Contents

D1796798

Contents

PART 2: *In vitro* **simulation of digestion and absorption in the gastro-intestinal tract of pigs and poultry - methods and results**

PART 3: The way forward

Authors

Dr M.B. Assoumani
Sanders Aliments
17 Quai de L'Industrie
F.91200 Athis-MDNS
France

Dr S. Bardocz
The Rowett Research Institute
Greenburn Road
Bucksburn
Aberdeen AB2 9SB
UK

Dr R. Begbie
The Rowett Research Institute
Greenburn Road
Bucksburn
Aberdeen AB2 9SB
UK

Dr S. Boisen
National Institute of Animal Science
Foulum
PO Box 39
DK 8830 Tjele
Denmark

Dr B. Carré
Institut National de la Recherche
Agronomique
Centre de Tours-Nouzilly
Station de Recherches Avicoles
37380 Monnaie
France

Dr A. Chesson
The Rowett Research Institute
Greenburn Road
Bucksburn
Aberdeen AB2 9SB
UK

Dr A.P. Drake
Gallina Blanca Purina S.A.
08730 Sta. Margarita Y Monjos
Barcelona
Spain

Dr S.W.B. Ewen
Department of Pathology
University of Aberdeen
Aberdeen AB9 2ZD
UK

Dr M.F. Fuller
The Rowett Research Institute
Greenburn Road
Bucksburn
Aberdeen AB2 9SB
UK

Dr S. Furuya
Kyushu National Agricultural
Experiment Station
Ministry of Agriculture, Forestry and
Fisheries
Nishigoshi
Kumamoto 861-11
Japan

Dr H. Graham
Deputy General Manager
Finnfeeds International Ltd
Forum House
41-51 Brighton Road
Redhill RH1 6YS
UK

Dr G. Grant
The Rowett Research Institute
Greenburn Road
Bucksburn
Aberdeen AB2 9SB
UK

Dr B. Hardy
Research and Technical Project
Manager
Dalgety Agriculture Limited
180 Aztec West
Almondsbury
Bristol BS12 4HQ
UK

Dr A.C. Longland
Institute for Grassland and Animal
Production
Shinfield
Reading RG2 9AQ
UK

Dr W. Löwgren
Department of Animal Nutrition and
Management
Swedish University of Agricultural
Sciences
S-750 07 Uppsala
Sweden

Dr J.M. McNab
AFRC Institute of Animal
Physiology and Genetics Research
Edinburgh Research Station
Roslin
Midlothian EH25 9PS
UK

Dr C.M. Parsons
Department of Animal Sciences
College of Agriculture
University of Illinois at
Urbana-Champaign
328 Mumford Hall
1301 West Gregory Drive
Urbana IL 61801
USA.

Dr A.J. Pusztai
The Rowett Research Institute
Greenburn Road
Bucksburn
Aberdeen AB2 9SB
UK

Authors

Dr B. Ratcliffe
The Robert Gordon Institute of Technology
School of Food and Consumer Studies
Kepplestone
Queen's Road
Aberdeen AB9 2PG
UK

Dr L. Savoie
Department of Nutrition
Université Laval
Quebec
Canada G1K 7P4

Introduction

There has been growing interest in recent years in the development of *in vitro* methods for assessing the digestibility of feedstuffs for pigs and poultry. This interest, which is now widespread, stems from a need for better evaluation of the very diverse raw materials available for inclusion in animal diets. There is now general recognition that feedstuffs cannot be fully evaluated solely in terms of their overall digestion in the gastrointestinal tract and that proper estimation of nutritive value requires that the site and end products of particular components of the digestive process must be separately assessed. This has led to the use of cannulated animals and precision feeding assays to estimate these components. *In vivo* methods, especially those based on the use of surgically modified animals, require special facilities not usually available to feed compounders. In addition, they are expensive and slow. Furthermore, there is increasing concern about the use of animals in routine testing. For all these reasons, *in vitro* methods that could be used in any laboratory and which could give rapid and reproducible results would be used very widely.

The simulation of the digestive processes is also important in nutrition research. By establishing and testing simulation models researchers can evaluate their hypotheses and, from the results, both generate new hypotheses and focus on areas for further research.

Several research groups round the world have been involved in the development of *in vitro* methods, using a variety of approaches. To foster this research, to discuss the scope for future collaboration and to consider the way forward towards the development of standard methods, a workshop was held at the Rowett Research Institute on the 4th and 5th of October 1990, to which many of those working on this subject were invited to contribute.

In addition to the speakers, a number of representatives of major feed compounders were invited to participate. All these delegates have a serious interest in the topic and the meeting provided an important opportunity to share ideas on the requirements of a practical assay.

Introduction

The workshop and this publication would not have been possible without the help of many individuals and organizations. The organizers are most grateful to Ajinomoto Inc., Eurolysine S.A. and Heartland Lysine Inc. for their financial contributions to the workshop. They are also much indebted to those organizations who allowed their employees to contribute and especially to those who provided their travel expenses. However, the greatest debt of gratitude is to the speakers for preparing the papers published here and to all those who participated in the discussions. Finally, the painstaking work of Miss Helen Martin in the technical editing of the text, of Mrs Vera Smith in correcting the copy and of Mr Bob Duthie in preparing it for printing is most gratefully acknowledged.

Malcolm Fuller
Aberdeen, December 1990

Part 1

What are we trying to simulate?

Chapter 1

Digestive Enzyme Activities in Pigs and Poultry

A.C. Longland

This paper contains a brief description of the digestive tracts of both pigs and poultry, the major sites of digestive enzyme activity, the manner in which feedstuffs are digested by these species and some of the factors which can affect digestive enzyme activity. Finally, some of the factors that might be considered when developing an *in vitro* digestibility method are outlined.

Morphology of the Digestive Tract

Pigs

The oral cavity contains tongue, lips, cheeks and teeth. The teeth include incisors for cutting food and molars which grind food into smaller particles. Saliva, which serves to lubricate food and contains α-amylase, varies in consistency depending on the diet fed; it is secreted by the three salivary glands, under the control of the autonomic nervous system. Food only remains in the mouth for a short time, passing into the oesophagus, which secretes mucus (from the tubuloacinar glands) lubricating the food bolus on its passage to the stomach. The stomach is differentiated into the oesophageal, cardiac, gastric and pyloric regions and is both a temporary storage organ, and the first major region for digestive activity - in terms of both proteolysis and of the further mechanical breakdown of feeds, facilitating subsequent enzymic degradation in the small intestine.

The duodenum, jejunum and ileum collectively comprise the small intestine, the jejunum accounting for ≃ 85% of its length. The majority of digestion by host enzymes and the absorption of their reaction products occurs in the small intestine. Nutrient absorption is facilitated by the greatly increased surface area provided by the villi, which occur along the length of the small intestine. There is a microflora throughout the small intestine which becomes progressively greater towards the large intestine. The large intestine consists of a short, blind-ended caecum which continues into the colon at the point of ileal attachment. The majority of microbial fermentation occurs in the large intestine, the end products of which are absorbed

3

across the mucosa. Thus the large intestine retrieves potential nutrients flowing from the small intestine before the undigested residue is excreted via the rectum and anus.

Poultry

The oral cavity of birds lacks lips and teeth which are replaced functionally by the beak. Salivation is minimal, the saliva being highly viscous, which serves to lubricate food but does not contain α-amylase. The oesophagus of poultry has a diverticulum, the crop, situated about two-thirds down its length, where it enters the thorax. The crop stores food, and there wetting and some digestive and microbial activities take place. The proventriculus, caudal to the oesophagus, contains gastric secretory glands, and leads to the gizzard, a highly muscular organ which mechanically grinds the feed, with or without the aid of grit, and combines this with substantial proteolytic activity. The small intestine of poultry is comparatively short compared with that of pigs but in terms of general structure and function, the avian small intestine is similar to that of mammals. As in the pig, there is a microflora in the small intestine, greatest near the large intestine. In contrast to pigs, poultry have large caeca and a small colon. The twin caeca are blind-ended, muscular organs, with a substantial microflora; they have long villi, mucus-secreting goblet cells and lymphoid tissue throughout. The mobility of the caeca results in mixing of the digesta which aids fermentation and subsequent absorption of end products. The short colon has a very limited capacity for fermentation and absorption; it links the ileo-caeco-colic junction with the cloaca. The cloaca is a common chamber which receives the excretory products of the urogenital and digestive tracts, and opens to the exterior via the vent.

Digestive Enzymes and their Secretion

Carbohydrate Digestion

Carbohydrates in animal feeds can generally be classified as storage carbohydrates, e.g., starch (or glycogen) and certain disaccharides which can be hydrolyzed by the host's enzymes to their constituent monomers, and the non-starch polysaccharides (NSP) of plant cell walls, e.g. cellulose, hemicellulose and pectins. NSP cannot be digested by the host's enzymes but must be fermented by the gut microflora, yielding volatile fatty acids (VFA) and gases. In addition to these, animal feeds may contain variable, but usually low amounts of free sugars and oligosaccharides, which may be absorbed directly or fermented.

Starch consists of varying proportions of amylose and amylopectin. Amylose consists of long, linear chains of α 1-4 linked glucose residues, whereas amylopectin generally has shorter linear chains of α 1-4 linked glucose units which are branched by α 1-6 linkages. The disaccharide sucrose, the storage carbohydrate of some plants e.g. sugar cane and sugar beet, contains glucose and fructose. Non-starch polysaccharides are described in Chapter 3.

In Pigs

The first starch-degrading enzyme encountered by the ingested feed in pigs is α-amylase (EC 3.2.1.1.) secreted by the submaxillary and sublingual salivary glands. The internal linkages of amylose are hydrolysed with equal ease but the breakdown of terminal linkages is considerably slower (Walker and Whelan, 1960) resulting in a mixture of dextrins, maltose and maltriose. The linear chains containing amylopectin and glycogen are hydrolyzed by α-amylase, but the α 1-4 links near branch points and the α 1-6 links themselves are not degraded. These unhydrolyzed portions of one or more α 1-6 linkages are the α-limit dextrins (Roberts and Whelan, 1960). The pH optimum for α-amylase is near neutral, and maximum activity depends on the presence of calcium.

The α-amylase digestion of starch continues during its passage to, and residence in the oesophageal region of the stomach, until mixing with HCl-containing gastric juice reduces the pH to less than 3.5 - the lower pH limit of α-amylase activity. Some starch, hemicellulose and sugar breakdown may also occur in the upper regions of the stomach, due to the fermentative activity of the gastric microflora, the main end product being lactic acid (Friend *et al.,* 1963). The main site for digestion of storage carbohydrates in pigs is in the small intestine. The pH of the gastric digesta flowing into the duodenum is gradually raised to a level suitable for carbohydrase activity by the secretion of alkaline pancreatic juice, bile and the products of Brunner's glands. These secretions are largely stimulated by the presence of food of low pH in the small intestine. Starch hydrolysis continues as a result of secretion of α-amylase by the pancreas. The action of pig pancreatic α-amylase differs from that of salivary amylase by its unequal action on susceptible bonds in the early stages of hydrolysis, producing relatively large amounts of reducing sugars (especially maltose) compared to products of longer chain lengths (Banks *et al.,* 1970). Pancreatic α-amylase is produced in very large amounts , usually being sufficient to hydrolyse 5-10 times the amount of substrate eaten by pigs. This is in contrast to the low levels of α-amylase in saliva.

A number of carbohydrases are produced in the brush border of the small intestinal mucosa. The major enzymes are four maltases, lactase and trehalase. Although the primary substrates of the maltases are the end-products of α-amylolytic starch digestion, they also hydrolyse several other substrates, being specific for their α-glucose moieties. Maltase Ia (isomaltase) (EC 3.2.1.10.) attacks isomaltose and limit dextrins; maltase Ib (sucrase) (EC 3.2.1.48.) degrades sucrose; maltose II (glucoamylase) (EC 3.2.1.20.) hydrolyses maltodextrose, starch, isomaltose, limit dextrins, tyranose, maltosucrose and melezitose as does its heat-stable iso-enzyme maltase III (Dahlquist, 1962). The pH optimum for maltases Ia and b lie between 6.0 and 6.5, that of maltases II and III between 6.5 and 7.0 (Dahlquist,

1960).

After hydrolysis of 1-6 linkages by maltases Ia, II and III, the resulting end-products can be degraded either by α-amylase or maltases. The brush border enzymes can break down soluble starch to glucose, though much more slowly than α-amylase (Ruttloff *et al.*, 1967, 1968). In contrast, the α-glucosidase activity of brush border glucoamylases (maltases II and III) results in more rapid degradation of small maltodextrins than does α-amylase. Thus, these enzyme activities complement each other, their combined action resulting in the release of glucose that can be absorbed by the intestinal mucosa.

Lactase (EC 3.2.1.108.), like the maltases, has multiple activities. In addition to lactose, lactase can also hydrolyze cellobiose and gentibiose with activities relative to lactose of 0.25 and 0.18 respectively at its pH optimum of 6.0, (Dahlquist, 1961); thus lactase has both β-galactosidase and β-glucosidase activity. Trehalase (EC 3.2.1.28.) is specific for α-α^1 trehalose with a pH optimum of 6.0 (Labat *et al.*, 1973) hydrolyzing it to two molecules of α-glucose.

Any starch or sugars which escape digestion by the hosts enzymes may, together with the non-starch polysaccharides, be fermented by the gut microflora.

In Poultry

Poultry saliva is thought not to contain α-amylase, but fairly intensive hydrolysis of starch may occur in the crop due to microbial action (Bolton, 1965). Little breakdown of carbohydrates occurs in the gizzard; the small intestine is the main site of carbohydrate digestive activity in the fowl. Small intestinal carbohydrase activities in poultry appear to be similar to those in the pig, except that fowl pancreatic α-amylase activity acts truly randomly on the internal linkages of starch molecules. Lactase and trehalase are not produced.

Protein Digestion

In Pigs

Proteins are first acted on by various pepsins in the stomach, which are secreted as inactive precursors, the pepsinogens. Pepsinogens are hydrolyzed to pepsin by the removal of a peptide from the N-terminal end of the molecule; this occurs rapidly at pH 2 and more slowly at pH 4 (Taylor, 1962), pepsin and hydrochloric acid being the main autocatalytic agents at pH 2 and 4 respectively.

The pepsins have two pH optima, at 2 and 3.5, and activity declines above pH 3.6 with no activity at pH > 6.0 (Taylor, 1959). Pepsins A and D (EC 3.4.23.1.), which are secreted by the gastric fundic mucosa, have higher optima than B and C (also called parapepsins I and II, EC 3.4.23.3.), which are secreted by the pyloric mucosa where the pH is lower (Taylor, 1959; Ryle, 1960). Of the different forms of pepsin, pepsin A predominates followed by pepsin C. The specificity of pepsin A has been investigated by a number of workers, e.g. Bovey and Yanari (1960).

Pepsin A only attacks peptide bonds between L-amino acids and has greatest preference for those with aromatic (hydrophobic) side chains, e.g. tyrosine and phenylalanine, followed by glutamic acid and then cysteine or cystine; hydrolysis is most rapid when both amino acids are aromatic (Inouye and Fruton, 1967). The specificities of the other pepsins differ slightly from that of pepsin A (Etherington and Taylor, 1971); consequently the rate of protein digestion will vary from one type of protein to another. The pH of the contents in the fundic and pyloric regions of the stomach falls rapidly to pH < 5.0 and then progressively to 2.0 so that peptic hydrolysis of protein is initially slow and becomes more rapid (Lawrence, 1972). Although it was originally believed that mixtures of large and small peptides were to be found in peptic hydrolysate, sequential gel-chromatography experiments by Steinhart and Kirchgessner (1973) indicate that, for soya-protein at least, digestion by pig pepsins results in progressively smaller peptides.

Very young pigs secrete chymosin (renin, EC 3.4.23.4.) which is secreted as the inactive precursor prochymosin in the gastric mucosa (Foltmann et al., 1981). Its proteolytic activity is limited and it functions mainly as a milk-clotting enzyme at pH < 5.5. Chitin, the structural amino-polysaccharide of insect exoskeletons and many fungal cell walls, is hydrolyzed by chitinase which is secreted by the porcine gastric mucosa (Jeuniaux, 1961).

On entry to the small intestine the increased pH renders the pepsins inactive, and the proteolytic enzymes secreted by the pancreas and intestinal brush border take over (Boyer, 1971). These proteases can be divided into three groups, the endopeptidases, the exopeptidases, and the aminopeptidases. The endopeptidases and exopeptidases are secreted by the pancreas, the former hydrolysing any susceptible peptide link in the chain, the latter cleaving only the terminal bonds from the carboxyl end of the peptide chains. The major endopeptidases of the pancreas are trypsin (EC 3.4.21.4.), chymotrypsin (EC 3.4.21.1.) and elastase (EC 3.4.21.36.); the main exopeptidases are the carboxypeptidases A (EC 3.4.17.1.) and B (EC 3.4.17.2.). Aminopeptidases are produced by the small intestinal mucosa and are located both on the brush border and in the cytoplasm.

All pancreatic proteases are secreted into the duodenum as inactive precursors, or zymogens. The duodenum mucosa secretes enterokinase, which activates trypsinogen to trypsin by removing a peptide from the N-terminal end of trypsino-gen (Charles et al., 1963). Formation of trypsin is then autocatalytic and, once formed, trypsin catalyses the activation of the other pancreatic proteases. Trypsin is the most important pancreatic endopeptidase both in terms of quantity and in its ability to activate other pancreatic proteases. Trypsin is the most specific of the pancreatic endopeptidases, its activity being limited to those bonds where the carboxyl group is contributed by an amino acid with a basic side-chain (i.e. arginine and lysine) (Travis, 1967). The chymotrypsins are less specific than trypsin, acting most swiftly on bonds of which the carboxyl group is contributed by an aromatic side chain e.g. tyrosyl, phenylalanyl and tryptophanyl. They also attack, but less rapidly, many bonds in which the amino acid has an aliphatic side chain, e.g. leucyl, methionyl, asparginyl and glutaminyl. The chymotrypsins are inactive against arginine and lysine, the trypsin substrates. Elastase acts most rapidly on alanyl bonds but also hydrolyses glycyl, sinyl, valyl and occasionally, leucyl bonds (Narayanan and Anwar, 1969).

Large amounts of carboxypeptidases (exopeptidases) are secreted in pancreatic juice and hydrolyse a single amino acid from the carboxyl end of a peptide. As they are exo-enzymes they degrade large proteins slowly due to a limited number of terminal amino acids, but rapidly degrade short peptides where there are many more terminal linkages for a given number of amino acid units. Carboxypeptidase A is particularly effective on peptides of which the terminal amino acid has an aromatic side-chain, as in hydrolysates produced by chymotrypsin (Folk and Schirmer, 1963). Carboxypeptidase B on the other hand acts most rapidly where the terminal amino acid has a basic side-chain, as in trypsin hydrolysates. Thus, the carboxypeptidases continue the proteolysis effected by the pancreatic endopeptidases.

Pig pancreatic juice also contains ribonuclease (EC 3.1.4.22.) (Zendzian and Barnard, 1967) and deoxyribonuclease (EC 3.1.4.5.) (Marchis-Mouren, 1965).

The aminopeptidases of the intestinal mucosa complete protein digestion, by removing a single amino acid residue from the amino end of a peptide chain. The aminopeptidases located in the brush border hydrolyse peptides in the intestinal lumen whereas those in the cytoplasm obviously only hydrolyse peptides which have been absorbed.

The major brush border hydrolases include the following enzymes. Amino-oligopeptidase (EC 3.4.11.2.) plays a key role in the hydrolysis of peptides in the lumen, shortening oligopeptides by stepwise hydrolysis. It is most active against neutral and basic amino acids and hydrolysis ceases when proline or 5-hydroxyproline is the final or penultimate N-amino acid (Kim et al., 1974). Dipeptidyl-aminopeptidase IV (EC 3.4.14.5.) complements the activity of amino-oligopeptidase, hydrolysing N-terminal dipeptides most effectively when the penultimate amino acid is proline (Bella and Kim, 1972); activity is much lower when a neutral amino acid occupies the penultimate position. Aminopepti-dase A (EC 3.4.11.7.) preferentially hydrolyses peptides with aspartic acid and glutamic acid in the N-terminal position (Andria et al., 1976). Because of their specificity, and because of end-product inhibition, the brush border peptidases do not completely hydrolyse the peptide mixture from the intestinal lumen to free amino acids (Friedrich et al., 1980). The digestion of absorbed peptides is completed by cytoplasmic di- and tri-peptidases.

At least three cytoplasmic hydrolases are important in the hydrolysis of absorbed peptides. Glycylleucine-dipeptide hydrolyase (EC 3.4.13.9.) is largely limited to dipeptides containing neutral amino acids (Das and Radhakrishnan, 1973), and aminoacylproline-dipeptide hydrolase, prolinase (EC 3.4.13.9.) is limited to dipeptides with C-terminal proline or hydroxyproline (Sjöstrom *et al.,* 1973). Amino tripeptidase (EC 3.4.11.4.) only hydrolyses tripeptides, its activity being highest for N-terminal proline and less for other neutral amino acids (Doumeng and Maroux, 1979).

In Poultry

In the fowl, 'gastric' digestion occurs in the proventriculus and gizzard, where oxynticopeptic cells secrete HCl and pepsinogen. The lumen of the gizzard parallels that of the pyloric antrum in pigs as the area for gastric proteolysis, and its effectiveness is considerably enhanced by vigorous mixing. Such mixing is limited in the pig, where 'layering' of consecutive meals can occur. Poultry produce more HCl and pepsin per unit of body weight than pigs and although the proteases secreted into the small intestine of poultry are also generally similar to those in pigs, chymotrypsin rather than trypsin is the predominant enzyme.

Digestion of Fat

Dietary fat is predominantly triglyceride with some phospholipids, sterols and sterol esters. Pancreatic lipase (EC 3.1.1.3.) secreted into the lumen of the small intestine initiates the digestion of triglycerides. High lipase activity requires that the enzyme be complexed with bile salts and the co-factor co-lipases whereupon the complex adsorbs at an aqueous/lipid interface where it is enzymatically active (Borgström, 1975). Lipase acts on the esters of primary alcohols and therefore hydrolyses ester groups on the 1- and 3- positions of the glycerol moiety, yielding 1,2-diglyceride and then 2-monoglycerides and free fatty acids (Schonheyder and Volqvartz, 1954). These two reactions are reversible so that there is a constant exchange of fatty acids at the 1- and 3- positions during hydrolysis, and thus equimolar concentrations of tri-, di- and mono-glycerides soon emerge (Borgström, 1954). Continued net hydrolysis will only occur when the reaction products are absorbed. A certain amount of isomerisation of mono- and di-glyceride occurs in the small intestine, with acyl groups moving from position 2 to positions 1 and 3, and thus all of the ester bonds become susceptible to lipase activity; this is most rapid in glycerides with short-chain fatty acids (Benzonana *et al.,* 1964). Lipase will also hydrolyse 1-monoglycerides if they are dissolved in the lipid phase: if they are in micellar solution they will be degraded by cholesterol esterase (EC 3.1.1.13.) (Morgan *et al.,* 1968) allowing complete hydrolysis to glycerol and free fatty acids. The final hydrolysis to glycerol is not a reversible reaction. Pancreatic cholesterol esterase, in the presence of bile salts, hydrolyses sterol esters to free sterol and free fatty acids (Swell *et al.,* 1953).

Pancreatic phospholipase (EC 3.1.1.4.) hydrolyses dietary phospholipid by removing the fatty acid in the 2 position of the glycerol yielding lysolecithin (de Haas *et al.,* 1965). The intestinal mucosa secretes alkaline phosphatase, which

9

could hydrolyse lysolecithin further, but it is thought that lysolecithin is absorbed directly by the mucosa.

In the presence of bile salts, the end products of fat digestion, i.e. the monoglycerides, free fatty acids, lysolecithin, free sterols and sterol esters, pass into micellar solution which is absorbed by the mucosa.

Control of Digestive Enzyme Secretion

The secretion of digestive enzymes into the various regions of the GI tract is not a continuous process, but is regulated by the actions of hormones and of the vagus nerve. The effects of the hormones or the nervous impulses may be stimulatory or inhibitory to secretion, the net result being to provide appropriate secretions in quantities appropriate to the type of feed being digested.

The secretion of saliva is thought to be under the control of the autonomic nervous system. Gastric secretion is stimulated by the presence of certain dietary peptides, which act on the pyloric mucosa causing secretion of the hormone gastrin, which, together with the action of the vagus nerve, mediate the secretion of HCl and fluid from the oxyntic cells. Pepsin is secreted in response to the presence of certain food components in the stomach, to vagal nerve stimulation, to gastrin and also in response to the small intestinal hormones secretin and chole-cystokinin (CCK). Secretin also serves to inhibit further secretion of gastric juice.

Although pancreatic juice is produced continuously, its secretion increases markedly after feeding. The major stimulus is the presence of acidic gastric digesta in the duodenum which causes the release of secretin and CCK from the intestinal mucosa, and initiates vagal nerve stimulation of the pancreas. Secretin stimulates the pancreatic secretion of fluid and bicarbonate, whereas CCK stimulates the secretion of pancreatic enzymes. Pancreatic secretion is suppressed by feed-back regulation, elicited by the presence of pancreatic fluid in the small intestine and it is thought that the regulatory factor is active trypsin (Schneeman and Lyman, 1975).

Another regulatory hormone of digestive enzyme secretion is somatostatin. Somatostatin is present in the stomach and small intestine of the pig, and inhibits pancreatic bicarbonate and protein secretion, gastric pepsin and small intestinal juice secretion. The control of digestive secretions in the fowl is thought to parallel that of the pig, except that pancreatic secretion in the fowl is less influenced by secretin and more related to vasoactive polypeptide (Moran, 1982).

Factors Affecting Digestive Enzyme Activity

The digestive enzyme activities present in pigs and poultry, described above, are affected by a number of factors including the age and physiological status of the animal, the diet fed, and by feed-back or end-product inhibition.

Digestive enzymic activities develop with age. The neonatal piglet has very low levels of pepsin, which increase slowly during the first two weeks of life, and then rapidly thereafter (Braude *et al.*, 1958). Kvanitskii (1951) reported the secretion of acid in the stomach to be low initially and free acid undetectable until pigs were three weeks old. Acid secretion increased rapidly after four weeks of age to reach near-adult levels in eight to ten week old piglets. Chymosin concentrations are highest in piglets up to seven days old, but decline thereafter (Foltmann *et al.*, 1981). Trypsin and chymotrypsin secretion is substantial at birth but proteolytic activity in the small intestine shows a marked increase from four to 36 days of age (Braude *et al.*, 1958). Efird *et al.* (1982) found that total trypsin activity had increased 20-fold, and that of chymotrypsin three-fold in pigs of four to eight weeks old.

Pancreatic α-amylase is very low at birth but increases rapidly with age (Kitts *et al.*, 1956). Tacu and Bianu (1974) found that the low activity at birth increased nine-fold in the first week of life and 20-fold by eight weeks. Values for adult pigs were ≈ 45 times the neonatal level. The activity of salivary α-amylase is generally fairly low in both newborn and adult pigs (Hudman *et al.*, 1957). Lactase is present at birth, but its activity falls rapidly during the next seven days; by 10 days activity was below half the neonatal value and then declined more slowly with age (Manners and Stevens, 1972). In the newborn piglet there is no sucrase, trehalase or isomaltase, and very little maltase activity (Bailey *et al.*, 1956), and feeding sucrose to young piglets is frequently fatal (Johnson, 1949). Sucrase activity gradually increases during the first 30 weeks of life, and then remains reasonably constant (Manners and Stevens, 1972). Trehalase, isomaltase, maltases II and III all increase with age, reaching maximum levels in adulthood (Kidder and Manners, 1978).

The small intestinal brush border peptidase activities may change with pig development. For example, Lindberg and Karlsson (1970) found that neonatal piglets had high levels of dipeptidase activity against L-alanyl-L-glutamic acid, and glycyl-L-leucine, but these had declined to adult levels in pigs six to eight weeks old.

Gestating and lactating sows also show differences in digestive enzyme activities compared with their non-reproducing counterparts. The protein, α-amylase and chymotrypsin contents of the pancreas were reduced at the end of gestation. During lactation, however, pancreatic weight, enzyme and protein contents increased considerably (Charbonneau *et al.*, 1982).

The chick shows increases in digestive enzyme activity with age generally similar to those in the pig, although newly hatched chicks have sufficient α-amylase and proteases for their somewhat different needs (Moran, 1982), and these increase substantially with age. Sucrase activity in the chick increases sharply shortly after hatching, to eight-fold its hatching level at four weeks of age; the greatest increase (five-fold) between one and four days after hatching (Brown and Moog, 1967). In contrast to the pig the newly hatched chick has high maltase and palatinase and low lactase activity; chicks do not have trehalase activity. In terms of total activity, Siddons (1969) found that all of the enzymes measured were lowest on the day of hatching and increased substantially over the following 42-day experimental period.

The effect of diet can be quite marked on both the levels of digestive enzyme activities and on the amounts of digestive tract secretions. Secretion of saliva in pigs is usually most copious when dry feed is given and minimal when diets are moist and liquid. Kvanitskii (1951) and Zebrowska et al. (1983) found that secretion of gastric juice by pigs on a barley-soya diet was approximately double that of pigs fed a starch-casein diet.

The pH of gastric juice can also be affected by dietary composition. When wheat bran was fed in conjunction with maize to growing pigs, the initial rise in gastric pH due to the presence of food was $\approx$ 1.25 pH units less than when maize alone was fed, and the time taken for the gastric pH to fall sufficiently for peptic hydrolysis to occur was substantially shorter (Lawrence, 1972).

In a study on the influence of diet on exocrine pancreatic secretion in growing pigs, Partridge et al. (1982) found that a diet based on barley, wheatings and fishmeal (diet BWF) stimulated $\approx$ 5 l/d of pancreatic juice, whereas with a semi-purified diet based on starch and casein (SSC) there was only 1.2 l/d of pancreatic juice. The protein contents of the pancreatic secretions were significantly different for the two diets, diet BWF and SSC eliciting the secretion of $\cong$ 12g and 6.5 g protein/day, respectively. The specific activities and total outputs of α-amylase and lipase were 2.3 and 4 times higher respectively with diet BWF than with diet SSC. However, although the specific activity of trypsin in pancreatic juice was higher with diet BWF than with diet SSC the difference was not significant. Chymotrypsin specific activities were similar for both diets as were those of the carboxypeptidases. It is of note that although the types of protein differed substantially between the two diets, this did not lead to a significant change in the amounts of proteases or peptidases secreted.

Pancreatic enzyme synthesis and secretion appear to be regulated to meet the particular needs of the diet fed. Low amylase and high chymotrypsin levels were reported in five to six week old piglets fed on low-starch, high-protein diets; when the protein was replaced by starch, the relative levels of amylase and chymotrypsin were switched (Aumaitre, 1971). Likewise, when low-starch, high-fat and high-starch low-fat diets were alternately fed at weekly intervals, high lipase and low α-amylase activity was found for the former diet, the reverse for the latter (Corring, 1975). Such responses in the pig can occur very rapidly with a change in diet composition. When a high carbohydrate diet was fed instead of a high lipid diet pancreatic α-amylase increased significantly within two hours of the diet change (Simoes-Nunes and Corring, 1979). Levels of trypsin do not, however, appear to respond to dietary change (Corring and Saucier, 1972).

The activities of pancreatic enzymes in poultry are also affected by diet composition. When chickens were fed low or high fat diets, it was found that the high fat diet decreased the activities of trypsin and chymotrypsin and increased that of lipase. Feeding the low fat diet, which contained high levels of protein and starch, led to increases in trypsin, chymotrypsin and α-amylase (Hulan and Bird, 1972).

Certain feeds contain antinutritional factors which decrease digestive enzyme secretion and activity. Two of the most well known are trypsin inhibitors which decrease porcine trypsin and chymotrypsin activity (Yen *et al.*, 1974), and tannins which can form complexes with enzymes or feed proteins (Griffiths, 1981). Trypsin inhibitors have a somewhat different effect on the chicken, causing pancreatic hypertrophy and hyperplasia (Liener and Kakade, 1980).

The condition under which animals are kept can also alter their pancreatic enzyne output. Szabo *et al.* (1976) found that four to five week old piglets kept at a high temperature had lower lipase and α-amylase levels than piglets kept at a lower temperature.

Digestive enzyme activities may also be affected by end-product inhibition which occurs with lipase and certain proteases when end products accumulate, instead of being absorbed.

Simulation of Digestive Enzyme Activity *in Vitro*

From the above review, it is clear that the digestion of feeds by pigs and poultry is a highly dynamic, integrated process, under hormonal and neural control, which responds to a number of stimuli. To simulate such a complex system in its entirety using a comparatively static, unresponsive *in vitro* method would be extremely difficult, and would be unlikely to be cheap, quick or easy to perform or to allow many samples to be analysed simultaneously - criteria often set for the adoption of *in vitro* methods. However, there are several important aspects to be considered when devising an *in vitro* digestibility method, if results akin to those found *in vivo* digestibility experiments are to be obtained. These include:

1. the sequential use of digestive enzymes which can degrade all of the linkages that would be hydrolysed by the animal's digestive enzymes, to reduce feeds to an absorbable form. The amounts of enzymes to be used should be considered, for although it is generally acknowledged that α-amylase and proteases are produced in excess of requirements *in vivo* in adult animals, it is known that various factors can influence their production. Consideration should be given to the animal the *in vitro* system is trying to simulate, particularly its age, to allow appropriate enzyme mixtures to be used;

2. the provision of the appropriate pH for the enzymes being used, in addition to the relevant co-factors, co-enzymes, bile salts, etc.

3. the removal of end-products of enzyme activity to a) allow separation of digested and undigested portions of the feed and b) prevent the problem of end-product

A.C. Longland

inhibition;
4. the provision of some degree of mixing appropriate to each stage of the digestion process. This would differ quite markedly between pigs and poultry;
5. the incubation time for each digestive step should be considered, as it is likely that *in vivo* greater digestion of feeds could occur in particular parts of the digestive tract if the residence times were longer. Factors affecting transit *in vivo* other than species differences include type of diet, health and age of the animals.

References

Andria, F., Marzi, A. and Auricchio, S. (1976) α-glutamyl-β-naphthylamide hydrolase of rabbit small intestine. Localisation in the brush-border and separation from other brush-border peptidases. *Biochimica et Biophysica Acta* 429, 42-50.

Aumaitre, A. (1971) Le developpement des enzymes dans le tube digestif due jeune porcelet. Importance pour le sévrage et signification nutritionelle. *Annales Zootechnica* 20, 551-75.

Bailey, C.B., Kitts, W.D. and Wood, A.J. (1956) The development of digestive enzyme system of the pig during its pre-weaning phase of growth. B. Intestinal lactase, sucrase and maltase. *Canadian Journal of Agricultural Science* 36, 51-8.

Banks, W, Greenwood, C.T. and Khan, K.M. (1970) The initial stages of action on amylose of the α-amylase from *B. subtilis*, human saliva malted rye and porcine pancreas. *Carbohydrate Research* 12, 79-87.

Bella, A. and Kim Y.S. (1972) Rat small intestine mucin. Isolation and characterisation of a water-soluble mucin fraction. *Archives of Biochemistry and Biophysics* 150, 679-89.

Benzonana, G., Entressangles, B., Marchis-Muren, G., Paséro, L., Sarda, L. and Desnuelle, P. (1964) Further studies on pig pancreatic lipase. In: Dawson, R.M.C., and Rhodes, D.N. (eds) *Metabolism and Physiological Significance of Lipids* 141-5. Wiley, New York.

Bolton, W. (1965) Digestion in the crop of fowl. *British Poultry Science* 6, 97.

Borgström, B. (1954) On the mechanism of pancreatic lipolysis of glycerides *Biochimica et Biophysica Acta* 13, 149-50.

Borgström, B. (1975) On the interaction between pancreatic lipase and colipase and the substrate and the importance of bile salt. *Journal of Lipid Research* 5, 522-31.

Bovey, F.A. and Yanari, S.S. (1960) Pepsin. In: Boyer, P.D., Lardy, H. and Myrbäck, K. (eds), *The Enzymes*. Academic Press, New York, pp. 61-3.

Boyer, P.D. (ed) (1971) *The Enzymes*. Academic Press, New York.

Braude, R., Dollar, A.M., Mitchell, K.G., Porter, J.W.G. and Walker, D.M. (1958) Proteolytic enzymes and the clotting of milk in the stomach of the young pig. *Proceedings of the Nutrition Society* 17, xv - xvi.

Brown, K.M. and Moog, F. (1967) Invertase activity in the intestine of the developing chick. *Biochimica et Biophysica Acta* 132, 185-7.

Charbonneau, P., Pelletier, G. and Monisset, J. (1982) Development of the pancreas during gestation and lactation in swine. *Canadian Journal of Physiology and Pharmacology* 60, 1229-35.

Charles, M., Rovery, M., Guidoni, A. and Desnuelle, P. (1963) Sur le trypsinogène et la trypsine du porc. *Biochimica et Biophysica Acta* 69, 115-29.

Corring, T. (1975) *Adaptation de la secretion du pancréas exocrine aux regime alimentaire chez le porc, physiologie comparee, étude experimentale*. Thesis. University of Paris, VI.

Corring, T. and Saucier, R. (1972) Pancreatic secretion in the fistulated pig: adaptation to dietary protein levels. *Annales de Biologie Animale, Biochimie Biophysique* 12, 233-41.

Dahlquist, A. (1960) Characterisation of three hog intestinal maltases. *Acta Chemica. Scandinavia* 14, 1-8.

Dahlquist, A. (1961) Pig intestinal β-glucosidase activities. 1. Relation to β-galactosidase (Lactase). *Biochimica et Biophysica Acta* 50, 55-61.

Dahlquist, A. (1962) Specificity of human intestinal disaccharidases and implications for hereditary disaccharide intolerance. *Journal of Clinical Investigation* 41, 463-70.

Das, M. and Radhakrishnan, A.N. (1973) Studies on a wide-spectrum intestinal dipeptide uptake system in the monkey and the human. *Biochemical Journal* 135, 609-15.

Doumeng, C. and Maroux, S. (1979) Aminotripeptidase, a cytosol enzyme from rabbit intestinal mucosa. *Biochemical Journal* 177, 801-8.

Efird, R.C., Armstrong, W.D. and Herman, D.L. (1982) The development of digestive capacity in young pigs: effect of age and weaning systems. *Journal of Animal Science* 55, 1380-7.

Etherington, D.J. and Taylor, W.H. (1971) The separation and preparation of human pepsins 3 and 5 from the gastric juice of single individuals, and the mode of action of human and swine pepsins on α chain of oxidised insulin. *Biochimica et Biophysica Acta* 236, 92-8.

Folk, J.E. and Schirmer, E.W. (1963) The porcine pancreatic carboxypeptidase A system. 1. Three forms of the active enzyme. *Journal of Biological Chemistry* 238, 3884-94.

Foltmann, B., Jensen, A.L., Lonblad, P., Smidt, E. and Alexsen, N.H. (1981) A developmental analysis of the production of chymosin and pepsin in pigs. *Comparative Biochemistry and Physiology* 68B, 9-13.

Friedrich, M., Schenk, G. and Noack, R. (1980) Studies on the physiological significance of brush border leucinanylamidase for the completion of protein digestion. *Nahrung* 24, 723-34.

Friend, D.W., Cunningham, H.M. and Nicholson, J.W.G. (1963) Volatile fatty acids and lactic acid in sections of the alimentary tract of the young pig. *Canadian Journal of Animal Science* 43, 174-81.

Griffiths, D. W. (1981) The polyphenolic content and enzyme inhibiting activity of testas from Bean (*Vicia faba*) and Pea (*Pisum sativum*) varieties. *Journal of the Science of Food and Agriculture* 32, 797-804.

Haas, de, G.H., Sarda, L. and Roger, J . (1965) Positional specific hydrolysis of phospholipids by pancreatic lipase: *Biochimica et Biophysica Acta* 106, 638-40.

Hudman, D.B., Friend, D.W., Hartman, P.A., Ashton, G.C. and Catron, D.V. (1957) Digestive enzymes of the baby pig. Pancreatic and salivary amylase. *Journal of Agriculture and Food Chemistry* 5, 691-3.

Hulan, H.W. and Bird, F.H. (1972) The effect of fat level in isonitrogenous diets on the composition of avian pancreatic juice. *Journal of Nutrition* 102, 459-68.

Inouye, K. and Fruton, J.S. (1967) Studies on the specificity of pepsin. *Biochemistry* 6, 1765-77.

Jeuniaux, C. (1961) Digestion de la chitine chez les oiseaux et les mammifères. *Annales de la Société Zoologique de Belgique* 92, 27-45.

Johnson, S.R. (1949) Comparison of sugars in the purified diet of baby pigs. *Federation Proceedings* 8, 387.

Kidder, D.E. and Manners, M.J. (1978) *Digestion in the Pig,* Kinston Press, Bath.

Kim, Y.S., Kim, Y.W. and Sleisenger, M.H. (1974) Studies on the properties of peptide hydrolases in the brush border and soluble fractions of small intestinal mucosa of rat and man. *Biochimica et Biophysica Acta* 370, 283-96.

Kitts, W.D., Bailey, C.D. and Wood, A.J. (1956) The development of the digestive enzyme system of the pig during its pre-weaning phase of growth. A. Pancreatic amylase and lipase. *Canadian Journal of Agricultural Science* 36, 45-50

Kvanitskii, A.V.(1951) *Problems of Digestive Physiology in Pigs.* Sel' Khozogiz, Moscow.

Labat, J., Baumann, F. and Courtis, J.E. (1973) Hydrolyse du tréhalose par la tréhalase de porc: configuration anomerique α du D-glucose liberé. *Carbohydrate Research* 26, 341-9.

Lawrence, T.J.L. (1972) The effect of certain dietary factors on *in vivo* pH changes and pepsin activity in the stomach of the growing pig. *British Veterinary Journal* 128, 402-11.

Liener, I.E. and Kakade, M.L. (1980) Protease inhibitors. In: Liener, I.E. (ed) *Toxic Constituents of Plant Foodstuffs.* Academic Press, New York, 7-71.

Lindberg, T. and Karlsson, B. (1970) Changes in dipeptidase activities during fetal and neo-natal development of the pig as related to the ultrastructure of mucosal cells. *Gastroenterology* 59, 247-56.

Manners, M.J., and Stevens, J.A. (1972). Changes from birth to maturity in the pattern of distribution of lactase and sucrase activity in the mucosa of the small intestine of pigs. *British Journal of Nutrition* 28, 113-27.

Marchis-Mouren, G. (1965) *Etude comparée de l'equipment enzymatique du suc pancréatique de diverses éspèces.* Thesis. Marseilles.

Moran, E.T. Jr. (1982) Starch digestion in fowl. *Poultry Science* 61, 1257-67.

Morgan, R.G.H., Barrowman, J., Filipek-Wender, H. and Borgström, B.C. (1968) The lipolytic enzymes of cat pancreatic juice. *Biochimica et Biophysica Acta* 106, 638-40.

Narayanan, A.S. and Anwar, R.A. (1969) The specificity of purified porcine elastase. *Biochemical Journal* 114, 11-17.

Partridge, I.G., Low, A.G., Sembrook, I.E.M. and Corring, T. (1982). The influence of diet on the exocrine pancreatic secretion of growing pigs. *British Journal of Nutrition* 102, 459-68.

Roberts, P.J.P. and Whelan, W.J. (1960) The mechanism of carbohydrase action. 5. Action of human salivary α-amylase on amylopectin and glycogen. *Biochemical Journal* 76, 246-53.

Ruttloff, H., Friese, R. and Täufel, K. (1967) Zur Bestimmung der intestalen allpha-amylase. *Nahrung* 11, 205-13.

Ruttloff, H, Friese, R. and T ufel, K. (1968) Zur Bedeutung de α-amylase bei der intestalen stärkehydrolyse . *Ernährungsforschung* 13, 141-45.

Ryle, A.P. (1960) Parapepsinogen II. The zymogen of parapepsin II. *Biochemical Journal* 75, 145-50.

Schneeman, B.O. and Lyman, R.L. (1975) Factors involved in the intestinal feedback regulation of pancreatic enzyme secretion in the rat. *Proceedings of the Society for Experimental Biology* 148, 897-903.

Schonheyder, F. and Volqvartz, K. (1954) studies on lypolitic enzyme action V1. Hydrolysis of trilauryl glycerol by pancreatic lipase. *Biochimica et Biophysica Acta* 15, 288-90.

Siddons, R.C. (1969) Intestinal disaccharidase activities in the chick. *Biochemical Journal* 12, 51-9.

Simoes Nunes, C. and Corring, T. (1979) Pancreatic exocrine secretion in the pig following test meals of different composition and intra-duodenal loads of glucose and maltose. *Hormone and Metabolic Research* 11, 346-51.

Sjöstrom, H., Norén, O. and Josefsson, L. (1973) Purification and specificity of pig intestinal prolidase. *Biochimica et Biophysica Acta* 327, 457-70.

Steinhart, H. and Kirchgcssner, M. (1973) Peptidverteilung auf molekulargewichts blöcke bei der In-vitro-verdauung von sojaprotein mit pepsin unter der Einfluss verschiedner Verdauungszeiten *Zeischrift für Tierphysiologie Tierernährung und Futtermittelkunde* 32, 55-64.

Swell, L., Field, H. and Treadwell, C.R. (1953) Role of bile salts in the activity of cholesterol esterase. *Proceedings of the Society for Experimental Biology*

84, 417-20.

Szabo, J., Ribiczeyne-Szabo, P., and Rafai, P. (1976) A pancreas hidrolazok aktivitasanak vizsgalata kulonbozo kornyezeti homesekletan tartott sertesekben. *Magyar Allatorvosok Lapja* 31, 325-8.

Tacu, A. and Bianu, G. (1974) Maltaza intestinala si pancreatica la porcine. Luckrarile stiintifice ale institutului de Cercetari pentru. *Nutritia Animalelor* 3, 155-76.

Taylor, W.H. (1959) Studies on gastric proteolysis. 4. *Biochemical Journal* 71, 627-32.

Taylor, W.H. (1962) Proteinases of the stomach in health and disease. *Physiological Reviews* 42, 519-53.

Travis, J. (1967) Specificity of porcine trypsin. *Biochemical and Biophysical Research Communications* 29, 294-7.

Walker, G. I. and Whelan, W.J. (1960) The mechanism of carbohydrase action. 7. Stages in the salivary α-amylolysis of amylose, amylopectin and glycogen. *Biochemical Journal* 86, 257-63.

Yen, J.T., Jensen, A.H. and Simon, J. (1974) Effects of dietary raw soybean and soybean trypsin inhibitor on trypsin and chymotrypsin activities in the pancreas and in the small intestinal juice of growing swine. *Journal of Nutrition* 107, 156-65.

Zebrowska, T., Low, A.G., and Zebrowska, H. (1983) Studies on gastric digestion of protein and carbohydrate, gastric secretion and exocrine pancreatic secretion in the growing pig. *British Journal of Nutrition* 49, 401-10.

Zendzian, E.N. and Barnard, E.A. (1967) Distributions of pancreatic ribonuclease, chymotrypsin and trypsin in vertebrates. *Archives of Biochemistry* 122, 699-713.

Chapter 2

The Role of the Microflora in Digestion

B. Ratcliffe

Introduction

The gut microflora is inextricably involved in the digestive processes. Much of what is known of the activities of the micro-organisms of the gastrointestinal tract is inferential or qualitative in nature because it is extremely difficult to study the activities of the microflora *in situ* and there is a dearth of quantitative studies. The collection of papers for this workshop is specifically related to digestion in pigs and poultry but because of the lack of comprehensive literature on the activities of the gut microflora of these species, it will be necessary to make reference to work in other species. Studies of the gut microflora over the last 20-30 years have illuminated the roles of micro-organisms in the digestive tract and have helped to show something of the complexity and extent of the microbial involvement in the digestive processes. The breakdown of dietary fibre in the large intestine has been well reviewed and is widely appreciated by research workers. Many, however, are still unfamiliar with the wide-ranging effects of the micro-organisms of the alimentary canal and believe that these effects are limited to the digestion of fibre in the large bowel. The contemporary view of the activities of the gut microflora is very complex and involves both digestive gains and losses for the host. It is generally held that the most important function of the indigenous microflora of the gut is the provision of the 'barrier effect' or 'colonization resistance' which is outside the scope of this paper.

The microflora of the alimentary canals of pigs and poultry are substantial in terms of density of colonization and species variety and tend to be present in greatest numbers in the caeca and large intestines (Salanitro *et al.*, 1978; Allison *et al.*, 1979; Robinson *et al.*, 1981; Mead, 1989). Most of the species are anaerobic and many are strictly obligate anaerobes. Micro-organisms colonize the mucosal epithelia and are intimately associated with these surfaces either by specific attachment to epithelial cells or by being bound up in the mucous layers around the villi. Bacteria can also be found deep in the crypts of Lieberkühn. They 'seed' the digesta in the lumen and may become intimately associated with dietary particles, particularly fibrous components. There are substantial changes in the gut microflora in response to diet, in terms of numbers, types and activities.

Effects on Enzyme Activity

Comparisons between germ-free (GF) and conventional (CV) animals have often been made to assess the contribution of the microflora to gastrointestinal enzyme activity. This type of comparison is not straightforward because of differences in intestinal morphology and rates of cellular renewal between GF and CV animals. The gut flora appears to have little effect on the levels of trypsin (Coates *et al.*, 1970) or total pancreatic proteolytic activity in the small intestines of chickens (Lepkovsky *et al.*, 1964). It has also been suggested that pancreatic enzyme activity is essentially the same for GF and CV piglets (Szabo, 1979). There is no difference in glycolytic activity between GF and CV chickens (Siddons, 1969; Coates *et al.*, 1970). There also appears to be no difference in the activity of pancreatic lipases in rats (Reddy *et al.*, 1969).

Bacteria are involved in the rapid inactivation of enzymes in the enteron (Cheredkova and Nikitin, 1970; Szabo, 1979). In GF animals, endogenous digestive enzyme activity persists into the large intestine whereas in CV animals such activity is non-existent or at a very low level beyond the terminal ileum (Szabo, 1979; Norin *et al.*, 1986). In enterocytes, the activity of enzymes, particularly those associated with absorption, may be influenced by the presence of gut bacteria. Evidence from mice suggests that phosphodiesterase I may be decreased whereas thymidine kinase may be increased and alkaline phosphatase is unaltered by the presence of micro-organisms (Whitt and Savage, 1988). Palmer and Rolls (1983) found that the activities of alkaline phosphatase, acid phosphatase and isocitric dehydrogenase were not different in enterocytes isolated from GF and CV chicks. These authors acknowledged the extreme difficulties involved in studying the microbial influence on enzyme activities in mucosal cells.

Digestion of Nitrogenous Compounds

Digestibility of nitrogenous compounds is markedly affected by the activities of gut micro-organisms. A large proportion of the protein and amino acids present in faeces is of microbial or endogenous origin. Relatively few of the nitrogenous compounds present in faeces are likely to be of undigested dietary origin, which may be as little as 6% of faecal nitrogen (N) in pigs (Low *et al.*, 1978). The gut bacteria are capable of catabolizing all amino acids (Michel, 1966) and are involved in deamination and decarboxylation of amino acids, urea hydrolysis and microbial protein synthesis. End-products found in the gut include amines, ammonia, volatile fatty acids (VFA) and microbial amino acids. The gut microflora requires N for its own synthetic processes and this may be obtained from dietary sources, other micro-organisms and endogenous sources including excreted urea, muco-protein, sloughed epithelial cells and enzymic secretions from the host. Many micro-organisms use ammonia as the main or only source of N and some preferentially use ammonia for the synthesis of bacterial amino acids, even in the presence of large amounts of peptides and amino acids (Takahashi *et al.*, 1980). It is generally held that N is normally in plentiful supply for microbial growth, but that the availability of energy is the limiting factor. Ahrens and Kaufmann (1983) showed that infusing carbohydrate at the rate of 75g/d into the caecum of mini-pigs increased bacterial protein from 70 to 85% of faecal protein. Morgan and Whittemore (1988) examined the effects of dietary fibre on the excretion and retention of N by male pigs of 45-50 kg. They used three sources of fibre (straw, oatfeed and sugar beet pulp) and three levels of inclusion in the diet. They found that increasing levels of fibre tended to decrease the digestibility of N and decrease the amount of urinary N. Bird *et al.* (1990) have shown that incorporation of lactitol or lactulose into the diets of mini-pigs can produce respectively a 20% or 70% increase in faecal N.

These effects probably reflect the increasing incorporation of N into microbial cells as energy supplied to the gut bacteria as fermentable carbohydrate ceases to be limiting. The cycling of ammonia and urea between the gut and the liver is probably altered so that more ammonia is incorporated into amino acids synthesized by bacterial cells. This lowers the load on the liver which uses the ammonia for the formation of amino acids or urea. Fermentation of the fibre also produces VFA which reduce the pH of the large bowel; this has the effect of suppressing bacterial urease activity and increasing the amount of urea voided in faeces.

Apart from the effects of fibre as an energy substrate for micro-organisms, there is increasing evidence from work with rats that the VFA produced have a stimulatory effect on the mucosal epithelia leading to cellular proliferation (Sakata, 1987; Goodlad *et al.*, 1989). Such proliferation is probably associated with increased loss of epithelial cells which will increase endogenous losses of N in both the small and large intestines. All this contributes to greater faecal N and, therefore, to the decreased apparent digestibility of N. Findings such as this have led to uncertainty about the validity of measurements of apparent digestibility of N. The extent of the involvement of the gut microflora in determining faecal N is shown by the discrepancies between apparent digestibilities of N measured at the terminal ileum and in the faeces (Holmes *et al.*, 1974; Low, 1979). The differences between ileal digestibility and apparent digestibility measured in faeces do not appear to be constant and can vary with different diets. For example, Taverner (1984) compared a diet based on soyabean meal with one based on meat and bone meal. He found that discrepancies between faecal digestibility and ileal amino acid digestibility were much greater for the meat and bone meal diet (Table 2.1).

Microbial activity and synthesis of amino acids may not only contribute to faecal N but may affect N present in digesta throughout the alimentary canal. Visek (1984) stated that 25% of urea produced in the liver is excreted *via* the gastrointestinal

tract. Urea present in the gut, either from endogenous or dietary sources, may be degraded by bacterial ureases. Uric acid also enters the gut and is hydrolysed to urea and other products which are further degraded to ammonia. The resulting ammonia may be taken up by the host for the synthesis of purines, pyrimidines and amino acids or may be reconverted to urea. Some of the ammonia will not be taken up but will be utilized by the microflora for synthesis of microbial amino acids and protein. Henderickx and Decuypere (1972) have shown that ammonia levels in the large bowel of young pigs could be reduced by half with small supplements of antibiotics and, indeed, intestinal urease seems to be entirely microbial in origin (Levensen et al., 1959; Delluva et al., 1968). Visek (1984), however, maintained that endogenous enzymes can account for 25% of urease activity in the alimentary canal, but this is not supported by germfree (GF) studies (Deguchi and Namioka, 1989). Wise et al. (1983) have demonstrated that urease activity in the caecum of rats increases with increasing level of protein intake.

Table 2.1. Differences between faecal digestibility (%) and ileal digestibility (%) of amino acids.

Amino acid	Soyabean meal	Meat & bone meal
Lysine	-3.3	-14.7
Threonine	-7.1	-21.5
Methionine	+2.1	- 9.3
Average of all amino acids	-2.9	-16.5

(After Taverner, 1984)

Can amino acids from microbial, endogenous or dietary sources, which enter the large bowel, be absorbed intact? The nutritional significance of amino acids entering the large intestines of chickens and pigs has not been elucidated but its potential contribution to host nutrition should not be ignored. Zebrowska (1975) has shown that amino acids disappear from the large intestine but do not appear to be absorbed intact. In contrast, Niiyama et al. (1978) have shown that, in piglets, intact microbial amino acids appear to be taken up and can be detected in the venous blood of the colon. Just et al. (1981) have indicated that under normal circumstances, the value of such nitrogenous compounds for protein synthesis in pigs may be low. Payne et al. (1968) suggested that microbial amino acids may be absorbed from the caeca of poultry. Moreto and Planas (1989) stated that the proximal region of the caeca of chickens has well-developed villi and microvilli and is able to absorb sugars and amino acids. Further work is needed in this area since such evidence brings into question the reliability of measurements of ileal digestibility of amino acids and the assumption that further hydrolysis and absorption does not occur distal to the terminal ileum. The effects of the microbial flora in the caeca of poultry may be less marked than those seen in pigs. Although significant changes can occur in the amino acid profile of digesta as a result of microbial activity in the hindgut (Parsons *et al.*, 1982), Salter and Fulford (1974), having studied GF and CV chicks, concluded that the influence of the microflora on the amino acid composition of excreta was not large. Raharjo and Farrell (1984) examined the effects of caecectomy and antibiotics on amino acid digestibility in adult cockerels. They found that the mean apparent digestibility of several amino acids showed no significant differences between seven diets. Caecectomy and antibiotic supplementation caused an increase in digestibility of isoleucine on some diets. These findings have to be viewed with caution since the authors were unable to demonstrate that the methods used had significantly suppressed microbial activity in the hindgut. Caecectomy may have effects on the distribution and activity of the gut microflora, on gastrointestinal physiology and endogenous N losses which would further hinder interpretation of such studies.

Assumptions that microbial effects on ileal digestibility of N are negligible can also be questioned. Some studies have shown that ileal digesta of pigs contain large amounts of bacterial protein and perhaps 20-30% of the total N present is of bacterial origin (Dierick *et al.*, 1983; Poppe *et al.*, 1983; Drochner, 1984). Work with GF rats has shown that dead bacteria can be digested in the small intestines and that this may contribute to host nutrition (Midvedt and Gustafsson, 1981). Interestingly, these authors showed that Gram-negative bacteria and certain strains of clostridia were well digested but Gram-positive strains appeared to be resistant to digestion.

The involvement of the microflora in the digestion of N compounds in avian species is further complicated by the evidence that urine is back-flushed into the caeca, rinsing water soluble substances and small particles of digesta out of the colon and into the caeca (Bjornhag, 1989). This provides easily fermentable substrates to the caecal microflora and poorly fermentable material can be rapidly excreted. Uric acid contained in the urine can provide a source of energy and N to the microflora and end-products may be available to the host. Bjornhag (1989) has suggested that back-flushed urine could even enter the ileum. He indicated that the value of this fermentable N source to the host and the amount of urine back-flushed to the caeca are inversely related to dietary N.

Decarboxylation reactions are carried out by the gut microflora. They yield amines which represent a nutritional loss to the host and have physiological or potentially toxic effects on the host. Dierick *et al.* (1986b) studied the influence of the gut flora on N metabolism and urine production. To suppress microbial activity, they fed groups of pigs a 20 ppm dietary supplement of either virginiamycin (seven animals) or spiramycin (six animals) and compared these groups with

23

controls (nine animals). The distribution of amines along the gastrointestinal tract was examined after slaughter and their results are given in Table 2.2. The greatest amounts of amines were found in the proximal and middle small intestine where the pH is acid and large amounts of free amino acids occur, which favours the bacterial decarboxylation of amino acids. Studies of gut micro-organisms *in vitro* by the same authors (Dierick *et al.*, 1986a) showed that *Escherichia coli* seemed to be the most active in the production of amines. Schneider *et al.* (1989) have also examined the occurrence of amines in the digesta of pigs. Although diets contained only small amounts of putrescine equal proportions of histamine, cadaverine, tyramine and putrescine were found in the stomachs of pigs. Most cadaverine occurred in the colon. Weaned pigs (12-14 kg live weight) given a diet with a crude protein (CP) concentration of 240 g/kg had concentrations of total amines of 4.2, 10.2 and 9.6mmol/kg dry matter (DM) in stomach, small intestine and large intestine, respectively. On a diet with 180 g CP/kg, these concentrations fell to 0, 5.5 and 4.9mmol/kg DM. Concentrations of amines in the digesta of finishing pigs (121 kg live weight) were 2.1-8.7, 1.0-4.8 and 0.2 - 2.2 mmol/kg DM in jejunem, caecum and colon, respectively. Increasing crude fibre and antibacterials in the feeds did not significantly decrease the concentration of amines in any section of the gut.

Digestion of Dry Matter and Dietary Fibre

Undoubtedly, energy is made available to the host through the fermentation of substrates which are not readily utilized by host enzymes. Substrates such as physiologically resistant starch (Englyst, 1989), which, although they can be utilized by host enzymes, escape digestion in the small intestine, can also be fermented. Indeed, all organic materials leaving the ileum are potentially substrates for fermentation. In pigs, VFA are readily taken up and provide energy to local intestinal tissue and *via* the systemic circulation are incorporated into peripheral tissues (Imoto and Namioka, 1978; Kass *et al.*, 1980; Latymer and Woodley, 1984; Latymer and Low, 1984).

The average total concentration of VFA in caecal contents of pigs is around 100 mM but the concentration in the rectum or faeces may be twice as high (Von Engelhardt *et al.*, 1989). This probably reflects continued microbial activity but reduced absorption of VFA in the lower parts of the large bowel. The amount of VFA absorbed by pigs has been estimated as 95 mmoles/ kg body weight per d (Stevens *et al.*, 1980).

The processing of dietary fibre seems to be quite different in the guts of pigs and poultry. The anatomical differences between avians and mammals may be partly responsible for this and there seem to be differences in the extent of fibre degradation which may be related to differences in the gut microflora. The microflora of the chicken caeca is diverse and highly complex. Although many species have been identified and their ability to metabolize various substrates has been assessed (Mead, 1989), the fastidious nature of some of the obligate anaerobes in the caeca means that they have yet to be cultured and identified *in vitro*. If such species make significant contributions to the overall metabolism of the caeca this could make it difficult to simulate exactly post ileal digestion *in vitro*. McBee (1977) has indicated that no caecal strain of bacteria yet tested has cellulolytic ability, supporting the general view that cellulose fermentation does not occur in the caeca of domestic chickens. In contrast, cellulolytic bacteria have been isolated from the caecum, colon and faeces of pigs of 26 to 32 kg live weight (Varel *et al.*, 1984). Interestingly, the predominant cellulolytic bacteria were *Bacteroides succinogenes* and *Ruminococcus flavefaciens;* strains of both these species are found in the rumen and in the caeca of rats (Montgomery and Macy, 1982).

Table 2.2. The effects of virginiamycin and spiramycin on the average concentrations of amines (μmol N/g DM) in the contents of segments of the gastrointestinal tracts of pigs at slaughter.

			Segment				
		Stomach	Small intestine			Caecum	Rectum
		1	3	5	7	9	12
Histamine	C	trace	3.3	1.7	1.5	0.6	0.1
	V	0.1	0.4	0.5	1.3	0.1	0.1
	S	trace	0.6	0.5	0.3	0.4	0.2
Putrescine	C	0.1	0.2	0.3	0.2	0.7	0.1
	V	0.1	0.1	0.2	0.3	0.7	0.1
	S	0.1	0.2	0.1	0.1	0.2	0.1
Cadaverine	C	0.3	11.2	6.7	5.4	1.5	0.4
	V	0.0	0.4	1.1	2.3	1.0	0.3
	S	0.1	0.5	0.5	0.4	0.6	0.1
Tyramine	C	0.2	1.5	2.2	0.8	0.4	0.3
	V	0.2	3.3	1.9	1.4	0.4	0.0
	S	0.1	2.3	0.6	0.4	0.1	0.1
Total amines	C	0.6	16.2	10.9	8.4	3.2	0.9
	V	0.4	4.2	5.0	7.0	2.2	0.5
	S	0.3	3.6	1.7	1.2	1.3	0.5

(From Dierick *et al.*, 1986b)

C=control, n=9; V=virginiamycin (20 ppm), n=7; S=spiramycin (20 ppm), n=6

Varel *et al.* (1982) have shown that cellulolytic micro-organisms in the hind gut can increase by 80% in a three week period after a change to a high fibre diet (alfalfa) and may increase by a further 70% from three to eight weeks after the dietary change. Other workers have detected changes in the faecal flora of pigs in response to high fibre diets (Moore *et al.*, 1987).

Microbial activity in the hind gut has a significant effect on the apparent digestibility of DM. Attempts to suppress the effects of gut micro-organisms in poultry using caecectomy and the addition of dietary antibiotics can produce a 20% reduction in DM digestibility (Raharjo and Farrell, 1984). Eggum *et al.* (1982) used an antibiotic mixture (Nebacitin) to suppress microbial activity in pigs (22-26 kg live weight) and found that DM digestibility was reduced from 67% to 62% on a high fibre diet (105 g crude fibre/kg diet) and from 80% to 77% on a lower fibre diet (47g crude fibre/kg diet). This nevertheless reflects suppression of all fermentative activity rather than just the degradation of non-starch polysaccharides (NSP).

Traditionally, fermentation of dietary fibre has been considered to be a post-ileal activity of the indigenous microflora. There is increasing evidence that some NSP is at least partly degraded anterior to the large intestine. Sambrook (1979) showed that pigs fitted with re-entrant cannulas had pre-caecal digestibilities of ADF of 8-50% depending on the diet. He suggested that part of this degradation might be facilitated by the prolonged retention of fibrous material in the stomach (Sambrook, 1980). Similar suggestions had been made previously (Kidder and Manners, 1978). It is conventionally assumed that the acid environment of the stomach would inhibit extensive fermentation but Bolduan *et al.* (1988) claim that digesta in the porcine stomach may have low acidity for several hours after feeding, allowing microbial growth and inhibiting gastric emptying with concomitant gastric fermentation. If this occurs, however, the more likely substrates are starches and simple sugars. Zoiopoulos *et al.* (1983) recorded crude fibre digestibilities at the terminal ileum of 25-40%. More recently Mathers (1991) has claimed that dietary fibre may be up to 60% digestible in the small intestine of pigs and that on average 40% of NSP in peas is digested anterior to the caecum. Mathers further maintained that similar levels of fibre degradation can occur before the terminal ileum in poultry, possibly as a result of microbial action in the crop, gizzard or both. Drochner (1984), from trials with cannulated mini-pigs, concluded that cellulose and pectin were not digested in the small intestine but that precaecal digestibility of hemicellulose was about 42%. Millard and Chesson (1984 a, b), using pigs with simple cannulas and a sophisticated marker system, demonstrated that pectic polysaccharides and cellulose were degraded anterior to the terminal ileum. Ileal digestibilities of pectic polysaccharides were 46-50% and of cellulose were 10-24%. Furthermore, Chesson *et al.* (1985) have shown that cellulolytic and pectinolytic anaerobic bacteria may be isolated from the ileal digesta of pigs.

There is evidence that fibre-degrading bacteria adhere closely to fibrous material and digest the plant cell wall material which is in intimate contact with the bacterial cell. This forms depressions in the material which can be distinguished by electron microscopy (Hungate, 1984). Similar adherence of bacteria to fibrous material has been reported for ruminants (Akin *et al.*, 1974; Czerkawski, 1990). It seems possible, therefore, that fermentative micro-organisms could become attached to particles of dietary fibre in relatively proximal regions of in the gut and travel with the flow of digesta to complete some preliminary degradation prior to arrival in the caecum.

Effects of Cannulation on the Activities of the Gut Microflora

The effects of cannulation on bacterial populations have not been widely studied. Cannulation might affect the micro-ecosystem of the gut, the anaerobic conditions at the site of the cannula and perhaps the digestive processes. Evidence from human ileostomy patients shows that the micro-ecology of the gut is altered in the region of the stoma (Gorbach *et al.*, 1967). The number of micro-organisms is 80 times greater than in the normal terminal ileum and the populations present are more like those found in faeces of normal patients. Finegold *et al.* (1970) found higher ratios of aerobes to anaerobes in ileostomy effluent than might be expected in the terminal ileum. Ileal stomata may not, however, be directly comparable with ileal cannulas. Livingstone and McWilliam (1985) examined pigs of 35 kg live weight with simple cannulas in the terminal ileum and compared them with their unoperated littermates. They found that cannulation caused a 7% reduction in the efficiency of food utilization which perhaps provides circumstantial evidence of changes occurring in the micro-ecology of the gut. Evidence that N digestibility measured at the terminal ileum is not affected by cannulation comes from Moughan and Smith (1987) and from George *et al.* (1988). These workers compared ileal digestibilities of N by slaughter techniques with those obtained by cannulation methods and found no difference. Other workers have shown that caecal cannulation appears to have little effect on the normal metabolic processes of pigs of around 40-60 kg live weight (Close *et al.*, 1984).

Other Effects of Intestinal Micro-organisms

Triacylglycerols are not readily synthesized by bacteria but the activities of the gut microflora can have a significant effect on both the quality and quantity of lipid detected in faeces. Suppression of the gut microflora of pigs, using antibiotics, increased the apparent digestibility of fat (Mason and Just, 1976). Faecal lipids are derived from unabsorbed dietary fat, endogenous losses and from gut micro-organisms. All these may be modified by microbial lipases. Biohydrogenation of unsaturated fatty acids is a significant activity which seriously hampers attempts to determine digestibilities of these compounds (Eyssen *et al.*, 1973). CV chicks

27

excrete at least twice as much cholesterol and bile acids in their faeces as GF birds (Eyssen *et al.*, 1969). This may reflect impaired absorption of microbially modified bile acids and cholesterol in the enterohepatic circulation. Primary bile acids are modified by the gut microflora to form secondary and tertiary bile acids by processes involving deconjugation, desulphation and dehydroxylation. Such activities have been well reviewed by Eyssen and Van Eldere (1984) who have also reviewed the influence of gut micro-organisms on cholesterol metabolism. In addition, gut bacteria both produce vitamins and use dietary vitamins. Whether or not this has significance in the digestive processes, particularly enzyme activities, is unknown.

Conclusions

The gut microflora is highly complex. Microbial populations differ in terms of numbers and types between the caecum, colon and rectum of pigs. Furthermore, the luminal populations may be quite different from those adhering to the intestinal epithelia (Allison, 1989).

Micro-organisms compete with the host animal for nutrients and this can affect the disappearance of dietary components at all levels of the gut. While fibre digestion provides additional energy to the host via the production of VFA and may contribute to intestinal well-being, other activities of the microflora may deprive the host of some nutrients.

The microflora appears to adapt to changes in diet; the digestibility of fibre, in particular, may show a steady increase over a considerable time, perhaps several months. This raises questions about the appropriate time to be allowed for adaptation to diets during measurements of digestibility *in vivo*.

The contribution of microbial amino acids to host nutrition requires further investigation.

Although the effects of micro-organisms on digestion *in vivo* may be difficult, if not impossible, to simulate exactly, this should not invalidate attempts to model the system *in vitro*. Model systems can be useful tools even if they are simplistic and do not exactly simulate the habitat which they have been set up to represent. If the aims of the modellers are to produce systems *in vitro* which simply correlate well with accepted values for digestibility obtained *in vivo*, as a means for rapid evaluation of feeds, then it may not be necessary to know fully the composition and activites of the gut microflora. Indeed, values obtained from fermentations with rumen liquor seem to serve as reasonable models for fermentation in the hind gut of pigs (Vervaeke *et al.*, 1989), although such studies would probably prove difficult to standardize.

References

Ahrens, F. and Kaufmann, W. (1983) The role of hind gut fermentation on protein digestibility. *Kieler Milchwirtschafliche Forschungsberichte* 35, 285-7.

Akin, D.E., Burdick, D. and Michaels, G.E. (1974) Rumen bacterial interrelationships with plant tissue during degradation revealed by transmission electron microscopy. *Applied Microbiology* 27, 1149-56.

Allison, M.J. (1989) Characterization of the flora of the large bowel of pigs: a status report. *Animal Feed Science and Technology* 23, 79-90.

Allison, M.J., Robinson, I.M., Bucklin, J.A. and Booth, G.D. (1979) Comparison of bacterial populations of the pig caecum and colon based upon enumeration with specific energy sources. *Applied and Environmental Microbiology* 37, 1142-51.

Bird, S.P., Hewitt, D., Ratcliffe, B. and Gurr, M.I. (1990) Effects of lactulose and lactitol on protein digestion and metabolism in conventional and germfree animal models: relevance of the results to their use in the treatment of portal systemic encephalopathy. *Gut* 31, 1403-6.

Bjornhag, G. (1989) Transport of water and food particles through the avian caeca and colon. *Journal of Experimental Zoology Supplement* 3, 32-7.

Bolduan, G., Jung, H., Schneider, R. and Schnabel, E. (1988) Hinweise zur schweineerahrung nach neueren erkenntnissen uber die mikrobielle verdauung. *Monatshefte für Veterinarmedizin* 43, 764-6.

Cheredkova, A.N. and Nikitin, Y.I. (1970) [Intestinal fluid and its enzymes along the porcine intestine.] Uchenye Zapiski Vitebskii Veterinarnyi Institut 22, 138-44.

Chesson, A., Richardson, A.J. and Robertson, J.A. (1985) Fibre digestion and bacteriology of the digestive tract of pigs fed cereal and vegetable fibre. In: Just, A., Jørgensen, H. and Fernandez, J.A. (eds), *Digestive Physiology in the Pig.* Statens Husdyrbrugsforsøg, Copenhagen, pp. 272-5.

Close, W.H., Heavens, R.P., Stephens, D.B. and Sambrook, I.E. (1984) The influence of gastrointestinal cannulation on the energy metabolism of the pig. *Proceedings of the Nutrition Society* 43, 66A.

Coates, M.E., Hewitt, D. and Golob, P. (1970) A comparison of the effects of raw and heated soyabean meal in diets for germ-free and conventional chicks. *British Journal of Nutrition* 24, 213-25.

Czerkawski, J.W. (1990) Relation between bacterial colonization of fibrous residues and digestibility of dry matter in the rumen simulation technique (Rusitec). *Biological Wastes* 32, 219-24.

Deguchi, E. and Namioka, S. (1989) Synthesis ability of amino acids and protein from non-protein nitrogen and the role of intestinal flora in this utilization in pigs. *Bifidobacteria and Microflora* 8, 1-12.

Delluva, A.M., Markley, K. and Davies, R.E. (1968) The absence of gastric urease in germ-free animals. *Biochimica et Biophysica Acta* 151, 646-50.

Dierick, N.A., Decuypere, J.A., Lannoye, J., Vervaeke, I. and Henderickx, H.K. (1983) Digestion ileale et fecale de la matiere seche, des proteines et des acides amines de quelques rations conventionelles pour les porc a l'engrais. *Revue de l'Agriculture (Bruxelles)* 36, 1713-26.

Dierick, N.A., Vervaeke, I.J., Decuypere, J.A. and Henderickx, H.K. (1986a) Influence of the gut flora and of some growth-promoting feed additives on nitrogen metabolism in pigs. I. Studies *in vitro*. *Livestock Production Science* 14, 161-76.

Dierick, N.A., Vervaeke, I.J., Decuypere, J.H. and Henderickx, H.K. (1986b) Influence of the gut flora and some growth-promoting feed additives on nitrogen metabolism in pigs. II. Studies *in vivo*. *Livestock Production Science* 14, 177-93.

Drochner, W. (1984) The influence of changing amounts of crude fibre and pectic components on precaecal and postileal digestive processes in the growing pig. *Advances in Animal Physiology and Animal Nutrition Supplement* 14, 1-125.

Eggum, B.O., Thorbek, G., Beames, R.M., Chwalibog, A. and Henckel, S. (1982) Influence of diet and microbial activity in the digestive tract on digestibility and nitrogen and energy metabolism in rats and pigs. *British Journal of Nutrition* 48, 161-75.

Englyst, H. (1989) Classification and measurement of plant polysaccharides. *Animal Feed Science and Technology* 23, 27-42.

Eyssen, H. and Van Eldere, J. (1984) Metabolism of bile acids. In: Coates, M.E. and Gustafsson, B.E. (eds), *The Germfree Animal in Biomedical Research*. Laboratory Animals Ltd., London, pp. 291-316.

Eyssen, H., Van Messom, G. and Van Den Bosch, J. (1969) Effect of type of diet on cholesterol absorption and bile salt excretion in germ-free and conventional chicks. In: Mirand, E.A. and Back, N. (eds), *Germfree Biology: Experimental and Clinical Aspects*. Plenum Press, New York, pp. 97-105.

Eyssen, H., Depauw, G. and De Somer, P. (1973) Biohydrogenation of long-chain fatty acids by intestinal micro-organisms. In: Heneghan, J.B. (ed), *Germfree Research: Biological Effect of Gnotobiotic Environments*. Academic Press, New York, pp. 277-83.

Finegold, S.M., Sutter, V.L., Baule, J.D. and Shmida, K. (1970) The normal flora of ileostomy and transverse colostomy effluents. *Journal of Infectious Diseases* 122, 376-81.

George, S.A., Elliot, R. and Batterham, E.S. (1988) A comparison of the ileal digestibility of nitrogen in sugar based diets for growing pigs determined by slaughter or cannulation techniques. *Proceedings of the Nutrition Society of Australia* 13, 116.

Goodlad, R.A., Ratcliffe, B., Fordham, J.P. and Wright, N.A. (1989) Does dietary fibre stimulate intestinal epithelial cell proliferation in germ- free rats? *Gut* 30, 820-5.

Gorbach, S.L., Nahas, L., Weinstein, L., Leviton, R. and Patterson, J.F. (1967) Studies of intestinal microflora. iv. The microflora of ileostomy effluent: a unique microbial ecology. *Gastroenterology* 53, 574-80.

Henderickx, H.K. and Decuypere, J.A. (1972) Influence of nutritional levels of spiramycin and virginiamycin on the bacterial metabolites in the gastrointestinal tract and urine of artificially reared early weaned piglets. In: Heneghan, J.B. (ed.), *Germfree Research: Biological Effect of Gnotobiotic Environments*, Academic Press, New York, pp. 361-8.

Holmes, J.H.G., Bayley, H.S., Leadbeater, P.A. and Horney, F.D. (1974) Digestion of protein in small and large intestine of the pig. *British Journal of Nutrition* 32, 479-89.

Hungate, R.E. (1984) Microbes of nutritional importance in the alimentary tract. *Proceedings of the Nutrition Society* 43, 1-11.

Imoto, S. and Namioka, S. (1978) VFA production in the pig large intestine. *Journal of Animal Science* 47, 467-78.

Just, A., Jorgensen, H. and Fernandez, J.A. (1981) The digestive capacity of the caecum-colon and the value of the nitrogen absorbed from the hind gut for protein synthesis in pigs. *British Journal of Nutrition* 46, 209-19.

Kass, M.L., Van Soest, P.J. and Pond, W.G. (1980) Utilization of dietary fibre from alfalfa by growing swine. II. Volatile fatty acid concentrations in and disappearance from the gastrointestinal tract. *Journal of Animal Science* 50, 192-7.

Kidder, D.E. and Manners, M.J. (1978) In: Digestion in the Pig. *Scientechnica*, Bristol.

Latymer, E.A. and Low, A.G. (1984) Tissue incorporation and excretion of ^{14}C in pigs after injection of [U-^{14}C] sodium acetate into the caecum. *Proceedings of the Nutrition Society* 43, 12A.

Latymer, E.A. and Woodley, S.C. (1984) *In vivo* incorporation of 14C into plasma fractions of pigs after injection of [U-14C] sodium acetate into the caecum. *Proceedings of the Nutrition Society* 43, 22A.

Lepkovsky, S., Wagner, M., Furuta, F., Ozone, K. and Koike, T. (1964) The proteases, amylase and lipase of the intestinal contents of germfree and conventional chickens. *Poultry Science* 43, 722-6.

Levenson, S.M., Crowly, J.V., Moriwitz, R.E. and Malm, O.J. (1959) The metabolism of carbon labelled urea in germ-free rats. *Journal of Biological Chemistry* 234, 2061-2.

Livingstone, R.M. and McWilliam, R. (1985) The effect of terminal ileum cannulation on the performance of growing pigs. *British Veterinary Journal* 141, 186-91.

Low, A.G. (1979) Studies on digestion and absorption in the intestines of growing pigs. 6. Measurements of the flow of amino acids. *British Journal of Nutrition* 41, 147-56.

Low, A.G., Sambrook, I.E. and Yoshimoto, J.T. (1978) Studies on the true digestibility of nitrogen and amino acids in growing pigs. *EAAP Annual Meeting,* Stockholm Paper PV9.

McBee, R.H. (1977) Fermentation in the hind gut. In: Clarke, R.T.J. and Bauchop, T. (eds), *Microbial Ecology of the Gut.* Academic Press, London, pp. 185-222.

Mason, V.C. and Just, A. (1976) Bacterial activity in the hind gut of pigs. I. Its influence on the apparent digestibility of dietary energy and fat. *Zeitschrift für Tierphysiologie, Tierernahrung und Futtermittelkunde* 36, 301-10.

Mathers, J.C. (1991) Digestion of non-starch polysaccharides by non-ruminant omnivores. *Proceedings of the Nutrition Society* 50, 161-72

Mead, G.C. (1989) Microbes of the avian caecum: types present and substrates utilized. *Journal of Experimental Zoology Supplement* 3, 48-54.

Midvedt, T. and Gustafsson, B.E. (1981) Digestion of dead bacteria by germ- free rats. *Current Microbiology* 6, 13-15.

Millard, P. and Chesson, A. (1984a) Modifications to swede (*Brassica napus L.*) anterior to the terminal ileum of pigs: some implications for the analysis of dietary fibre. *British Journal of Nutrition* 52, 583-94.

Millard, P. and Chesson, A. (1984b) Glycosidic linkages of swede cell walls and their residues recovered from the terminal ileum of the pig. *European Journal of Biochemistry* 142, 367-9.

Montgomery, L. and Macy, J.M. (1982) Characterization of rat caecum cellulolytic bacteria. *Applied and Environmental Microbiology* 44, 1435-43.

Moore, W.E.C., Moore, L.V.H., Cato, E.P., Wilkins, T.D. and Kornegay, E.T. (1987) Effect of high-fiber and high-oil diets on the faecal flora of swine. *Applied and Environmental Microbiology* 53, 1638-44.

Moreto, M. and Planas, J.M. (1989) Sugar and amino acid transport properties of the chicken caeca. *Journal of Experimental Zoology Supplement* 3, 111-6.

Morgan, C.A. and Whittemore, C.T. (1988) Dietary fibre and nitrogen excretion and retention by pigs. *Animal Feed Science and Technology* 19, 185-9.

Moughan, P.J. and Smith, W.C. (1987) A note on the effect of cannulation of the terminal ileum of the growing pig on the apparent ileal digestibility of amino acids in ground barley. *Animal Production* 44, 319-21.

Niiyama, M., Deguchi, E., Kagota, K. and Namioka, S. (1978) Appearance of [15]N- labelled intestinal microbial amino acids in the venous blood of the pig colon. *American Journal of Veterinary Research* 40, 716-8.

Norin, E.K., Midvedt, T. and Gustafsson, B.E. (1986) Influence of intestinal microflora on tryptic activity during lactation in rats. *Laboratory Animals* 20, 234-7.

Palmer, M.F. and Rolls, B.A. (1983) The activities of some metabolic enzymes in the intestines of germ-free and conventional chicks. *British Journal of Nutrition* 50, 783-90.

Parsons, C.M., Potter, L.M., Brown, R.D., Wilkins, T.D. and Bliss, B.A. (1982)

Microbial contribution to dry matter and amino acid content of poultry excreta. *Poultry Science* 61, 925-32.

Payne, W.L., Combs, C.F., Kifer, R.R. and Snyder, D.G. (1968) Investigation of protein quality: ileal recovery of amino acids. *Federation Proceedings* 27, 1199-203.

Poppe, S., Meier, H., Benneke, H.J. and Struwe, E. (1983) On the protein and amino acid digestibility in various sections of the digestive tract of pigs. 3. Composition of the amino acids in the chyme and faecal protein. *Archiv für Tierernährung* 33, 743-8.

Raharjo, Y.C. and Farrell, D.J. (1984) Effects of caecectomy and dietary antibiotics on the digestibility of dry matter and amino acids in poultry feeds determined by excreta analysis. *Australian Journal of Experimental Agriculture and Animal Husbandry* 24, 516-21.

Reddy, B.S., Pleasants, J.R. and Wostmann, B.S. (1969) Pancreatic enzymes in germ-free and conventional rats fed chemically defined, water-soluble diet free from natural substrates. *Journal of Nutrition* 97, 327-34.

Sakata, T. (1987) Stimulatory effect of short-chain fatty acids on epithelial cell proliferation in the rat intestine: a possible explanation for trophic effects of fermentable fibre, gut microbes and luminal trophic factors. *British Journal of Nutrition* 58, 95-103.

Salanitro, J.P., Blake, I.G., Muirhead, P.A., Maglio, M. and Goodman, J.R. (1978) Bacteria isolated from the duodenum, ileum and caecum of young chicks. *Applied and Environmental Microbiology* 35, 782-90.

Salter, D.N. and Fulford, R.J. (1974) The influence of gut microflora on the digestion of dietary and endogenous proteins: studies of amino acid composition of excreta of germfree and conventional chicks. *British Journal of Nutrition* 32, 625-37.

Sambrook, I.E. (1979) Studies on digestion and absorption in the intestines of growing pigs.8.Measurements of the flow of total lipid, acid-detergent fibre and volatile fatty acids. *British Journal of Nutrition* 42, 279-87.

Sambrook, I.E. (1980) Digestion and absorption of carbohydrates and lipid in the stomach and small intestine of the pig. In: Low, A.G. and Partridge, I.G. (eds), *Current Concepts of Digestion and Absorption in Pigs*. NIRD, Reading, Technical Bulletin 3, pp. 78-93.

Schneider, R., Kreienbring, F., Bolduan, G. and Beck, M. (1989) Biogenic amines in the digesta of pigs. *Archives of Animal Nutrition* 39, 1021-9.

Siddons, R.C. (1969) Intestinal disaccharidase activities in the chick. *Biochemical Journal* 112, 51-7.

Stevens, C.E., Argenzio, R.A. and Clemens, E.T. (1980) Microbial digestion: Rumen versus large intestine. In: Ruckebusch, Y. and Thivend, P. (eds), *Digestive Physiology and Metabolism in Ruminants*. MTP Press, Lancaster, pp. 685-706.

Szabo, J. (1979) Protein, carbohydrate and fat degrading enzymes in the intestine of germfree and conventional piglets. In: Fliedner, T., Heit, H., Niethammer, D. and Pflieger, H. (eds), *Clinical and Experimental Gnotobiotics*. Gustav Fischer Verlag, Stuttgart, pp.125-8.

Takahashi, M., Benno, Y. and Mitsuoka, T. (1980) Utilization of ammonia nitrogen by intestinal bacteria isolated from pigs. *Applied and Environmental Microbiology* 39, 30-5.

Taverner, M.R. (1984) Protein digestion in the pig - applied aspects. Proceedings of the Australian Society for Animal Production, 15, 150-3.

Van Eldere, J. and Eyssen, H. (1984) Metabolism of cholesterol. In: Coates, M.E. and Gustafsson, B.E. (eds), *The Germfree Animal in Biomedical Research*. Laboratory Animals Ltd., London, pp. 317-32.

Varel, V.H., Pond, W.G., Pekas, J.C. and Yen, J.T. (1982) Influence of high-fiber diet on bacterial populations in intestinal tracts of obese- and lean-genotype pigs. *Applied and Environmental Microbiology* 44, 107-12.

Varel, V.H., Fryda, S.J. and Robinson, I.M. (1984) Cellulolytic bacteria from pig large intestine. *Applied and Environmental Microbiology* 47, 219-21.

Vervaeke, I.J., Dierick, N.A., Demeyer, D.I. and Decuypere, J.A. (1989) Approach to the energetic importance of fibre digestion in pigs. 2. An experimental approach to hindgut digestion. *Animal Feed Science and Technology* 23, 169-94.

Visek, W.J. (1984) Ammonia: its effects on biological systems, metabolic hormones and reproduction. *Journal of Dairy Science* 67, 481-98.

Von Engelhardt, W., Ronnau, K., Rechkemmer, G. and Sakata, T. (1989) Absorption of short-chain fatty acids and their role in monogastric animals. *Animal Feed Science and Technology* 23, 43-53.

Whitt, D.D. and Savage, D.C. (1988) Influence of indigenous microbiota on activities of alkaline phosphatase, phosphodiesterase I and thymidine kinase in mouse enterocytes. *Applied and Environmental Microbiology* 54, 2405-10.

Wise, A., Mallett, A.K. and Rowland, I.R. (1983) Dietary protein and cecal microbial metabolism in the rat. *Nutrition and Cancer* 4, 267-72.

Zebrowska, T. (1975) The apparent digestibility of nitrogen and individual amino acids in the large intestine of pigs. Roczniki Nauk Rolniczych, B, 97 (1), 117-23.

Zoiopoulos, P.E., Topps, J.H. and English, P.R. (1983) Fibrous agri-industrial by-products as protein sources for bacon pigs. 2. Study of digestion with pigs cannulated at the terminal ileum. *Zeitschrift für Tierphysiologie, Tierernährung und Futtermittelkunde* 49, 219-28.

Chapter 3

The Physical and Chemical Constitution of Foods: Effects on Carbohydrate Digestion

H. Graham

Introduction

Modern non-ruminant husbandry systems are based on the use of cereal-based feeds, and profitability is dependent on access to cost-effective diets. Thus sophisticated least-cost methods are widely used for formulation, with, in some cases, over 20 feedstuffs included in complete diets. Although these methods have enjoyed considerable success they are subject to the constraint that a feedstuff must be assigned a particular nutritive value whereas it is known that there is a considerable variation in composition within each feedstuff and that inclusion of some can affect the nutritive value of others. Nutritional evaluation of diets is traditionally performed in time-consuming and costly animal experiments, while chemical analysis, even with modern equipment, is also rather laborious. Consequently only a limited number of feeds can be examined in this way and the results obtained are then extrapolated to other similar formulations. This has led to an increasing interest in recent years in the development of fast and accurate *in vitro* methods for the evaluation of the nutritive value of pig and poultry diets. To be successful, however, such methods must be based on an understanding of the physical and chemical composition of feeds and the processes of digestion and metabolism in the animal.

Physical Constitution of Feeds

It is unfortunate that a plant feedstuff is not homogeneous but rather a mixture of ordered tissues. Thus it cannot be considered as a single entity but rather as a collection of widely differing parts. Each plant tissue is composed of cells which normally have unique shapes, sizes, contents and cell wall structures, depending on their function. For example, the aleurone layer which surrounds the starchy endosperm in cereal grains is made up of relatively large cells with thick and rather intransigent cell walls. These cells contain many of the enzymes necessary for germination, and the function of the thick cell walls is presumably to enclose these enzymes and protect the dormant grain from destruction. However these cell walls are also relatively resistant to degradation in non-ruminant animals and may pass intact through the intestinal tract, still enclosing their high quality protein (Bach Knudsen and Eggum, 1984). Feed manufacturers can adopt several measures, including physical treatments such as milling or pelleting and other techniques, such as enzyme treatment, to disrupt cell structure (Graham *et al.*, 1989) but extensive disruption can be expensive and can also lead to dust and animal health problems. It is likely that ingestion of intact plant cell feeds can result in a loss of nutrients both as a result of enclosure and because larger feed particles can give rise to a higher digesta passage rate (Wrick *et al.*, 1983).

Carbohydrates in Feeds

Plant carbohydrates are the predominant component for non-ruminant feeds, generally contributing over 70% of the dry matter. They are a complex group of compounds which differ considerably in chemical structure and physiological activity. From a chemical viewpoint they can be sub-divided into five groups:

1. mono- and disaccharides, including mainly glucose, fructose, sucrose, lactose and maltose;
2. oligosaccharides, with the raffinose series (raffinose, stachyose and verbascose) of particular interest;
3. storage polysaccharides, including primarily starch and fructans;
4. cell wall storage polysaccharides, including mannans, galactans and xyloglucans;
5. cell wall structural polysaccharides, usually classified as cellulose, hemicelluloses and pectins.

The last two groups, which together are often referred to as the non-starch polysaccharides (NSP), are closely associated with lignin with which they form the dietary fibre complex.

Mono-, Di- and Oligosaccharides

Sucrose, the rather inert sugar employed in plants for carbohydrate transport, is generally the main simple sugar in cereal-based feeds, although in some cases appreciable amounts of maltose, glucose and fructose may be present. While monosaccharides can be directly absorbed from the small intestine, disaccharides are hydrolyzed by enzymes on the brush border surface prior to absorption. Simple sugars normally make up only 3-4% of common diets (Table 3.1), and are essentially completely absorbed in the small intestine. Lactose will also be encountered in milk products, and this sugar may partially escape enzymatic hydrolysis in older pigs (Low, 1980).

Dietary oligosaccharides originate mainly from plant protein sources such as soyabean meal and peas (Table 3.1). These compounds pass through the small intestine unabsorbed, but, in common with other simple sugars, are rapidly fermented by the bacteria present in the hind-gut. This rapid fermentation can cause nutritional disturbances and these oligosaccharides are therefore generally considered to be antinutritional components.

Storage Polysaccharides

Starch is the main component of cereal grains (Table 3.1) and is usually the primary energy source for pigs and poultry. However average compositional data such as those presented in Table 3.1 should be treated with a certain amount of suspicion. A Swedish study of about 100 samples each of wheat, barley and oats found that starch contents varied from 60-73% (mean 68%, CV 4%) in wheat, 53-67% (mean 62%, CV 4%) in barley and 39-55% (mean 46%, CV 6%) in oats (Graham *et al.*, 1987). Thus quite a few barley samples had higher starch contents than some of the wheats. There was also a significant negative correlation between the contents of starch and those of total fibre and protein. Thus a decrease of 1 percentage unit in starch content was associated with an increase in crude protein 0.20%-units in oats, 0.31%-units in barley and 0.44%-units in wheat. The corresponding figures for the relationship between starch and total fibre were 0.75%-units for oats, 0.58%-units for barley and 0.53%-units for wheat. Thus low starch contents were primarily associated with high fibre contents, although in wheat a considerable increase in protein was also observed.

Table 3.1. Typical contents (g/kg DM) of the main carbohydrates and Klason lignin in some common feedstuffs.

	Maize	Wheat	Barley	Soyameal	Peas
Simple	10	30	20	40	33
Oligosaccharides	-	2	4	30	27
Starch	690	670	600	-	420
NSP residues					
total	88	98	166	185	164
arabinose	17	24	21	20	24
xylose	22	35	43	13	16
galactose	5	3	4	47	22
glucose	35	33	91	53	111
uronic acids	4	2	3	35	21
Klason lignin	6	10	20	10	9

Starch is digested by the alpha-amylases present in the upper gastro-intestinal tract to dextrins which are further hydrolyzed by brush border enzymes prior to absorption. Thus starch is potentially totally digestible in the small intestine.

However certain types of starch, as typified by potato starch, are difficult to hydrate and must be cooked or otherwise gelatinized before they become accessible to digestive enzymes. Retrograded starch, resistant to α-amylase can be formed during heating and cooling cycles, but is not found to any significant extent in present-day feeds.

Table 3.2. Variation in content and composition of dietary fibre (% of DM) in Swedish oats (n=16), barley (n=16) and wheat (n=24) samples with a wide variation in starch contents

Fibre component		Oats	Barley	Wheat
Dietary fibre	mean	29.6	19.0	11.1
	range	20-39	16-25	10-14
	CV (%)	17	16	9
β-glucans	mean	3.2	3.4	0.8
	range	2.7-3.6	2.4-4.2	0.7-1.0
	CV (%)	10	18	10
Arabinoxylans	mean	8.0	7.0	6.0
	range	4-15	6-11	5-7
	CV (%)	37	25	7
Cellulose	mean	9.1	5.3	2.5
	range	6-13	3-7	2 3
	CV (%)	21	26	24
Klason lignin	mean	8.4	2.2	0.8
	range	5-13	2-3	0.5-1
	CV (%)	29	26	27

from Graham *et al.*, 1987.

The other important storage polysaccharides, fructans, generally constitute less that a few percent in feeds, with contents ranging from about 0.1% in oats to about 0.8% in wheat. In some novel feedstuffs such as Jerusalem artichokes, however, fructans may constitute more than 50% of the dry matter. This component is resistant to degradation by host enzymes. However, some degradation would appear to take place in the fore-gut, presumably due to acidic hydrolysis, bacterial activity or the action of enzymes present in the diet (Graham and Åman, 1986a). As with starch, any fructans entering the hind-gut are rapidly fermented.

Cell Wall Storage Polysaccharides

Cell wall storage polysaccharides occur widely, particularly in dicotyledonous seeds. Three main types are found, the mannans, including pure mannans and gluco- and galacto-mannans, the galactans and the xyloglucans. Examples of their occurrence in feedstuffs are the mannans in palm kernel meal, galactans in lupin seeds and xyloglucans in peas. These components are often associated with thickening of the cell wall, which may lead to a reduction in the availability of enclosed nutrients. All are resistant to hydrolysis by host enzymes, but are highly susceptible to degradation by the bacteria in the hind-gut.

Cell Wall Structural Polysaccharides

Plant cell wall polysaccharides are primarily built of up to ten monosaccharide residues. These are the pentoses arabinose and xylose, the hexoses glucose, mannose and galactose, the deoxy-hexoses rhamnose and fucose, and the hexuronic acids galacturonic, glucuronic and 4-O-methyl-glucuronic acids. Potentially, these residues could combine to give a staggering array of polysaccharides and to some extent they do. Glucose residues tend to predominate in most feedstuffs (Table 3.1), coming mainly from cellulose, which is thought to be the most abundant organic molecule on Earth. There may also be a significant contribution from the mixed-linked β-glucans in the endosperm cell walls of barley and oats (Table 3.2). Cereals also have a high content of arabinoxylans, and this component, together with the mixed-linked β-glucans are of particular nutritional significance since they make up the cereal endosperm cell walls and can give rise to viscous solutions. Dicotyledonous protein supplements tend to have a high pectin content, typified by uronic acid, arabinose and galactose residues. The pectins are also partially soluble and can give rise to viscous conditions within the intestinal tract. The cell wall polysaccharides are not hydrolyzed by animal enzymes but are degraded to a greater or lesser extent by bacteria present in the gastro-intestinal tract.

Table 3.3. Carbohydrate content (g/kg DM) of a barley-based diet and resultant digesta.

Site	Fructose+ Glucose	Sucrose	Maltose	Starch	NSP
Feed	3	12	-	510	185
Duodenum	50	10	30	375	173
Ileum	tr[+]	tr[+]	tr[+]	70	356
Faeces	-	-	-	tr[+]	331

Graham *et al.*, 1986

NSP - non-starch polysaccharides; tr - trace

Digestibility of Feed Carbohydrates

Starch and Simple Sugars

As could be expected of such a divergent group of compounds, the pattern of digestion and absorption of carbohydrates in the intestine is rather complex. A study of digestibility up to the duodenum (distal to the pancreatic and bile ducts), terminal ileum and overall of a barley based diet in 40 kg pigs revealed that some starch was hydrolyzed early in the gastro-intestinal tract, with a duodenal apparent digestibility of 27% (Graham *et al.*, 1986). However, when the quantities of hydrolysis products, primarily glucose and maltose, were considered, the apparent digestibility was 10% (Table 3.3). Recovery of NSP residues at the duodenum was complete. At the ileum only traces of soluble sugars were recovered, demonstrating the efficient absorption mechanisms for these components. Starch, however, still constituted 70 g/kg of digesta dry matter, giving an ileal apparent digestibility of 96%; the remainder was completely degraded in the hind-gut. The apparent digestibilities of non-starch polysaccharide residues at the ileum and in the faeces were 17% and 44%, respectively. Similar patterns were observed in chicks (Table 3.4), in which ileal starch digestibility approximated to 95% in cereal-based diets. Again, some fibre degradation occurred prior to the ileum, but with birds it would appear that only soluble fibres enter and are degraded in the caeca.

Table 3.4. Apparent digestibility (%) in the last third of the small intestine (ileum) and in excreta of 20 day old broiler chicks fed a wheat/rye/soya-based diet.

Component	Ileal digestibility	Overall digestibility
Organic matter	71	73
Starch	96	100
Crude protein	70	76
Fibre polysaccharides	33	40

Pettersson and Åman, 1989

It is of interest to note that there is some microbial degradation of fibre prior to the ileum in both poultry and pigs. *In vitro* studies have shown that inocula taken from the pig intestine will degrade starch in preference to fibre, and it could be assumed that the microbes present in the fore-gut would also degrade starch and free sugars *in vivo* more readily than fibre. However, the extent of such degradation and what this means in terms of loss of energy to the host animal are unknown.

It would also appear that the ability to digest starch may be attained early in the life of piglets and chicks, although this may be disturbed somewhat during periods of stress such as weaning (Low, 1980; Moran, 1982). Indeed, it has been suggested that under optimal conditions a growing pig could produce sufficient amylases to hydrolyze half of its body weight of starch (Low and Longland, 1990). However, starch is rarely if ever completely digested prior to the ileum. There is evidence to suggest that starch digestibility may depend on botanical source, pretreatment and feeding practice. For example, it would appear that amylose is more digestible that amylopectin, perhaps not surprisingly considering the greater chemical complexity of the latter (Low and Longland, 1990). Further, starch from sources such as peas and potatoes would appear to be less digestible than cereal starch, and this may be a function of the structure of the starch granule or of the cell-wall composition of the feedstuff. Treatments which disrupt the cell wall, such as pelleting or enzyme supplementation, can improve ileal starch digestibility (Graham *et al.*, 1989). Indeed any mild heat treatment which partially disrupts the cell wall and gelatinizes the starch could be expected to increase digestibility, although excessive heat may lead to the formation of retrograded starch. There is also evidence that much of the starch which escapes digestion in the small intestine may do so immediately after feeding, presumably due to a rapid digesta flow during this time (Graham and Åman, 1986b).

Table 3.5. Pig ileal and faecal degradation (%) of dietary components in a barley-based diet or the same diet with 15% wheat fibre or 15% potato fibre included.

Site and component	Basal diet	+wheat fibre	+potato fibre
Ileum			
-starch	88[a]	87[a]	78[b]
-crude protein	69[a]	59[b]	55[b]
-NSP - arabinose	18	16	9
- xylose	13[ab]	24[a]	3[b]
- galactose	6	-4	8
- glucose	39[a]	25[b]	17[b]
- uronic acids	3[a]	1[a]	21[b]
- total	26[a]	17[ab]	12[b]
Faeces			
-crude protein	84[a]	76[b]	76[b]
-NSP - arabinose	73[a]	58[b]	76[a]
- xylose	57	66	54
- galactose	79[a]	69[b]	93[c]
- glucose	76[a]	61[b]	79[a]
- uronic acids	64[a]	46[b]	90[c]
- total	71[a]	61[b]	79[c]

[a-c]Means in a row that do not share a common superscript are significantly different (P<0.05).

H. Graham

Fibre Polysaccharides

Although it has long been known that the entire gastrointestinal tract is colonized with an active microflora essentially from birth, it was assumed that the rather inclement conditions in the fore-gut, the intransigence of the substrate and the relatively rapid digesta flow would limit any significant degradation of fibre there. However, it is now apparent that some fibre sources are highly degraded and that part of this degradation may occur in the small intestine of both the pig and the chick (Tables 3.4 & 3.5; Low and Longland, 1990; Longland *et al.*, 1990). Indeed, fibre polysaccharide degradation in the pig can approach 75% even in cereal-based diets and be much higher in the presence of other fibre sources (Table 3.5; Longland *et al.*, 1990). With fibre contents generally exceeding 15% of dry matter, and likely to increase with the now inevitable move to more vegetarian diets, this could obviously represent a considerable energy source for the animal.

Little is known of the processes of microbial degradation of carbohydrates in the non-ruminant and much of what is accepted is extrapolated from ruminant studies. It is apparent that the micro-organisms present degrade the carbohydrates by way of extra-cellular and wall-bound enzymes, and that the eventual end-products of such degradation are lactate, acetate, propionate, butyrate, carbon dioxide, methane, hydrogen and water. The digestion of complex fibre polysaccharides will undoubtably require the synergistic action of a number of enzymes, and it is likely that the major part of the monosaccharides liberated are immediately further metabolized by the bacteria. It is also apparent that fibres vary considerably in their susceptibility to degradation, with differences between feedstuffs, within the same feedstuff and indeed possibly between monosaccharide residues within a particular polysaccharide. Thus mixed-linked β-glucans and pectins are particularly susceptible to degradation, while cellulose tends to be less degraded. The factors which ultimately determine degradability are primarily digesta retention time and the chemical structure of the particular fibres present, with degree of lignification likely to play an important role. Ability to degrade intransigent fibres increases with age (Longland *et al.*, 1990), although whether this is due to a longer digesta retention time or to a more prolific microflora is unclear. A limited solubilization of fibre can occur during passage through the fore-gut, but much of the soluble fraction is degraded in the hind-gut, particularly in the pig.

Attempts to estimate the energy value of fibre and other carbohydrates degraded in the gastro-intestinal tract have been bedevilled by several factors including the chemical complexity of fibre, the wide range of metabolites produced on microbial fermentation, the divergence in degradability of different components and the fact that fibre polysaccharides make up only a small proportion of the potentially degradable material entering the hind-gut (Table 3.3). Nevertheless it is now accepted that the energy value to the pig of microbial fermentation of carbohydrates is about 70% of that from glucose absorbed as such in the fore-gut (Graham, 1988). This is presumably the case irrespective of whether this fermentation occurs

42

in the fore- or hind-gut. Little is known of the energy value of fibre in poultry, but in this case degradation is relatively low and thus will not contribute significantly to the energy requirements of the animal.

It should also be borne in mind that fibre can influence feed intake, digesta passage rate, access of hydrolytic enzymes to substrates and the secretion of host enzymes (Graham, 1988). This in turn can affect the digestion of other nutrients, including starch, protein and fat (Table 3.5), influencing the flow into the hind-gut and thus the loss to the animal of potential energy.

Designing an *in Vitro* Method

Any *in vitro* method, whether designed for research or for predicting the nutritive value of commercial feeds, must be accurate, rapid, cheap, simple, robust and adaptable. While methods developed for research purposes may be more sophisticated, those for commercial use must be sufficiently simple and robust to give reproducible results when used with a wide range of feeds in many locations. If possible, results obtained should be additive, allowing feedstuffs to be assigned values irrespective of the diet in which they are included. The method must also be relevant to the processes of digestion and metabolism. From the above discussion, two important parameters that it should be possible to determine by *in vitro* methods are:

1. the extent of digestion of nutrients, particularly starch, protein and fat, in the fore-gut;
2. the extent of degradation in the hind-gut of undigested components.

There are several assumptions that need to be made in order to design a simple and workable *in vitro* method; some of these are of dubious validity and introduce weaknesses. For example, nearly all systems assume, with some justification, that all soluble material is digestible. The effects of antinutrients will often be lost in *in vitro* systems, while effects of some components on intake and transit time will be difficult to assess. Other interactions between nutrients and the host, such as the possible fibre-mediated reduction in starch digestion in the fore-gut and increase in endogenous secretions, will also confound results.

As with all prediction methods, any *in vitro* method will only be as good as the standards on which it is based. In this case most methods will be used to predict the ME of feeds, having been standardized against data produced in animal balance studies. However, such data are at best suspect since all apparently digested components do not have the same energy value. This could lead to an over-estimation of the nutritive value of feedstuffs high in degradable fibres. Ultimately any *in vitro* method should be standardized against growth data from the particular animal type of interest.

It is apparent that *in vitro* methods will in future be used widely in non-ruminant nutrition. Such methods will probably only be applicable to the comparison of similar feeds, but they could prove useful in screening such feeds, for example, in assessing the effects of processing. Obviously such methods will have limited commercial use as all samples of feedstuffs cannot be screened on entry to the feedmill. However, *in vitro* methods coupled with continuous analysis of feedstuffs by rapid methods should allow a better exploitation of the variations in raw materials and thus more accurate feed formulation.

References

Bach Knudsen, K.E. and Eggum, B.O. (1984) The nutritive value of botanically defined mill fractions of barley. 3. The protein and energy value of pericarp, testa, germ, aleuron, and endosperm rich decortication fractions of the variety Bomi. *Zeitschrift für Tierphysiologie, Tierernährung und Futtermittelkunde* 51, 130-48.

Graham, H. (1988) Dietary fibre concentration and assimilation in swine. *ISI Atlas of Science; Animal and Plant Sciences* 1, 76-80.

Graham, H. and Åman, P. (1986a) Composition and digestion in the pig gastrointestinal tract of Jerusalem artichoke tubers. *Food Chemistry* 22, 67-76.

Graham, H. and Åman, P. (1986b) Circadian variation in composition of duodenal and ileal digesta from pigs fitted with T-cannula. *Animal Production* 43, 133-40.

Graham, H., Hesselman, K., Jonsson, E. and Åman, P. (1986) Influence of β-glucanase supplementation on digestion of a barley-based diet in the pig gastrointestinal tract. *Nutrition Reports International* 34, 1089-96.

Graham, H., Åman, P. and Pettersson, D. (1987) Variation in composition of Swedish cereal grains. In: Munch, L. (ed.), *Proceedings from 23rd. Nordic Cereal Congress*. The Danish Cereal Society, Copenhagen, pp. 87-93.

Graham, H., Fadel, J.G., Newman, C.W. and Newman, R.K. (1989) Effect of pelleting and β-glucanase supplementation on the ileal and fecal digestibility of a barley-based diet in the pig. *Journal of Animal Science* 67, 1293-8.

Longland, A.C., Close, W.H. and Low, A.G. (1990) Effects of feeding plant cardohydrates from contrasting botanical sources on the performance of pigs. NJF Seminar 189, *Plant Carbohydrates and Associated Components* Herning, Denmark; 18-20 June 1990; 4 pp.

Low, A.G. (1980) Nutrient absorption in pigs. *Journal of the Science of Food and Agriculture* 31, 1087-130.

Low, A.G. and Longland, A.C. (1990) Carbohydrate and dietary fibre digestion in the pig and the possible influence of feed enzymes. *Feed Compounder* 10, 5-10.

Moran, E.T. (1982) Starch digestion in fowl. *Poultry Science* 61, 1257-67.

Pettersson, D. and Åman, P. (1989) Enzyme supplementation of a poultry diet containing rye and wheat. *British Journal of Nutrition* 62, 139-49.

Wrick, K.L., Robertson, J.B., van Soest, P.J., Lewis, B.A., Roe, D.A. and Hackler, L.R. (1983) The influence of dietary fiber source on human intestinal transit time and stool output. *Journal of Nutrition* 113, 1464-79.

Chapter 4

Indirect Effects of Food Antinutrients on Protein Digestibility and Nutritional Value of Diets

A. Pusztai, R. Begbie, G. Grant, S.W.B. Ewen and S. Bardocz

Introduction

It is a common experience in animal nutrition that plant proteins are more often resistant to breakdown in the alimentary tract than animal proteins (Pusztai, 1985; Begbie and Pusztai, 1989). With some plant proteins, such as the 7S legume seed proteins, this resistance may have its origin, at least in part, in structural features (Begbie and Pusztai, 1989). When rats are fed on such proteins, those parts of the protein structure which are not broken down by proteolytic enzymes in the small intestine are not nutritionally utilized by the animals. The resistant part(s) of these proteins pass into the large intestine where digestion occurs mainly through microbial action. The N released by this process is almost totally lost to the animal. Thus, the poor digestibility of plant proteins due to structural (or other) features seriously limits their full nutritional utilization.

The constraint that incomplete digestibility places on the nutritional utilization of plant proteins is relatively easy to predict from *in vitro* digestibility measurements. However, if the dietary protein survives fully or partly in the small intestine and is capable of interaction with enzymes or other components of the digesta or the cells lining the intestinal tract or with their secretions, this reactivity may not just interfere with the proper functioning of the digestive system but also makes it difficult for us to predict the magnitude of the deterioration in nutritional performance from *in vitro* measurements. In fact, the extent of disturbances in digestive or absorptive function or the occurrence of increased tissue catabolism due to destructive local and systemic immune (or other) responses to the food is usually gauged from the difference between nutrient utilization found in *in vivo* feeding experiments and that predicted from *in vitro* measurements (Fig. 4.1). Thus, due to the indirect effects on protein digestibility of dietary antinutrients in the small intestine, dietary proteins may appear to be less digestible *in vivo* than *in vitro* digestion tests would predict.

Of the many and various factors which may be present in foods, particularly in foods of plant origin, two main classes of protein antinutrients, the lectins and the proteolytic enzyme inhibitors, are probably the most important in nutrition.

A. Pusztai, R. Begbie, G. Grant, S.W.B. Ewen, and S. Bardocz

Fig. 4.1. Nutritional utilization of diets containing kidney bean proteins.

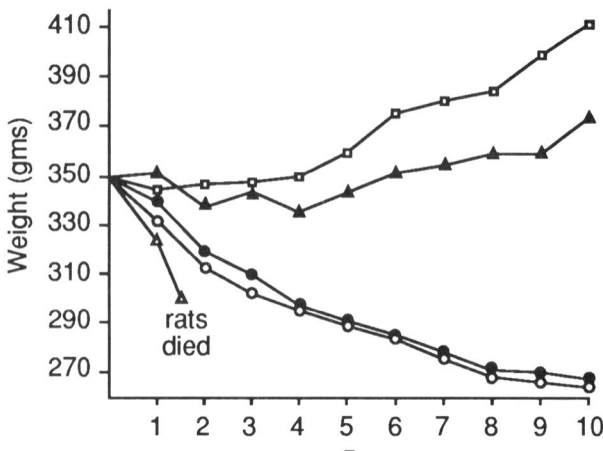

Rats, in groups of four, were fed for 10 days on a protein-free diet (O) or on diets with a total dietary protein concentration of 100 g/kg. The diets included: a mixture 1:1 of kidney bean and casein proteins (●); raw (▲) or cooked kidney bean proteins (▲) and casein (□).

Protease Inhibitors

Protease (trypsin) inhibitors have long been known to interfere with the proper digestion of dietary proteins in the small intestine (Pusztai, 1967; Liener and Kakade, 1980; Gallaher and Schneeman, 1984). It is less widely recognized that the direct effects of protease inhibitors on the digestibility of food proteins may be limited because, in normal healthy individuals, there is usually an ample supply of pancreatic proteases. Thus, the protease inhibitors present in the diet may neutralize only a part of the digestive enzymes. Clearly, the activity of the proteases which remain unattached to inhibitors will not be affected. Additionally, soyabean trypsin inhibitors are eventually degraded and inactivated during their passage through the small intestine, at least in chicks (Madar *et al.*, 1979). In contrast, the Bowman-Birk inhibitor from soyabean appears to be more resistant to breakdown in the alimentary tract (Troll and Yavelow, 1983). Even with the possibility that some inhibitors may be resistant to breakdown in the gut their amounts in the diets are limited and dietary protease inhibitors may, at most, only slow down the rate of luminal digestion. The net result of this is that a part of the nutrients will be digested in the more distal parts of the small intestine.

It is now widely accepted that one of the main antinutritive effects of protease (trypsin) inhibitors in the diet is due to their overstimulation of the secretion of digestive enzymes from the exocrine pancreas (Chernik *et al.*, 1948; Lyman and Lepkovsky, 1957). It is thought that the inhibitors in the lumen of the small intestine first react with the appropriate pancreatic protease(s). As a result, the concentrations of the endopeptidases in the lumen fall. This, by a mechanism not fully understood, induces the release of cholecystokinin from gut endocrine cells into the systemic circulation and this in turn stimulates the secretion of enzymes from the exocrine pancreas (Ihse *et al.*, 1979; Owyang *et al.*, 1986).

The mechanism of the release of the hormone is complex. Although the signal is dependent on the falling luminal concentrations of pancreatic enzymes, the effects of the enzymes are indirect. The mediation of the signal is probably through monitor peptide(s) originating from the pancreas or the jejunal mucosa. In the absence of the inhibitors, the monitor peptides are split and inactivated by the proteases present in the lumen. In the presence of inhibitors, the low levels of proteases in the lumen cannot inactivate the monitor peptides. Thus, their binding to and stimulation of the gut endocrine cells is no longer inhibited.

The net result of this stimulation of pancreatic enzyme secretion is the loss into the faeces of a part of the secreted pancreatic proteins which is not fully recycled. As most pancreatic enzymes are rich in sulphur-containing amino acids, their loss will aggravate the nutritional problems of legume seed proteins, most of which are particularly deficient in methionine. If the protease inhibitor-protease complexes escape digestion in the small intestine, this will lead both to inefficient utilization of dietary proteins and to increased losses of valuable endogenous proteins.

Lectins

Lectins constitute a specific class of proteins, widely distributed in nature, which are involved in recognition processes occurring in biological systems (Pusztai, 1989). Lectins, in highly specific ways, recognize and reversibly bind to simple or complex carbohydrates, both in solution and present on membranes or other biological surfaces. Lectins are different from carbohydrases or other sugar-specific enzymes as their binding is not followed by changes in the covalent structure of the ligands. Most lectins are bi- or tetra-valent and, therefore, can crosslink cells and agglutinate them.

Seeds, and particularly legume seeds, are rich sources of lectins. Diets based on raw legume seed meals usually contain lectins, some of which may possess strong antinutritive properties. Although some lectins are inactivated by proper heat treatments, such processes are expensive and, therefore, in commerce, are usually avoided. Additionally, 30-40% of the naturally occurring lectins are difficult to inactivate by heating. Accordingly, the digestive systems of both man and animals are regularly exposed to lectins as a part of the natural diet.

Resistance to Proteolysis

One of the main reasons why lectins can possess strong antinutritive properties is to be found in the extraordinary degree of their resistance to proteolytic breakdown

47

A. Pusztai, R. Begbie, G. Grant, S.W.B. Ewen, and S. Bardocz

in the gut (Pusztai, 1986; 1989; Pusztai *et al.*, 1986). Measurements by immunochemical techniques of the amounts of lectins which survive passage in the gut revealed that some lectins, such as *Phaseolus vulgaris* lectin (PHA), concanavalin A, snowdrop bulb (*Galanthus nivalis*) agglutinin (GNA), etc., may survive almost entirely (Pusztai *et al.*, 1990a). Even with less resistant lectins, such as the agglutinins isolated from *Vicia faba*, *Pisum sativum* or *Dioclea grandiflora*, the extent of survival was not less than 20% (Table 4.1).

Table 4.1. Survival and binding by the rat small intestinal epithelium of pure lectins 1 h after intragastric administration.

Lectins	Specificity	Binding	% Immunoreactive lectin recovered
PHA (*Phaseolus vulgaris*)	Complex	+++	>90
Con A (*Canavalia ensiformis*)	Man/Glco	++	>90
GNA (*Galanthus nivalis*)	Man	-	>90
SNA-I (*Sambucus nigra*)	α-2,6-neuraminyl-Gal	+	50-60
SNA-II (*Sambucus nigra*)	GalNAc	+++	>60
SBL (*Glycine max*)	GalNAc/Gal	++	40-50
LEL (*Lycopersicon esculentum*)	GALNAc	+	40-50
WGA (*Triticum vulgare*)	GlcNAc	+	50-60
PSL (*Pisum sativum*)	Man/Glc	±	20-30
VCF (*Vicia faba*)	Man/Glc	±	20-30
DGL(*Dioclea grandiflora*)	Man/Glc	±	18-20

Rats were intubated intragastrically with 10 mg of individual lectins. After 1 h, the rats were killed. The stomach was rinsed with saline (0.15 M)-phosphate buffer (0.05 M), pH 7.6 and the small intestine with the same buffer containing aprotinin (0.1 mg/ml). Small intestinal tissue was homogenized with the same buffer containing aprotinin and in the presence of 0.1 M of the appropriate haptenic carbohydrate. The amount of surviving lectin was estimated by rocket immunoelectrophoresis against the appropriate monospecific antibody.

It has often been suggested that it is their binding to receptors which protects the lectins from proteolytic breakdown. Protection by the lectin receptor is probably due to steric hindrance or even to complete shielding of those peptide bonds in the primary structure of the lectin which, in a free state, may be open to proteolytic enzyme attack. Thus, recent work (unpublished) has shown that kidney bean lectin, PHA, can be degraded *in vitro* by successive exposure of the lectin to pepsin and trypsin/chymotrypsin. However, in the presence of fetuin, a glycoprotein to which it binds avidly, the lectin becomes largely refractory to breakdown (Fig. 2). This protection by fetuin is even more remarkable in that it occurs at pH values as low as 2 (pepsin), whereas under normal conditions, PHA bound to fetuin-Sepharose-4B affinity columns is quantitatively displaced from the column below pH 3 (Pusztai and Palmer, 1977). However, although protection of lectins by binding to ligands definitely occurs, it does not necessarily follow that lectins which do not bind to the mucosa will be degraded. For example, although negligible amounts of the snowdrop bulb lectin, GNA, bind to the small intestinal mucosa on acute administration, over 93% of the lectin introduced initially remains undegraded, as judged by immunochemical criteria (Pusztai *et al.*, 1990a).

Fig. 4.2. The protective effects of glycoconjugate ligands (bovine fetuin) in the digestion of PHA by gastrointestinal proteases.

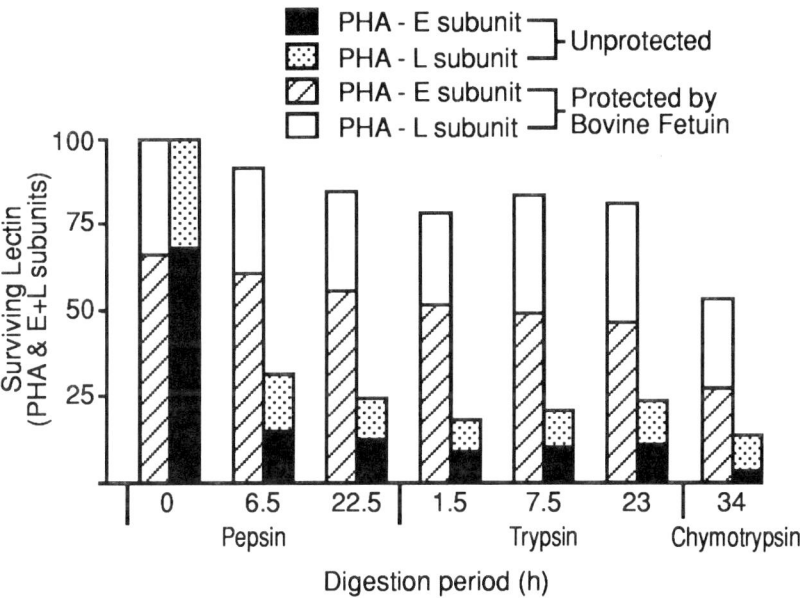

Affinity-purified PHA (E_2L_2, 5 mg) was treated with porcine pepsin at pH 2 and 37°; after adjustment to pH 7.4 further sequential hydrolysis was carried out with trypsin and chymotrypsin. Enzyme: substrate ratios were 1:50 (w/w). The protection afforded by inclusion of bovine fetuin (5 mg) in digests is illustrated. Porcine gastric mucin (10 mg) was similarly effective.

Binding to the Mucosa, Endocytosis and Intestinal Damage

The extraordinary effectiveness of lectins as antinutrients is due to their recognition of and binding to carbohydrate moieties. As the luminal membranes of epithelial cells or secretions in the small intestine contain carbohydrate structures of diverse composition and complexity, surviving lectins may bind to these membranes and secretions, depending on the sugar specificity of the lectin and the carbohydrate composition of the mucosal receptor. By crosslinking receptors in the membranes, the multivalent lectins are capable of severely distorting the structures of the lipid bilayer and of the proteins embedded in it. Accordingly, lectin binding may lead to an interference of varying severity with the morphology and proper functioning of the epithelial cells. For example, kidney bean lectin, PHA, by binding to the luminal surface of the proximal small intestine (King *et al.*, 1980a) causes severe damage to the architecture of the brush border of both rats

Fig. 4.3. Erosion of the microvilli of small intestinal epithelial cells by dietary PHA and the consequent overgrowth of bacteria.

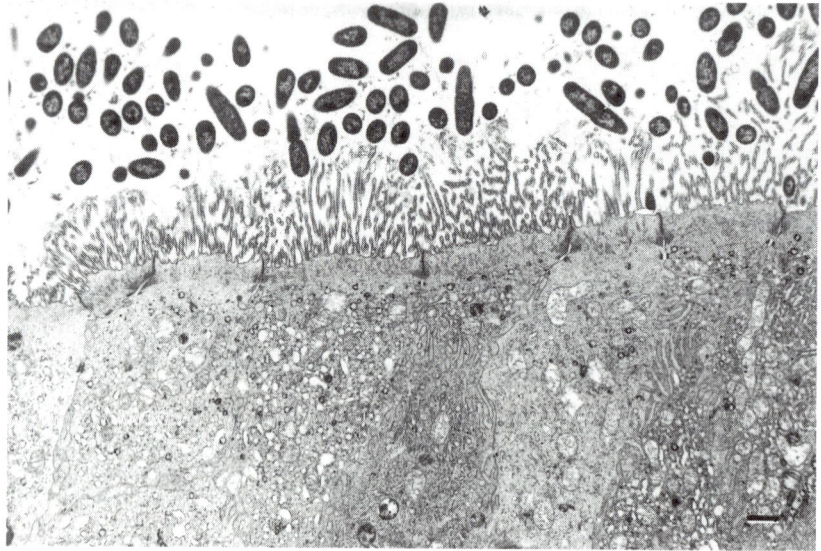

Rats were fed on kidney bean diets for 10 days. The electron micrograph of a section of the jejunum shows overgrowth of coliform bacteria associated with damaged microvilli. Scale bar: 1μm.

(Fig. 4.3; King *et al.*, 1980b; 1982) and pigs (King *et al.*, 1983). The binding of the lectin to epithelial cells is followed by extensive endocytosis (Fig. 4.4; King *et al.*, 1986) and an immediate near doubling of the rate of protein synthesis in the mucosa (Palmer *et al.*, 1987). Similar effects have been observed with all the other lectins which can bind to the mucosa (Pusztai, 1989; Begbie and Pusztai, 1989; Pusztai *et al.*, 1990a). Thus, concanavalin or wheat germ agglutinin (WGA), a lectin which is regarded as non-toxic, accelerate cell turnover and loss from the brush border of the proximal small intestine (Lorenzsonn and Olsen, 1982; Nakata and Kimura, 1986).

It is now generally recognized that lectins from food or bacteria and bacterial toxins may cause intestinal damage. However, in the absence of quantitative information on the extent of the damage caused by the different lectins, it is very difficult to predict the magnitude of their harmful effects. Nevertheless, it is clear that the erosion of the absorptive surface of the small intestine by exposure to dietary lectins will appreciably reduce the efficiency of nutrient conversion in the animal.

Fig. 4.4. Endocytosis by epithelial cells of dietary kidney bean lectin, PHA.

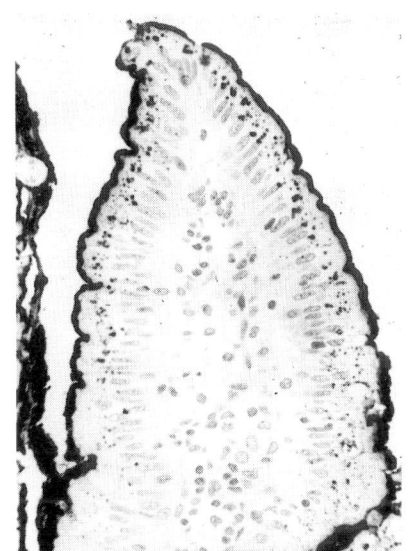

Specific immunoreactive PAP (peroxidase-antiperoxidase)-staining of a section from the jejunum of rats fed for 10 days on a diet containing PHA. The formalin-fixed section after trypsin treatment was reacted with monospecific rabbit anti-PHA antibody. The second antibody treatment (PAP) was followed by staining with 3,3'-diaminobenzidine and counterstained with haematoxylin. Bar represents 100 μm.

Lectins as Growth Factors

Despite their damaging effects on the microvilli, lectins which bind to epithelial cell membranes can also stimulate the growth of the small intestine and, therefore, function as exogenous growth factors for the gut (Pusztai *et al.*, 1990a). PHA, for instance, induces a dose-dependent and fully reversible hyperplastic growth of the small bowel (Fig. 4.5; Greer and Pusztai, 1985; de Oliveira *et al.*, 1988). Although the biochemical mechanism of the growth is not fully clear at present, the cellular proliferation which follows the binding and endocytosis of PHA by the epithelial cells strongly resemble the well-known, lectin-induced mitosis and proliferation of peripheral lymphocytes. In addition, like other hyperplastic or hypertrophic

51

A. Pusztai, R. Begbie, G. Grant, S.W.B. Ewen, and S. Bardocz

growth processes, the PHA-induced growth of the small intestine is coincident with an increased accumulation of polyamines in the tissue (Pusztai *et al.*, 1988; 1989; Bardocz *et al.*, 1990a,b). It appears that before proliferation can occur, the lectin first stimulates the uptake of polyamines from the circulation *via* the basolateral membrane of the epithelial cells. This increase in polyamine uptake is the first stage of the PHA-induced elevation of cellular metabolism and precedes the increases in the rates of RNA, protein and DNA synthesis (Palmer *et al.*, 1987; Bardocz *et al.*, 1990a,b) which, in turn, occur before the onset of crypt cell proliferation. Indeed, all lectins which can bind to mucosal cells, and not just PHA, stimulate the growth of the small intestine by a similar mechanism. These lectins do not just increase the size of the small intestine but also increase epithelial cell turnover and shedding of cells from the villi (Pusztai *et al.*, 1990a). Although it is not known what proportion of the constituents of the sloughed off cells are recycled, it is unlikely that their re-absorption reaches 100% efficiency. Thus, the dietary lectin-induced growth of the small intestine and the increased epithelial cell turnover may make an appreciable contribution to the overall loss of endogenous proteins and other constituents from the body.

Fig. 5. 5. The dependence of the weight of the small intestine on the amounts of pure PHA ingested in 10 days.

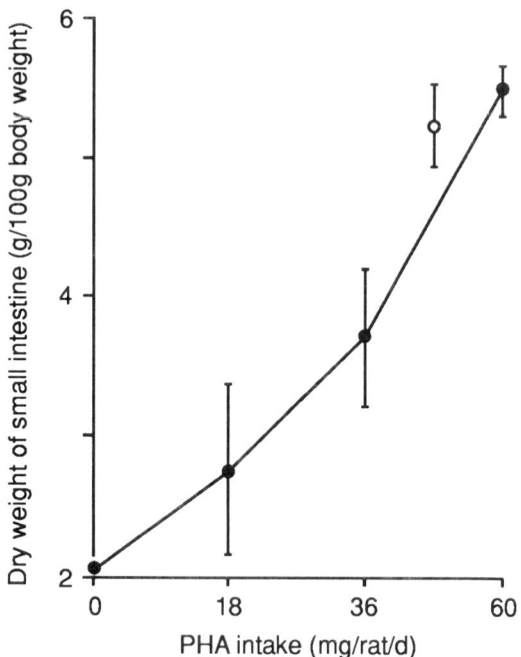

In fact, the increase in epithelial cell metabolism, including hyperplastic growth, occurs at the expense of nutritional efficiency. Approximate calculations show that if both the weight of the small intestinal mucosa and the turnover of its epithelial cells increase, a situation is soon reached when the total intake of nutrients is insufficient for the maintenance of mucosal continuity and integrity. Thus, because of the effects of the lectin on gut metabolism under such conditions, the animal could be losing more protein than it consumes, even with diets which were more than adequate for its nutritional requirements (Table 4.2).

Effects on Goblet Cell Mucin

Further reduction in nutritional efficiency occurs because some food lectins may increase not only the rate of tissue protein synthesis but also the rates of both synthesis and secretion of mucinous glycoproteins by epithelial goblet cells (Freed and Buckley, 1979; Greer and Pusztai, 1985). As the mammalian small intestine lacks enzymes which can degrade mucinous glycoproteins, the stimulation by lectins of mucin synthesis and secretion represents an increased loss from the body. Indeed, by blocking the binding to brush border receptors of injurious lectins from food or bacteria or of bacterial toxins, the shedding of membrane glycoproteins and increased secretory activity may be a protective mechanism for the small intestine (Fox, 1979; Weiser, 1984).

Table 4.2. The approximate protein cost of the PHA-induced hyperplasia and increased cell turnover in the small intestine (S.I.).

Diet	S.I.weight (mg/g body weight)	S.I. protein content (mg)	Cell turnover time (h)	Daily protein requirements of S.I. (assuming no recycling)	
				mg	%
Control	0.02	250-300	36-48	120-150	>20
Kidney bean (5%,7d)	0.04	500-600	24	500-600	>60-90
Kidney bean (5%,14d)	0.06	750-900	>24	700-900	>100

The total daily intake of protein in these calculations was 600-700 mg. Cell turnover times are approximate values.

A. Pusztai, R. Begbie, G. Grant, S.W.B. Ewen, and S. Bardocz

Allergenic Reactions

Loss of endogenous proteins may also result from hypersensitivity reactions to dietary lectins of the local (gut) immune system. Type-1 immediate hypersensitivity reactions occur generally to even highly degradable food proteins, despite the fact that these proteins disappear very quickly from the small intestinal lumen. The likelihood of similar allergenic reactions to lectins which persistently bind to mucosal cells is much higher.

Table 4.3. The leakage of rat serum proteins (RSP) into the wall and the lumen of the small intestine of rats due to gut anaphylactic reactions to PHA.

Diet:	Control		Kidney bean
Intubation:	Saline	PHA	PHA
Labelled RSP in wall + lumen (mg)	0.20±0.02	0.90±0.09	1.70±0.14

Groups of rats were fed on kidney bean or control diets for 11 days. Some of the rats on the control diet were given 10 mg of PHA by intragastric intubation; the others were given saline. Rats fed on the kidney bean diet were given 10 mg PHA only. 1 h later, the rats were injected intravenously with a single dose (10 mg) of radioactively labelled homologous rat serum protein (RSP) preparation. 1 h after that the rats were killed and the TCA precipitable counts in the lumen and in the gut wall were determined. The absolute amounts of RSP in the wall and lumen were calculated from the specific activity of the RSP sample injected.

The anaphylactic responses to lectins and other dietary proteins are usually measured by injecting rats intravenously with ^{125}I-labelled rat serum proteins and then, after an intragastric challenge with the sensitizing lectin or protein, the amounts of labelled proteins leaked into the gut wall and lumen are measured within a short time, such as 1 h. By such measurements it was shown that even a single dose of PHA, in rats never previously exposed to the lectin, could increase vascular permeability and the accumulation of serum proteins in the wall and the lumen of the small intestine (Pusztai and Greer, 1984; Greer and Pusztai, 1985). Indeed, it is known that lectins can bind to mast cells and induce their degranulation directly, without the mediation of the immune system (Bach and Brashler, 1975; Ennis *et al.*, 1981). It is possible that the increased permeability of the small intestine to large molecules found experimentally in rats after a single treatment with PHA (Table 4.3) is due to such direct effects of the lectin on gut mast cells (Pusztai and Greer, 1984; Greer and Pusztai, 1985). However, the extent of the leakage of serum proteins into the gut was much higher if rats had been prefed on diets containing PHA for 11 days (Table 4.3). This suggested that the original direct degranulation of mast cells was amplified by a local immune hypersensitivity (type-1) reaction to the lectin (Pusztai and Greer, 1984; Greer and Pusztai, 1985).

From our present knowledge it is difficult to predict the likely extent of protein loss due to the direct or indirect effects of lectins on gut mast cells. Undoubtedly, an unknown proportion of the serum proteins exuded into the intestinal wall and lumen is recycled. However, it is clear that, despite this re-absorption, lectins, because of their interactions with the local (gut) allergenic immune system, increase the wastage of endogenous proteins and thus reduce the efficiency of nutrient assimilation.

Effects on the Microbial Ecology of the Small Intestine

That infection of the gut with pathogenic bacteria is detrimental to nutritional efficiency and health is obvious. However, it is less widely appreciated that in the presence of large numbers of even non-pathogenic bacteria in the small intestine, nutrient utilization may be severely depressed. Moreover, the numbers and species of bacteria present in the small intestine are not static. Quite to the contrary, some dietary components, such as lectins, can cause appreciable and selective proliferation of individual species of bacteria in the digestive tract. For example, feeding conventional rats on diets containing raw kidney beans has very serious consequences for growth and health (Fig. 4.1). In germ-free rats, although the efficiency of nutritional utilization is not high, the same raw kidney bean diets are far less toxic for the animals without bacteria in the alimentary tract (Rattray *et al.*, 1974). Similar observations have been made with other animal species investigated (Jayne-Williams and Hewitt, 1972). Concurrent with the increased toxicity of kidney bean proteins for conventional rats, there is a substantial overgrowth of *E. coli* in their small intestine (Wilson *et al.*, 1980). It is now clear that both the nutritional toxicity and the bacterial proliferation are caused by the presence of PHA in kidney bean diets. Thus, with low-lectin cultivars, such as Pinto III, the overgrowth by *E. coli* is much reduced. As expected, diets based on Pinto III beans are utilized by conventional rats with about the same efficiency as the germ-free rats utilize the normal kidney bean cultivars (Wilson *et al.*, 1980). Moreover, because the *E. coli* overgrowth is dependent on the presence of PHA, when the lectin is removed from the diet of rats which have previously been fed on kidney bean-containing diets, the *E. coli* overgrowth is abolished. In all species tested studies have confirmed that the causative agent of kidney bean in bacterial overgrowth and nutritional toxicity is indeed the lectin PHA (Jayne-Williams and Burgess, 1974; Banwell *et al.*, 1984).

Several mechanisms have been proposed to explain the role of PHA in the bacterial overgrowth. One suggestion is that, by eliminating other competing species in the gut, PHA promotes the proliferation of *E. coli*. A similar promotion of *E. coli* overgrowth may occur if PHA agglutinates the cells of *E. coli* to each other, to mucosal cells or to both. It has also been suggested that the mannose-containing carbohydrate side chains of PHA, already bound to mucosal surfaces, may provide attachment points for the mannose-fimbriated *E. coli* (King *et al.*, 1983; Banwell *et al.*, 1984; Boldt and Banwell, 1985).

Recent detailed studies give no support to these ideas. Indeed, no evidence of specific association between PHA and *E. coli* was found (Ceri *et al.*, 1988). Moreover, the presence of PHA made no difference to the extent of bacterial adhesion to washed small intestine mucosa in three different types of binding assay. Thus, although the involvement of PHA in the selective overgrowth of *E. coli* is not in doubt, the role of the lectin might be indirect (Banwell *et al.*, 1988; Ceri *et al.*, 1988). As mucosal surfaces in rats fed on PHA-containing diets were overgrown by *E. coli*, while those in control rats were essentially free of the bacteria, it is possible that the presence of the lectin in the lumen of the small intestine may promote access of the bacteria to the epithelial surface by some unknown mechanism (Ceri *et al.*, 1988).

Recent work on the effects of a variety of lectins on gut structure has shown how the diet affects the bacterial ecology of the small intestine indirectly, through changes in gut morphology. It was shown that the diet, or some components of it, could have profound effects on the structure and the receptor expression of the absorptive surface of the small intestine. Thus, chronic exposure to those dietary lectins which behave as exogenous growth factors for the small intestine affected the carbohydrate composition and structure of epithelial receptors by speeding up the rates of differentiation and maturation of crypt cells (Pusztai *et al.*, 1990a). For example, in the presence of PHA in the diet, an appreciable proportion of the villus cells might be immature. As these cells reacted with antibodies to crypt cell antigens they presumably retained polymannose residues in the carbohydrate side chains of their membrane glycoproteins rather than converting them to complex carbohydrate side chains characteristic of fully differentiated cellular envelopes (King and Pusztai unpublished). Such mannose-containing receptors may serve as new attachment points for *E. coli* in those rats which were fed on diets containing PHA. Other lectins may change the carbohydrate receptor expression in the small intestine by other mechanisms. Thus, continuous overstimulation by some lectins of mucus secretion may reduce the concentrations of those carbohydrate structures which feature prominently in goblet cells mucins (Pusztai *et al.*, 1990a). Long-term exposure to lectins may also increase the concentrations of particular receptors by displacing endogenous ligands which, under normal conditions, are bound to these receptors (Pusztai *et al.*, 1990a).

Chemical Probiosis

As the attachment of bacteria (Sharon, 1987) or parasitic protozoa (Lev *et al.*, 1986) to carbohydrate receptors on epithelial cells is mediated mainly by lectin-adhesins, those food constituents which resemble the carbohydrate moieties of receptors interfere with microbial binding to the gut wall. Moreover, the food lectins which possess carbohydrate specificities similar to those of the bacterial adhesins may competitively block the attachment and the consequent proliferation of particular species of bacteria. Alternatively, the presence in the gut of food lectins whose specificities are different from those of the bacterial adhesins may aggravate the damage to the small intestinal epithelium caused by the bacteria. Clearly, when several lectins bind to different receptors on the same epithelial cell, the damaging effects of the individual lectins may be additive or even synergistic. Interactions occur continuously between the diet, the microbes and the gut, as defined by the concept of chemical probiosis (Pusztai *et al.*, 1990b). Therefore, changes in any of these three components will have major effects on the bacterial ecology of the small intestine, on the effectiveness of the gut barrier function and, ultimately, on the efficiency of the utilization of nutrients.

Accordingly, the presence of bacteria in the digestive tract makes an unknown contribution to the reduction in nutritional efficiency often observed in practice. Clearly, some antinutritive components of the diet, such as the lectins, largely determine the extent of this bacterially-mediated interference in nutritional performance. Lectins either react directly with the bacterial species or may indirectly affect the microbial balance in the gut through modifying the structure of the small intestine. Unfortunately, based on our present knowledge, it is difficult to predict the extent of this interference which may depend on the carbohydrate specificity of the individual lectin. With some lectins, such as PHA, the effects will be serious and may lead to death. With some other lectins which do not bind to the mucosa, such as the lectin from broad bean (*Vicia faba*), the effects will be negligible (Pusztai *et al.*, 1990a).

Conclusion

The efficiency of the utilization of diets based on plant proteins is not easily predicted. Clearly, if the dietary proteins are not fully digested in the small intestine, their nutritional value is predictably reduced. However, if the dietary proteins are not digested fully and if they react with either the gut or its bacterial content, a further deterioration in the efficiency of both digestion and absorption will occur. According to our present understanding, some dietary components interact with the gut and modify the metabolism, digestive, absorptive, immune and endocrine functions of the small intestine and its bacterial content. The extent of the possible reduction in nutritional efficiency will, however, be variable and dependent on the composition of the diet and the bacterial status of the gut. The deterioration in the nutritional performance of the animals under such conditions will therefore be largely unpredictable from *in vitro* measurements. Thus, present studies with lectins, bacteria and the gut of model animals (rats, pigs, etc.) may give only a qualitative, rather empirical and vague prediction of the likely consequences of the dietary inclusion of food components defined as antinutrients. It appears that,

A. Pusztai, R. Begbie, G. Grant, S.W.B. Ewen, and S. Bardocz

at least for the time being, there are no reliable short-cuts to *in vivo* animal testing.

Acknowledgements

The Emeritus Fellowship from The Leverhulme Trust to Dr. Pusztai is gratefully acknowledged. The authors are also indebted to Dr. T.P. King for the electron micrograph (Fig. 4.3).

References

Bach, M.K. and Brashler, J.R. (1975) Inhibition of IgE and compound 48/80-induced histamine release by lectins. *Immunology* 29, 371-86.

Banwell, J.G., Abramowsky, C.R., Weber, F., Howard, R., and Boldt, D.H. (1984) Phytohemagglutinin-induced diarrheal disease. *Digestive Diseases and Sciences* 29, 921-9.

Banwell, J.G., Howard, R., Kabir, I. and Costerton, J.W. (1988) Bacterial overgrowth by indigenous microflora in the phytohemagglutinin fed rats. *Canadian Journal of Microbiology* **34**, 1009-13.

Bardocz, S., Grant, G., Brown, D.S., Ewen, S.W.B., Nevison, I. and Pusztai, A. (1990a) Polyamine metabolism and uptake during *Phaseolus vulgaris* lectin, PHA-induced growth of rat small intestine. *Digestion* 46 (suppl 2), 360-6.

Bardocz, S., Brown, D.S., Grant, G. and Pusztai, A. (1990b) Luminal and basolateral polyamine uptake by rat small intestine stimulated to grow by *Phaseolus vulgaris* lectin phytohaemagglutinin *in vivo*. *Biochimica et Biophysica Acta* 1034, 46-52.

Begbie, R. and Pusztai, A. (1989) The resistance to proteolytic breakdown of some plant (seed) proteins and their effects on nutrient utilization and gut metabolism. In: Friedman, M. (ed.) *Absorption and Utilisation of Amino Acids Vol.III*. CRC Press, Boca Raton, Fl, 244-63.

Boldt, D.H. and Banwell, J.G. (1985) Binding of isolectins from red kidney bean (*Phaseolus vulgaris*) to purified rat brush border membranes. *Biochimica et Biophysica Acta* 843, 230-7.

Ceri, H., Falkenberg-Anderson, K., Fang, R., Costerton, J.W., Howard, R. and Banwell, J.G. (1988) Bacteria-lectin interactions in phytohemagglutinin-induced bacterial overgrowth of the small intestine. *Canadian Journal of Microbiology* 34, 1003-8

Chernik, S.S., Lepkovsky, S. and Chaikoff, I.L. (1948) Dietary factor regulating the enzyme content of the pancreas - changes induced in size and proteolytic activity of the chick pancreas by the ingestion of raw soybean meal. *American Journal of Physiology* 155, 33-41.

de Oliveira, J.T.A., Pusztai, A. and Grant, G. (1988) Changes in organs and tissues induced by feeding of purified kidney bean (*Phaseolus vulgaris*) lectins. *Nutrition Research* 8, 943-7.

Ennis, M., Truneh, A. and Pearce, F.L. (1981) Lectin-induced histamine secretion from isolated rat and guinea pig mast cells. *Biochemical Pharmacology* 30, 2179-81.

Fox, R.A. (1979) Membrane glycoproteins shed in defense of cells of the gastrointestinal tract. *Medical Hypotheses* 5, 669-82.

Freed, D.L.J. and Buckley, C.H. (1979) Mucotractive effect of lectin. *Lancet* i, 585-6.

Gallaher, D. and Schneeman, B.O. (1984) Nutritional and metabolic response to plant inhibitors of digestive enzymes. *Advances in Experimental Medicine and Biology* 177, 299-320.

Greer, F. and Pusztai,A. (1985) Toxicity of kidney bean (*Phaseolus vulgaris*) in rats: Changes in intestinal permeability. *Digestion* 32, 42-6.

Ihse, I., Lilja, P. and Lundquist, I. (1979) Trypsin as a regulator of pancreatic secretion in the rat. *Scandinavian Journal of Gastroenterology* 14, 873-80.

Jayne-Williams. D.J. and Burgess, C.D. (1974) Further observations on the toxicity of navy beans (*Phaseolus vulgaris*) for Japanese quail (*Coturnix coturnix japonica*). *Journal of Applied Bacteriology* 37, 149-69.

Jayne-Williams, D.J. and Hewitt, D. (1972) The relationship between the intestinal microflora and the effects of diets containing raw navy bean (*Phaseolus vulgaris*) on the growth of Japanese quail (*Coturnix coturnix japonica*). *Journal of Applied Bacteriology* 35, 331-44.

King, T.P., Pusztai, A. and Clarke, E.M.W. (1980a) Immunochemical localization of ingested kidney bean (*Phaseolus vulgaris*) lectins in rat gut. *Histochemical Journal* 12, 201-08.

King, T.P., Pusztai, A. and Clarke, E.M.W. (1980b) Kidney bean (*Phaseolus vulgaris*) lectin-induced lesions in the rat small intestine. I. Light microscope studies. *Journal of Comparative Pathology* 90, 585-95.

King, T.P., Pusztai, A. and Clarke, E.M.W. (1982) Kidney bean (*Phaseolus vulgaris*) lectin-induced lesions in the rat small intestine. 3. Ultrastructural studies. *Journal of Comparative Pathology* 92, 357-73.

King, T.P., Begbie, R. and Cadenhead, A. (1983) Nutritional toxicity of raw kidney beans in pigs. Immunocytochemical and cytopathological studies on the gut and the pancreas. *Journal of the Science of Food and Agriculture* 34, 1404-12.

King, P.T., Pusztai, A., Grant, G, and Slater, D. (1986) Immunogold localization of ingested kidney bean (*Phaseolus vulgaris*) lectins in epithelial cells of the rat small intestine. *Histochemical Journal* 18, 413-20.

Lev, B., Ward, H., Keusch, G.T. and Pereira, M.E.A. (1986) Lectin activation in *Giardia lamblia* by host protease: a novel host-parasite interaction. *Science* 232, 71-3.

Liener, I.E. and Kakade, M.L. (1980) Protease inhibitors. In: Liener, I.E. (ed.) *Toxic Constituents of Plant Foodstuffs* 2nd edn Academic Press, New York,

A. Pusztai, R. Begbie, G. Grant, S.W.B. Ewen, and S. Bardocz

pp.7-71.

Lorenzsonn, V. and Olsen, W.A. (1982) *In vivo* responses of small intestinal epithelium to intraluminal dietary lectins. *Gastroenterology* 82, 838-48.

Lyman, R.L. and Lepkovsky, S. (1957) The effect of raw soybean meal and trypsin inhibitor diets on pancreatic enzyme secretion in the rat. *Journal of Nutrition* 62, 269-84.

Madar, Z., Gertler, A. and Birk, Y. (1979) The fate of the Bowman-Birk trypsin inhibitor from soybeans in the digestive track of chicks. *Comparative Biochemistry and Physiology* 62A, 1057-61.

Nakata, S. and Kimura, T. (1986) Behavior of ingested concanavalin A in the gastrointestinal tract of the rat. *Agricultural and Biological Chemistry* 50, 645-9.

Owyang, C., Louie, D.S. and Tatum, D. (1986) Feedback regulation of pancreatic enzyme secretion. Suppression of cholecystokinin release by trypsin. *Journal of Clinical Investigation* 77, 2042-7.

Palmer, R., Pusztai, A., Bain, P. and Grant, G. (1987) Changes in rates of tissue protein synthesis in rats induced *in vivo* by consumption of kidney bean lectins. *Comparative Biochemistry and Physiology* 88C, 179-83.

Pusztai, A. (1967) Trypsin inhibitors of plant origin, their chemistry and potential role in animal nutrition. *Nutrition Abstracts and Reviews* 37, 1-9.

Pusztai, A. (1985) Constraints on the nutritional utilization of plant proteins. *Nutrition Abstracts and Reviews* (Ser.B) 55, 363-9.

Pusztai, A. (1986) The biological effect of lectins in the diet of animals and man. In: Bog-Hansen, T.C. and van Driessche, E.(eds) *Lectins Vol 5*. Walter de Gruyter, Berlin, pp. 317-27.

Pusztai, A. (1989) Lectins. In: Cheeke, P.R. (ed.) *Toxicants of Plant Origin Vol.III*. CRC Press, Boca Raton, 29-71.

Pusztai, A. and Greer, F. (1984) Effect of dietary legume proteins on the morphology and secretory responses to the rat small intestine. *Protides of the Biological Fluids* 32, 347-50.

Pusztai, A. and Palmer, R. (1977) Nutritional evaluation of kidney bean (*Phaseolus vulgaris*): the toxic principle. *Journal of the Science of Food and Agriculture* 28, 1037-46.

Pusztai, A., Grant, G. and de Oliveira, J.T.A. (1986) Local (gut) and systemic response to dietary lectins. *IRCS Medical Science* 14, 205-8.

Pusztai, A., Grant, G., Brown, D.S., Ewen, S.W.B. and Bardocz, S. (1988) *Phaseolus vulgaris* lectin induces growth and increases the polyamine content of rat small intestine *in vivo*. *Medical Science Research* 16, 1283-4.

Pusztai, A., Grant, G., Williams, L.M., Brown, D.S., Ewen, S.W.B. and Bardocz, S. (1989) *Phaseolus vulgaris* lectin induces growth and the uptake of polyamines by the rat small intestine *in vivo* . *Medical Science Research* 17, 215-7.

Pusztai, A., Ewen, S.W.B., Grant, G., Peumans, W.J., van Damme, E.J.M., Rubio, L. and Bardocz, S. (1990a) Relationship between survival and binding of plant lectins during small intestinal passage and their effectiveness as growth factors. *Digestion* 46 (suppl 2), 308-16.

Pusztai, A., Grant, G., King, T.P. and Clarke, E.M.W. (1990b) Chemical probiosis. In: Haresign, W. and Cole, D.J.A. (eds) *Recent Advances in Animal Nutrition*. Butterworth, London. pp. 47-60.

Rattray, E.A.S., Palmer, R. and Pusztai, A. (1974) Toxicity of kidney bean *(Phaseolus vulgaris L.)* to conventional and gnotobiotic rats. *Journal of the Science of Food and Agriculture* 25, 1035-40.

Sharon, N. (1987) Bacterial lectins, cell-cell recognition and infectious disease. *FEBS Letters* 217, 145-57.

Troll, W. and Yavelow, J. (1983) Protease inhibitors in the diet as anticarcinogens. In: Rae, D.A. (ed.) *Diet, Nutrition and Cancer*. Alan Liss, New York, pp. 167-76.

Weiser, M.M. (1984) Dietary lectins and the possible mechanism whereby they induce intestinal injury. In: Lebenthal, E. (ed.) *Chronic Diarrhea in Children,* Raven Press, New York, pp. 279-87.

Wilson, A.B., King, T.P., Clarke, E.M.W. and Pusztai, A. (1980) Kidney bean *(Phaseolus vulgaris)* lectin-induced lesions in the rat small intestine. 2. Microbiological studies. *Journal of Comparative Pathology* 90, 597-602.

Discussion - Part 1

The question was raised as to whether current *in vitro* systems include all known digestive enzyme activities in the animal or whether there might be particular ingredients the digestion of which would not be simulated by current simple systems. It was suggested that brush border enzymes might exert activities which were not usually included *in vitro* systems. There was a strong case for the use of pancreatin on the basis of its wide range of activities and its cost; some other enzyme activities would be prohibitively expensive. In the rat, under normal circumstances, about half of the endopeptidase activity is not of pancreatic origin. Pancreatic secretion adapts to major changes of diet in two to three days though some authors have reported detecting changes as soon as two hours after feeding.

It appears that there is an important difference between pigs and poultry in passage rate but with some exceptions such as the lack of trehalase in poultry the enzyme activities seem similar. Differences in digestibility between the species probably depend on the feed being considered and on the developmental state of the animal. Salivary amylase probably plays only a minor role in the pig, pancreatic α-amylase being much more important.

The practice of evaluating feeds in poultry after a period of starvation may lead to erroneous estimates. Even quite short periods of starvation can lead to atrophy of gut tisue and although these changes can be reversed there is a hypertrophic response to re-alimentation.

In discussion of the role of fibre in gut function the question was raised as to how the effects of fibre on crypt cell production rate were brought about. The fibre in question was a mixture of matrix and soluble fibres. This might be a question of the physical properties of the fibre, but infusion of volatile fatty acids without fibre also increased crypt cell production rate, suggesting that the effect is brought about by the fermentation of the fibre and the production of VFAs. This was thought to be due to gastrin. Urease activity and ammonia levels increase when dietary fibre is given but decarboxylation is not affected by fibre or antibiotics.

It was considered difficult to differentiate between transient microflora in the small intestine and a stable population. The adherent population seems to be quantitatively and qualitatively different from the population in the lumen.

In comparing enzyme activities in germ-free and conventional animals, when the weight of gut tissue is altered, it is important to distinguish between specific activities of enzymes and the values for a whole animal. On a body weight basis there does not seem to be any difference in pancreatic enzyme activity. As far as brush border enzymes are concerned there seem to be no differences, whichever way the results are expressed. It may be that the difference arises in the enzymes concerned with absorption rather than digestion. The mechanism of this is not clear but it may have something to do with the attachment of micro-organisms.

There seem to be differences in digestibility between amylopectin and amylose. The problem with starches is not so much the chemical structure but the structure of the starch granules and the difficulty in hydration, limiting access by water soluble enzymes. Microbes *in vitro* certainly degrade starch but the extent to which they do so in the small intestine depends on diet composition. Since, *in vitro*, they degrade starch before they degrade fibre it would seem likely that they have the same preference *in vivo*.

In animals given the kidney bean lectin PHA for the first time, gastric emptying seems to be slow. Animals previously exposed to PHA show more rapid emptying. Some lectins are resistant to microbial proteolysis; some are not. It would probably be possible to find bacterial enzymes to break down lectins before feeding. There is very little difference between ileal and overall digestibilities of lectins. The extent of their disappearance in the large intestine will depend on the specific lectin and on the nature of the flora present. The major lectins in practical diets for pigs or poultry would be in seeds, such as wheat germ agglutinin. At present this would cause no problem but plant breeders are interested in improving disease resistance in plants by introducing the genes for lectins and this could have a major impact on the nutritional value of the plant. The normal legume lectins are more heat sensitive than trypsin inhibitors. Inclusion of *Vicia faba* lectin at three times its normal concentration in the diet had no effect on the rat gut but this result cannot be extrapolated to other species since the different species will express different receptors.

Part 2

In vitro simulation of digestion and absorption in the gastro-intestinal tract of pigs and poultry
- methods and results

Chapter 5

The Chemical and Biological Bases of a Calculation System Developed for Predicting Dietary Energy Values: a Poultry Model

B. Carré

Introduction

The quality of a compound feed for poultry depends to a large extent on its energy value; precision and accuracy are therefore required for the evaluation of energy values. Several methods can be used for this:

1. *in vivo* determination ;
2. prediction equations based on chemical measurements;
3. prediction equations based on *in vitro* digestibility values.

The first method is the most accurate but *in vivo* determinations are expensive and time consuming. The second and third methods are much less expensive and thus have been studied extensively. It is clear that, until now, equations based on chemical analysis have been developed much more than those based on *in vitro* digestibility values. This can be explained by the fact that the equations based on *in vitro* digestibility have not been shown to be more efficient than those based on chemical parameters (Fisher, 1982). The other reason is that the objectives of the *in vitro* digestibility methods have not been well defined. *In vitro* digestibility methods must be developed when chemical measurements show limitations in their efficiency.

Over the last 15 years a great deal of work in various countries of Europe has been devoted to the improvement of prediction equations based on chemical analysis (see Carré, 1990, for review). Special attention has been given to the improvement of predictions based on cell-wall related parameters (Carré, 1990). A new system was set up (Carré *et al.*, 1984) and showed high efficiency (Carré, 1990) : this was developed as far as possible. The aim of the present paper is to show how this new system was developed and what limitations appeared. This will allow us to define precisely the direction to be taken for future research on *in vitro* digestibility methods. Some principles of the chemistry of plant cell walls are first reviewed; second, data on the digestibility of plant cell walls in poultry are given; third, the bases and recent developments of equations based on water-insoluble cell wall (WICW) are explained and their limitations are put forward.

B. Carré

The Plant Cell Walls

Terminology

Many words are used for designating plant cell walls or related materials. Some of them have been chosen because they represented one of the properties of plant cell walls : for instance, the word 'pulp' represents the soft texture and water-binding capacity of cell walls, especially of those from parenchymatous cells. The word 'fibre' is given for the form, pliability and resistance of some cell walls, especially those from vascular bundles. Other words are related to the chemical constitution of cell walls such as 'cellulose', 'lignocellulose' or 'non starch polysaccharides'. Adjectives or substantives are sometimes added to these latter words to make them a bit more precise : the old term 'crude fibre' designates an analysis which is related to plant cell wall components but also designates the least digestible part of plants. 'Crude fibre' remains ambiguous because it contains two concepts, one chemical and one nutritional and because the words 'crude' and 'fibre' are not precise and thus support an ambiguous meaning. Other methods have been set up for the determination of cell wall-related components because the crude fibre method did not appear fully satisfactory : acid detergent fibre (ADF: Van Soest, 1963), neutral detergent fibre (NDF: Van Soest and Wine, 1967) and total dietary fibre (Prosky *et al.*, 1985). The ambiguous meaning attached to the word 'fibre' was retained for all three of these methods. 'Dietary fibre' was defined as 'the skeletal remains of plant cells that are resistant to hydrolysis by the enzymes of man' (Trowell, 1972) and as 'the non-starch polysaccharides and lignin' (Cummings, 1981).

It is generally accepted that words used in the sciences need to be precise and unambiguous. It is clear that the word 'fibre' does not meet this requirement. In contrast, the term 'plant cell wall' relates to only one concept, a botanical one.

The main components of plant cell walls are non-starch polysaccharides (NSP), lignin and proteins. NSP are the major constituents making up 70-95% of the cell wall. The chemical features of cell wall NSP have been precisely described (Aspinall, 1980). Accordingly, the use of the term 'cell wall' is much less misleading than the use of the word 'fibre'. Despite this, animal (and human) nutritionists do not very often use the term 'cell wall' probably because they are familiar with animal or chemical concepts and not with botanical concepts. However, it will be seen below that the botanical concept attached to the term 'cell wall' is not a drawback for its use in animal nutrition sciences.

Animal nutrition needs precise quantification of most dietary components. So, if 'cell wall' is used to define a component of food, a precise method must be proposed for its determination. Without this, there would be little interest in using the term 'cell wall' for nutritional purposes. The approach which has been developed in our laboratory is described below.

68

Analytical Approach Developed for the Determination of Plant Cell Walls

NSP of plants occur not only in cell walls but also as intracellular components; fructans, for example, are intracellular polysaccharides (Aspinall, 1980). Thus, in the development of an analytical method for the determination of cell walls, the question arises of distinguishing cell wall NSP from those in the intracellular space. The intracellular NSP are, in general, readily soluble in aqueous solution. So too are some of the cell wall NSP, such as arabinoxylans and β-glucans from cereal endosperm, and the highly methylated pectins from fruits. Thus, the differential extraction procedure is not appropriate for selectively quantifying the cell wall NSP. Only structural analysis can distinguish intracellular from cell wall NSP (Aspinall, 1980). Such methods are tedious and time-consuming and cannot be used in routine analysis.

However, the fact that intracellular NSP are readily soluble in aqueous solution means that a residue insoluble in water does not contain intracellular NSP. If such a residue is devoid of starch and intracellular protein, it can be described as a cell wall material. The gravimetric determination of such a residue can be used as a rapid measurement related to cell walls. The term for this determination can incorporate the words 'cell wall', but requires an adjective to qualify the fraction of cell walls that has been isolated since a part of the cell walls is not recovered in the residue. The nature of the residue depends on the choice of chemical and physical factors used in the isolation procedure. This choice will be made for precise reasons related to practical, nutritional or chemical aspects. Considering the practical aspects, the cost of analysis is a good reason and can justify fractionation schemes similar to that used for crude fibre determination. From a nutritional viewpoint, it can be considered that the cell wall components which are rapidly digested by the animal have not to be recovered in the cell wall residue : that was the logic developed for the NDF method (Van Soest and Wine, 1967) for application in ruminant nutrition. From chemical considerations the choice may be to recover one or several specific classes of components encountered in cell walls such as lignin, cellulose, hemicellulose or pectic substances. However, most differential extraction procedures fail to distinguish clearly between the different classes of cell wall components. One general trend in the chemical isolation of cell wall residues is to use procedures thought to minimize the solubilization and, hence, the loss of cell wall components (Morrison, 1973 ; Talmadge *et al.*, 1973; Selvendran, 1975; Whitmore, 1982; Brillouet and Carré, 1983; Shibuya, 1984; Brillouet *et al.*, 1988). This was the first aim of our procedure (Carré and Brillouet, 1989) for which the term 'water-insoluble cell wall' seemed to be suitable. The other aim was to develop an analysis that could be used routinely.

The cohesion of cell walls depends on inter- and intramolecular bonds, either covalent, ionic or hydrogen bonds. Any factor able to break these bonds is thought to increase the soluble part of cell walls. Such factors include pH, temperature, enzyme activities, chelating agents, hydrogen bond disrupting agents, irradiation and mechanical treatments. Of course, the time required for the procedure is also to be considered : the shorter the procedure, the lower the risk of breaking bonds, and the more convenient for routine analysis.

Grinding Conditions

In all procedures developed for the isolation of cell wall residues, a mechanical process is applied to the plant material to disrupt the plant cells and allow complete extraction of intracellular compounds. However, strong mechanical processes applied to plant materials, such as extrusion cooking (Björk *et al.*, 1984), freeze-milling (Brillouet *et al.*, 1988) or prolonged ball-milling (Lapierre *et al.*, 1982), increase the soluble fraction of cell walls probably by breaking covalent linkages. Ultrasonic treatment (Gebert, 1952) and γ-irradiation are also processes that can break covalent linkages of polysaccharides (Sacquet *et al.*, 1985). Accordingly, strong mechanical processes must be avoided, if possible. Prolonged ball-milling (15-20 h), recommended in some methods (Selvendran, 1975 ; Selvendran and Du Pont, 1980), may be expected to increase the soluble fraction of cell walls. However, the efficiency of the disrupting treatment must be sufficient to allow a nearly complete extraction of intracellular compounds.

Table 5.1. Effect of type of grinding on the yield of cell wall residues (% of DM).

Grinding	Water insoluble cell walls		NDF (+α-amylase)		Total dietary fibre not corrected for residual proteins	
	0.5 mm	1 mm	0.5 mm	1 mm	0.5 mm	1 mm
Maize	10.0	10.4	10.1	14.0	11.9	14.7
Wheat	9.9	10.7	11.0	12.6	12.5	12.7
Barley	15.4	17.0	15.8	20.7	20.1	19.6
Sorghum	10.9	12.6	11.8	15.7	16.8	18.0
Rapeseed meal	34.8	36.4	25.7	27.6	46.1	45.0
Soyabean meal	16.4	16.9	9.6	9.4	30.3	30.6
Peas	12.8	24.6	10.1	17.5	23.0	31.5
White lupin cotyledons	20.0	26.8	7.4	7.2	28.0	32.8

From Carré *et al.*, 1988.

In a previous experiment (Carré *et al.*, 1988), grinding to 1 mm instead of 0.5 mm increased the yield of cell wall residues of peas, with pronounced differences that cannot be attributed to differences in the solubilization of NSP (Table 5.1). Subsequent analyses revealed contaminating starch as the factor responsible. Grinding to 0.3-0.5 mm is generally considered a fair compromise between the possibilities of a low contamination of cell wall residues and a low degradation of them. Thus, this grinding procedure has been adopted in many methods related to cell walls (Asp *et al.*, 1983 ; Prosky *et al.*, 1985 ; Theander and Westerlund, 1986; Brillouet *et al.*, 1988 ; Carré and Brillouet, 1989). However, as stated above, some materials such as peas can be very sensitive to the type of grinding. For those samples, the purity of the cell wall material recovered after grinding to 0.5 mm cannot be assured. To reduce the possibilities of contamination, our method recommends 10 min ball-milling as a prerequisite for the determination of water-insoluble cell walls in mature starchy legume seeds.

Chemical Agents

As far as possible, the chemical agents used for the solubilization of intracellular compounds must preserve the integrity of cell walls. Ionic bonds between calcium cations and carboxylic anions of pectic polymers are thought to be responsible for the water-insolubility of much of the cell wall pectic substances (Thibault, 1980). Accordingly, chelating agents able to release calcium and, hence, pectic polymers from cell walls have to be avoided. The chelating agents that are most commonly used for pectic polymer extraction are ammonium oxalate and ethylenediaminetetra acetate (EDTA), the latter being used for the NDF procedure (Van Soest and Wine, 1967). The NDF residue is often designated 'insoluble cell walls' (Van Soest, 1978), which has introduced some confusion about pectic substances. Pectic substances are generally considered 'soluble' components in ruminant nutrition because their digestion rate in the rumen is similar to that of starch (Bailey, 1967). In this case, the word 'soluble' corresponds to a nutritional concept for the ruminant, not to a chemical concept. This has to be kept clearly in mind.

From a chemical point of view, it has previously been shown that, for many samples, a major part of pectic substances may be insoluble in water. This has been observed for testa and head from sunflower (Sabir *et al.*, 1975), for cotyledons from yellow lupin seeds (Matheson and Saini, 1977), for cabbage (Theander and Åman, 1979 ; Stevens and Selvendran, 1980), for carrot and lettuce (Theander and Åman, 1979), for peas (Theander and Åman, 1979; Brillouet and Carré, 1983), for soyabean and faba bean cotyledons (Brillouet and Carré, 1983), for white lupin cotyledons (Carré *et al.*, 1985), for kamranga fruits (Nahar *et al.*, 1990) and for tomato fruits (Seymour *et al.*, 1990). The amounts of water-insoluble pectic substances can be high in some plant materials such as soyabean (Brillouet and Carré, 1983) and white lupin cotyledons (Carré *et al.*, 1985) and this can lead to great differences between values of NDF and water-insoluble cell walls. In one study (Carré and Brillouet, 1986), NDF values of soyabean meal and whole seeds of white lupins, were found to be 8.5 and 18.3, while water-insoluble cell wall values were 17.1 and 30.9% of the dry matter, respectively. These differences were confirmed in another study (Carré and Brillouet, 1989) with NDF values of 8.2 and

B. Carré

6.5, and water-insoluble cell-wall values of 14.9 and 18.9% of the fresh matter, for soyabean meal and dehulled seeds of white lupins, respectively.

Hydrogen bonds are responsible for the constitution of cellulose microfibrils (Barnoud, 1980) and can be at the origin of binding between cellulose and hemicelluloses (Albersheim, 1976). Accordingly, hydrogen bond disrupting agents should not be used for the isolation of water-insoluble cell walls. Such agents, 8M urea for example, have been used for extracting polysaccharides from water-insoluble cell walls (Bauer *et al.*, 1973). Even if 8M urea treatment is considered a convenient method for extracting starch, its use for isolating cell wall components (Jeraci *et al.*, 1989) could be misleading if it is also used for the isolation of water-insoluble cell walls. Dimethylsulphoxide (DMSO) is another chemical agent used for the extraction of starch (Ring and Selvendran, 1978; Carpita, 1983; Brillouet *et al.*, 1988) but results in noticeable loss of cell wall polysaccharides with some samples such as cabbage (Stevens and Selvendran, 1980), white lupins and copra (Brillouet *et al.*, 1988) : the losses varied from 6.5% (copra) to 15.3% (white lupins) of the water-insoluble cell walls. DMSO would only be useful when starch is difficult to extract but, in such cases, already mentioned with peas, the difficulty may easily be overcome by 10 min ball-milling (Carré and Brillouet, 1989).

Detergents allow protein to be rapidly and efficiently extracted. First introduced by Van Soest (1963) for the determination of cell wall components, detergent has also been used in our procedure. The extraction properties of sodium dodecyl sulphate (SDS), the detergent used in our procedure (Carré and Brillouet, 1989), are due in part to its ability to participate in hydrophobic interactions. Because of the wide distribution of oxygen atoms throughout the carbon skeleton of polysaccharides, hydrophobic interactions are not expected to occur between SDS and polysaccharides. Hence, SDS is not expected to participate in the extraction of polysaccharides but probably acts only on the extraction of proteins and lipids.

pH Conditions and Temperature

Extractions of starch and proteins have to be done under pH conditions that minimize the disruption of inter- and intramolecular bonds occurring in cell walls. Low pH is known to hydrolyze glycosidic linkages, especially when they involve α-arabinofuranosyl residues. Increasing the temperature speeds up hydrolysis. It can be estimated that, near 100°C the risks of splitting α-arabinofuranosyl links begin below pH 4. Specific losses of arabinose residues at pH 3.2 and 100°C were clearly observed in our laboratory (unpublished data). Acidic pH could also be responsible for cleavage of ether bonds between lignin core and phenolic acids (Scalbert *et al.*, 1985), inducing subsequent solubilization of polysaccharides ester-linked to phenolic acids (Iiyama *et al.*, 1990). Cleavage of ether bonds between phenolic compounds can occur even with fairly mild acid treatments (Cyr *et al.*, 1988). Hence, the extraction procedures used in our method for the isolation of cell walls were not performed below pH 5.6. Boiling temperature was applied at the latter pH for extracting starch in order to shorten this step. However, owing to the risks of the hydrolytic reactions described above, the time of treatment at this temperature (93-100°C) and pH 5.6 was as short as possible (10 min). Moreover, in contrast to many methods developed for cell walls (Schweizer and Wursch, 1979; Englyst, 1981; Asp *et al.*, 1983; Prosky *et al.*, 1985; Theander and Westerlund, 1986; Brillouet *et al.*, 1988), this was not followed by a subsequent hydrolysis of starch under acidic conditions and lower temperature. This latter step, using amyloglucosidase, is usually included to split starch to free glucose in order to avoid any contamination of alcohol-insoluble water-soluble polysaccharides with amylodextrins. As this amyloglucosidase step mainly concerns the determination of water-soluble NSP it can be omitted in our procedure, since water-soluble NSP are not measured.

The second step of our procedure concerns the extraction of proteins which is performed after starch extraction and not before. The advantages of this are:

1. addition of boiling water at the beginning of the procedure quickly inactivates endogenous enzymes and avoids any enzymatic hydrolysis of cell wall polysaccharides ;
2. if protein extraction is applied first, filtration would be needed between the two extraction steps in order to remove SDS which could decrease the activity of α-amylase used in the second step;
3. the change in temperature is faster during cooling than heating.

Hence, the analysis is faster if destarching (93°C -100°C) is performed before deproteinizing (40°C). The extraction of protein after destarching does not affect the efficiency of protein release as shown by the low protein contamination of cell wall residues obtained with this sequence (Table 5.2).

Table 5.2. Protein content of water-insoluble cell walls (WICW).

	WICW content of feed (% of the feed dry matter)	Protein (N x 6.25) content of WICW (% of the WICW residue)
Wheat	11.7	6.4
Soyabean meal	17.6	8.9
Sunflower meal	43.2	4.9
Lucerne meal	48.1	5.9
Rapeseed meal		
(not dehulled)	35.8	12.1
(dehulled)	21.5	11.4

B. Carré

At basic pH, β-eliminations occur in the methylated galacturonic acids, which result in splitting and solubilization of pectins (Aspinall, 1980). This reaction may even take place at neutral pH if temperature is raised to near boiling (Aspinall, 1980). The protein extraction step of our procedure is carried out at pH 7.5, which is optimum for pronase and SDS, the protein-extracting agents used in our procedure. Accordingly, the temperature for this step must not be too high in order to limit, as far as possible, the solubilization of pectic polymers. A temperature near ambient (40°C) was chosen as a fair compromise between the need to avoid splitting polysaccharides and the need to develop a routine analysis.

Table 5.3. Comparison between methods of measuring water-insoluble cell walls (% of dry matter).

Diet no. (Carré et al., 1984)	Methods		Diet no. (Carré et al., 1984)	Methods	
	Carré et al., 1984	Carré and Brillouet, 1989		Carré et al., 1984	Carré and Brillouet, 1989
1	9.56	9.65	25	9.50	9.52
2	15.77	15.02	26	9.70	9.33
3	14.97	13.97	27	10.20	9.89
4	11.65	11.51	28	10.30	9.54
5	11.47	10.96	29	10.30	9.98
6	11.24	11.36	30	11.00	11.10
7	11.30	10.99	31	15.50	15.87
8	13.29	13.26	32	16.30	15.80
9	13.60	13.32	33	15.50	15.58
10	12.20	13.22	34	10.80	10.79
11	11.61	11.66	35	13.10	13.00
12	12.81	12.18	36	14.60	14.09
13	18.74	18.94	37	14.60	13.80
14	17.05	16.65	38	12.20	12.19
15	15.24	15.54	39	25.40	26.34
16	11.07	11.40	40	22.10	23.22
17	12.15	12.11	41	10.50	9.36
18	14.25	14.35	42	10.60	9.26
19	11.80	11.82	43	15.50	15.20
20	11.70	10.87	44	12.30	11.53
21	11.50	9.97	45	11.30	10.70
22	9.10	8.82	46	10.40	9.77
23	13.40	12.64	47	8.70	9.49
24	10.70	10.53	48	11.10	11.08

It was observed in our laboratory that extracting protein at pH 7.5 and boiling temperature instead of 40°C resulted in losses of polysaccharides that represented 2.1, 2.1 and 3.2% of the original dry raw material of soyabean meal, mature pea seeds and lucerne meal, respectively (unpublished data).

Of course, basic pH must be avoided for isolation of water insoluble cell walls (except at temperatures near 0°C), because this may result in splitting of many bonds such as glycosidic bonds of methylated pectins, ester linkages of cross-bridging phenolic acids (Iiyama et al., 1990), and hydrogen bonds.

Comparison Between Methods

The results of our method set up for routine analysis (Carré and Brillouet, 1989) show good agreement with other methods except for some samples (Table 5.4). There are differences with peas, when compared to the method of Prosky et al. (1985), because of starch contamination with the latter method; and differences with soyabean meal, rapeseed meal and white lupin cotyledons, when compared to NDF, because of solubilization of pectic polymers with the latter method. Good agreement was observed with our method set up in 1984 (Tables 5.3 and 5.4).

No correction for residual proteins is generally needed with our method except for tannin-containing samples in which the protein content of cell wall residues is often higher than 10%. For these samples, it is necessary to apply a correction for residual proteins in order to obtain a more accurate estimate of water-insoluble cell walls. The procedure developed by Prosky et al. (1985) needs a correction for residual proteins with most samples (Carré and Brillouet, 1989).

The time required for our procedure is 3 h for 12 different samples, including filtrations and rinsing. No filtration problems have been encountered. It can be concluded that our method can be used for routine analysis, and is suitable for laboratories involved in animal nutrition sciences.

Digestibility of Plant Cell Walls in Poultry

The chemical determinations of food components that relate to available nutrients are generally recognized to be of interest. Moreover, these determinations often have similar nutritional significance amongst various animal species because, very often, the digestibilities of available nutrients do not vary greatly between species. So, where available nutrients such as starch, proteins or lipids are concerned, one method of determination can be used for several animal species.

In contrast, the situation is much more complicated for the chemical determinations applied to plant cell walls in the field of nutrition sciences. First, these components are generally the least digested in diets. So, their nutritional significance is often indirect and, thus less easily understood than that of available nutrients. Second, great variations exist in their digestibility between animal species (Fonnesbeck et al., 1974 ; Carré et al., 1990). This introduces great

75

76

Table 5.4. Comparison between methods measuring water-insoluble cell walls (% of fresh matter).

Methods	Maize	Wheat	Barley	Sorghum	Tapioca root	Soyabean meal	Rapeseed meal	Peas	White Lupin cotyledons	Diet 1	Diet 2
Carré and Brillouet (1989)	9.06	8.97	13.66	10.03	4.32	14.88	31.50	11.12	18.87	10.95	9.56
Carré et al. (1984)	8.68	8.60	12.77	9.64	4.13	14.12	27.53	11.28	17.51	10.23	9.05
Prosky et al. (1985)[a]	9.38	8.60	13.38	9.16	3.79	12.92	26.52	17.27	18.22	10.43	9.38
NDF (Van Soest and Wine, 1967) + α-amylase	8.77	9.46	13.55	10.01	3.36	8.22	22.42	9.04	6.51	9.12	8.05

[a] Water-insoluble fraction, with correction for residual proteins on a duplicate sample, as described in the procedure. The other methods do not include correction for residual proteins.

difficulties among nutritionists in agreeing on methods related to cell walls. For this reason it is better to propose methods for cell walls that are based on chemical rather than on nutritional considerations. The variation in the digestibility of cell walls between species also implies that it is unlikely that one method related to cell walls can be used for all animal species. Laboratories that deal with several animal species have to keep in mind that they have to use several methods for cell walls. The choice of a method for a particular animal species will be made on the basis of the extent of the cell wall digestion by the species under consideration. The choice will also relate to the factors responsible for the variation in cell wall digestibility.

Methodology

The methods used for the *in vivo* determination of cell wall digestibility in poultry require attention for the following reason. These digestibilities are generally rather low; hence, errors in the recovery of excreta may have pronounced effects on cell wall digestibility values. For instance, if the actual cell wall digestibility is 10% and if the error in the excreta recovery reaches 20%, the cell wall digestibility values recorded can vary between -8 and 28%. For comparison, the same error applied to an actual protein digestibility of 84% results in estimates of protein digestibility ranging only between 80.8 and 87.2%. Accordingly, it is essential to apply sound methods in the *in vivo* balance experiments used to determine cell wall digestibility in birds. After 20 years of study in Europe, general agreement has been reached on a reference method for these determinations; it includes an adaptation period, a feeding level near to *ad libitum*, and a feeding period of several days (Bourdillon *et al.*, 1990). These three conditions were followed in all the studies conducted at Nouzilly for the determination of cell wall digestibility in poultry.

Moreover, the chemical methods used for determination of cell wall components in feed and excreta were as precise as possible. Gravimetric methods were not used because they were designed for feed, not for excreta: for example, the solubility of uric acid is rather low and would require modifications to gravimetric methods. The extraction of protein and lipids by gravimetric methods could also be different in feed and excreta and would require the level of contamination in residues of excreta to be checked. Accordingly, these methods would not be more rapid than those based on determination of individual sugars of NSP, the method used in Nouzilly.

The only contamination that can be expected with that method are from endogenous glycoproteins or glycolipids. Examination of polysaccharides in excreta from starved birds (Longstaff and Mc Nab, 1987) or from birds fed on cell wall free diets reveal a composition similar to that of remaining dietary cell walls (Carré and Leclercq, 1985). The sugar pattern of the excreta NSP of starved birds (Rha 0.13, Fuc 0.26, Ara 1, Xyl 1.96, Man 0.26, Gal 1.26, Glc 2.26; Longstaff and Mc Nab, 1987) does not differ greatly from that of a diet containing 70% maize and

B. Carré

25% soyabean meal (Rha 0.04, Fuc 0.04, Ara 1, Xyl 1.17, Man 0.11, Gal 0.50, Glc 1.88; Carré and Brillouet, 1986; Brillouet *et al.*, 1988). This suggests that the endogenous sugars are actually very low, causing little interference with the estimation of dietary NSP. Further support for this view is provided by a comparison of the digestibility of arabinose with that of total NSP : owing to the scarcity of arabinose in animals and bacteria, this sugar can be considered as a marker of plant cell walls. So, the similarity between digestibility values of arabinose and total NSP that is invariably encountered with poultry (Carré and Leclercq, 1985; Carré *et al.*, 1990) also suggests low influence of endogenous sugars on the estimation of total NSP.

NSP Digestibility in Poultry

Combining the data obtained in Nouzilly (Carré and Leclercq, 1985; Carré *et al.*, 1990, Carré *et al.*, unpublished data) in Fig. 5.1, it appears that poultry are able to digest only the water-soluble fraction of NSP. The water-insoluble fraction remains nearly undigested. In contrast to mammals, birds are not sensitive to the structural features of cell walls (Carré *et al.*, 1990).

Fig. 5.1. Digestibility of NSP in cockerels as a function of NSP solubility.

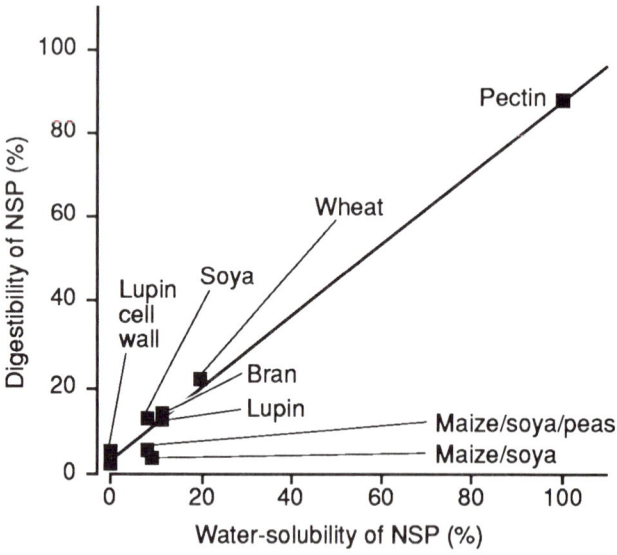

The pH and temperature conditions encountered in the digestive tract of poultry (40°C; pH 2.5 and 6.7 in gizzard and intestine, respectively; Herpol and Van Grembergen, 1967) are not really degradative for cell walls. Accordingly, the soluble fraction of plant cell walls in the poultry digestive tract is probably rather similar to that obtained in the fractionation scheme used for isolation of WICW and water-soluble polysaccharides (see above). So, if the latter molecules are soluble in the gut, they can be fermented very quickly even within the short transit time of poultry (< 8 h ; Sibbald, 1980). Moreover, soluble molecules can reach the caeca where extensive fermentation can occur. In contrast, the water-insoluble cell walls require longer to be degraded and do not enter the caeca (Bjornhag and Sperber, 1977). Accordingly, the gastrointestinal tract of poultry provides suitable conditions for fermentation of water-soluble polysaccharides but poor conditions for the fermentation of water-insoluble cell walls. This explains the NSP digestibility values observed in poultry (Fig. 5.1).

These data support the conclusion that WICW act as diluents of available nutrients. This principle was the basis of the calculation system developed for the prediction of AMEn.

Recent Developments and Limitations of AMEn Predictions Based on WICW

AMEn predictions based on WICW have been applied to diets (Carré *et al.,* 1984; Carré and Brillouet, 1989) and to raw materials (Carré, 1990; Carré and Rozo,

Fig. 5.2. Use of a theoretical equation for calculation of a regression adapted to a combination of different raw materials.

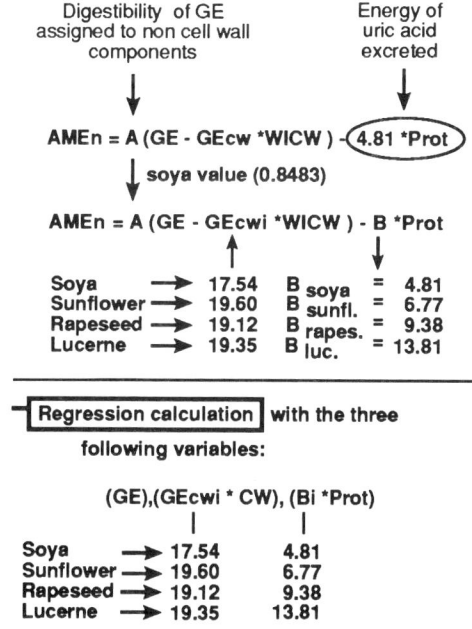

1990) and showed high efficiencies. The theoretical scheme based on a diluting effect of WICW was in very good agreement with experiments, especially with those based on gross energy (GE), WICW and proteins (Carré, 1990).

Because of its accuracy the theoretical scheme was used to improve the efficiency of AMEn predictions for protein meals. Different types of protein meal were combined in regressions to improve the accuracy and range of validity of the equations. But this raises the problem of taking into account the great variation in protein digestibility between types of protein meals. This has been solved using a theoretical equation that allows a coefficient to be calculated for each type of protein meal. This coefficient modulates a variable in the regression equation (Fig. 5.2). The theoretical equation (Carré *et al.*, 1984) is based on the principle of a diluting effect of cell walls. The 'A' value is calculated as the unknown factor of the equation and the experimental values of seven soyabean meals

Fig. 5.3. Prediction of AMEn values of protein meals.

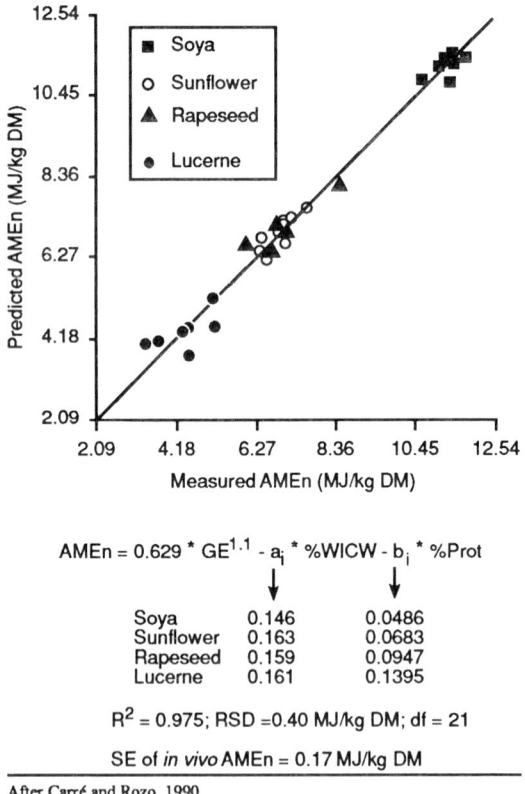

$$AMEn = 0.629 * GE^{1.1} - a_i * \%WICW - b_i * \%Prot$$

	a_i	b_i
Soya	0.146	0.0486
Sunflower	0.163	0.0683
Rapeseed	0.159	0.0947
Lucerne	0.161	0.1395

$R^2 = 0.975$; RSD $= 0.40$ MJ/kg DM; df $= 21$

SE of *in vivo* AMEn $= 0.17$ MJ/kg DM

After Carré and Rozo, 1990

are used to derive the other factors in the equation. Thereafter, the calculated A value is considered as a known value in the equation and the coefficient for each unknown protein is calculated as a B value for each individual sample. A mean B_i value is obtained for each i group (soya, sunflower, rapeseed, lucerne meals). A value for GEcwi is also given for each i group. This was measured on isolated cell walls from one sample of each i group. Then, the regression is calculated with (GE), (GEcwi x WICW) and (Bi x Prot) as the three independent variables (Fig. 5.3). The residual standard deviation (RSD) of the regression (0.397 MJ/kg DM) is higher than that obtained with diets (0.22 MJ/kg DM; Carré and Brillouet, 1989). This can be explained partly by the higher standard errors of *in vivo* AMEn values of feeds (0.167 MJ/kg DM) compared to those for diets (0.081 MJ/kg DM: Carré *et al.*, 1984). However, part of the difference must be attributed to a lower intrinsic efficiency of the prediction for protein meals compared to that for diets.

Adding other variables based on crude nutrients would probably not greatly improve the efficiency of the equation because its variables and the modulators applied to them are able to meet a wide range of chemical situations. The main factor that cannot be taken into account is the variation in protein digestibility between individual samples within the groups i. It is in this connection that *in vitro* digestibility values would be useful. Accordingly, the development of *in vitro* digestibility methods must be directed to protein digestibility to distinguish individual samples within type of raw material. Applying such methods for detecting differences between types of raw materials or between diets is of little interest because chemical methods, such as those using WICW, are able to do this.

References

Albersheim, P. (1976) The primary cell wall. In: Bonner, J., Varner, J.E. (eds), *Plant Biochemistry*. Academic Press, New York, pp. 225-74.

Asp, N.G., Johansson, C.G., Hallmer, H. and Siljeström, M. (1983) Rapid enzymatic assay of insoluble and soluble dietary fiber. *Journal of Agricultural and Food Chemistry* 31, 476-82.

Aspinall, G.O. (1980) Chemistry of cell wall polysaccharides. In: Press, J. (ed.), *The Biochemistry of Plants*, 3. Academic Press, New York, pp. 473-500.

Bailey, R.W. (1967) Quantitative studies on ruminant nutrition. II. Loss of ingested plant carbohydrates from the reticulo-rumen. *New Zealand Journal of Agricultural Research* 10, 15-32.

Barnoud, F. (1980) La cellulose. In: Monties, B. and Costes, C. (eds), *Les Polymères Végétaux : Polymères Pariétaux et Alimentaires non Azotés*. Gauthier-Villars-Bordas, Paris, pp. 66-86.

Bauer, W.D., Talmadge, K.W., Keegstra, K. and Albersheim, P. (1973) The structure of plant cell walls. II. The hemicellulose of the walls of suspension-cultured sycamore cells. *Plant Physiology* 51, 174-87.

Björck, I., Nyman, M. and Asp, N.G. (1984) Extrusion cooking and dietary fiber:

effects on dietary fiber content and on degradation in the rat intestinal tract. *Cereal Chemistry* 61, 174-9.

Björnhag, G. and Sperber, I. (1977) Transport of various food components through the digestive tract of turkeys, geese and guinea fowl. *Swedish Journal of Agricultural Research* 7, 57-66.

Bourdillon, A., Carré, B., Conan, L., Duperray, J., Huyghebaert, G., Leclercq, B., Lessire, M., McNab, J. and Wiseman, J. (1990) European reference method for the *in vivo* determination of metabolisable energy with adult cockerels: reproducibility effect of food intake and comparison with individual laboratory methods. *British Poultry Science* 31, 557-65.

Brillouet, J.M. and Carré, B. (1983) Composition of cell walls from cotyledons of *Pisum sativum, Vicia faba* and *Glycine max. Phytochemistry* 22, 841-7.

Brillouet, J.M., Rouau, X., Hoebler, C., Barry, J.L., Carré, B. and Lorta, E. (1988) A new method for determination of insoluble cell walls and soluble nonstarchy polysaccharides from plant materials. *Journal of Agricultural and Food Chemistry* 36, 969-79.

Carpita, N.C. (1983) Hemicellulosic polymers of cell walls of *Zea* coleoptiles. *Plant Physiology* 72, 515-21.

Carré, B. (1990) Predicting the dietary energy value of poultry feeds. In: Wiseman, J. and Cole, D.J.A. (eds), *Feedstuff Evaluation*. Butterworths, London, pp. 283-300.

Carré, B. and Brillouet, J.M. (1986) Yield and composition of cell wall residues isolated from various feedstuffs used for non-ruminant farm animals. *Journal of the Science of Food and Agriculture* 37, 341-51.

Carré, B. and Brillouet, J.M. (1989) Determination of water-insoluble cell walls in feeds : interlaboratory study, *Journal of the Association of Official Analytical Chemists* 72, 463-7.

Carré, B. and Leclercq, B. (1985) Digestion of polysaccharides, protein and lipids by adult cockerels fed on diets containing a pectic cell wall material from white lupin (*Lupinus albus* L.) cotyledon. *British Journal of Nutrition* 54, 669-80.

Carré, B. and Rozo, E. (1990) La prédiction de la valeur énergétique des matières premières destinées à l'aviculture. *INRA Productions Animales* 3, 163-9.

Carré, B., Prévotel, B. and Leclercq, B. (1984) Cell wall content as a predictor of metabolizable energy value of poultry feedingstuffs. *British Poultry Science* 25, 561-72.

Carré, B., Brillouet, J.M. and Thibault, J.F. (1985) Characterization of polysaccharides from white lupin (*Lupinus albus* L.) cotyledons. *Journal of Agricultural and Food Chemistry* 32, 285-92.

Carré, B., Perez, J.M. and Lebas, F. (1988) Mesure des fibres végétales dans les aliments pour animaux. *Rapport final de la convention de recherches DIAA/ IRTAC n° 86/02*. Institut de Recherches Technologiques Agro-alimentaires des Céréales, Paris.

Carré, B., Derouet, L. and Leclercq B. (1990) Digestibility of cell wall polysaccharides from wheat (bran or whole grain), soybean and white lupin meal in cockerels, Muscovy ducks and rats. *Poultry Science* 69, 623-33.

Cummings, J. (1981) Dietary fibre. *British Medical Bulletin* 37, 65-70.

Cyr, N., Elofson, R.M., Ripmeester, J.A. and Mathison, G.W. (1988) Study of lignin in forages and wood by 13C CP/MAS NMR. 1. Some evidence of polymerization and depolymerization. *Journal of Agricultural and Food Chemistry* 36, 1197-201.

Englyst, H. (1981) Determination of carbohydrate and its composition in plant materials. In: James, W.P.T. and Theander, O. (eds) *The Analysis of Dietary Fiber in Food.* Marcel Dekker, Inc., New York, pp.71-93.

Fisher, C. (1982) (ed.) *Energy Values of Compound Poultry Feeds.* Occasional publication n° 2, AFRC Institute for Grassland and Animal Production, Poultry Division, Roslin, Midlothian, United Kingdom.

Fonnesbeck, P.V., Harris, L.E. and Kearl, L.C. (1974) Comparative digestion of plant cell walls by animals. *Utah Academy Proceedings* 51, 85-92.

Gebert, F. (1952) Zur kinetik der ultraschall-depolymerisation. *Angewandte Chemie* 64, 625-6.

Herpol, C. and Van Grembergen, G. (1967) La signification du pH dans le tube digestif de *Gallus domesticus. Annales de Biologie Animale, Biochimie, Biophysique* 7, 33-8.

Iiyama, K., Lam, T.B.T. and Stone, B.A. (1990) Phenolic acid bridges between polysaccharides and lignin in wheat internodes. *Phytochemistry* 29, 733-7.

Jeraci, J.L., Lewis, B.A., Van Soest, P.J. and Robertson, J.B. (1989) Urea enzymatic dialysis procedure for determination of total dietary fiber. *Journal of the Association of Official Analytical Chemists* 72, 677.

Lapierre, C., Lallemand, J.Y. and Monties, B. (1982) Evidence of poplar lignin heterogeneity by combination of 13C and 1H NMR spectroscopy. *Holzforschung* 36, 275-82.

Longstaff, M. and McNab, J.M. (1987) Digestion of starch and fibre carbo-hydrates in peas by adult cockerels. *British Poultry Science* 28, 261-85.

Matheson, N.K. and Saini, H.S. (1977) Polysaccharide and oligosaccharide changes in germinating lupin cotyledons. *Phytochemistry* 16, 59-66.

Morrison, I.M. (1973) The isolation of plant cell wall preparations with low nitrogen contents. *Journal of Agricultural Science Cambridge* 80, 407-10.

Nahar, N., Rahman, S. and Mosihuzzaman, M. (1990) Analysis of carbohydrates in seven edible fruits of Bangladesh. *Journal of the Science of Food and Agri-culture* 51, 185-92.

Prosky, L., Asp , N.G., Furda, I., De Vries, J.W., Schweizer, T.F. and Harland, B.F. (1985) Determination of total dietary fiber in foods and food products : collaborative study. *Journal of the Association of Official Analytical Chemists* 68, 677-9.

Ring, S.G. and Selvendran, R.R. (1978) Purification and methylation analysis of cell wall material from *Solanum tuberosum*. *Phytochemistry* 17, 745-52.

Sabir, M.A., Sosulski, F.W. and Hamon, N.W. (1975) Sunflower carbohydrates. *Journal of Agricultural and Food Chemistry* 23, 16-19.

Sacquet, E., Leprince, C., Riottot, M. and Raibaud, P. (1985) Dietary fiber and cholesterol and bile acid metabolism in axenic (germfree) and holoxenic (conventional) rats. III. Effect of non-sterilized pectin. *Reproduction Nutrition Développement* 25, 93-100.

Scalbert, A., Monties, B., Lallemand, J.Y., Guittet, E. and Rolando, C. (1985) Ether linkage between phenolic acids and lignin fractions from wheat straw. *Phytochemistry* 24, 1359-62.

Schweizer, T.F. and Wursch, P. (1979) Analysis of dietary fibre. *Journal of the Science of Food and Agriculture* 30, 613-9.

Selvendran, R.R. (1975) Analysis of cell wall material from plant tissues : extraction and purification. *Phytochemistry* 14, 1011-7.

Selvendran, R.R. and Du Pont, M.S. (1980) An alternative method for the isolation and analysis of cell wall material from cereals. *Cereal Chemistry* 57, 278-83.

Seymour, G.B., Colquhoun, I.J., Du Pont, M.S., Parsley, K.R. and Selvendran, R.R. (1990) Composition and structural features of cell wall polysaccharides from tomato fruits. *Phytochemistry* 29, 725-31.

Shibuya, N. (1984) Phenolic acids and their carbohydrate esters in rice endosperm cell walls. *Phytochemistry* 23, 2233-7.

Sibbald, I.R. (1980) The clearance time and rate of passage of feed residues. *Poultry Science* 59, 374-7.

Stevens, B.J.H. and Selvendran, R.R. (1980) The isolation and analysis of cell wall material from the alcohol-insoluble residue of cabbage (*Brassica oleracea* var *capitata*). *Journal of the Science of Food and Agriculture* 31, 1257-67.

Talmadge, K.W., Keegstra, K., Bauer, W.D. and Albersheim, P. (1973) The structure of plant cell walls. I. The macromolecular components of the walls of suspension-cultured sycamore cells with a detailed analysis of the pectic polysaccharides. *Plant Physiology* 51, 158-73.

Theander, O. and Aman, P. (1979) Studies on dietary fibres. 1. Analysis and chemical characterization of water-soluble and water-insoluble dietary fibres. *Swedish Journal of Agricultural Research* 9, 97-106.

Theander, O. and Westerlund, E.A. (1986) Studies on dietary fiber. 3. Improved procedures for analysis of dietary fiber. *Journal of Agricultural and Food Chemistry* 34, 330-6.

Thibault, J.F. (1980) Les substances pectiques. In: Monties, B. and Costes, C. (eds), *Les Polymères Végétaux : Polymères Pariétaux et Alimentaires non Azotés*. Gauthier-Villars-Bordas, Paris, pp. 232-51.

Trowell, H. (1972) Ischemic heart disease and dietary fiber. *The American*

Journal of Clinical Nutrition 25, 926-32.

Van Soest, P.J. (1963) Use of detergents in the analysis of fibrous feeds. II. A rapid method for the determination of fiber and lignin. *Journal of the Association of Official Analytical Chemists* 46, 829-35.

Van Soest, P.J. (1978) Dietary fibers : their definition and nutritional properties. *The American Journal of Clinical Nutrition* 31, S12-S20.

Van Soest, P.J. and Wine, R.H. (1967) Use of detergents in the analysis of fibrous feeds. IV. Determination of cell wall constituents. *Journal of the Association of Official Analytical Chemists* 50, 50-5.

Whitmore, F.W. (1982) Lignin-protein complex in cell walls of *Pinus elliottii* : amino acid constituents. *Phytochemistry* 21, 315-8.

Chapter 6

Enzyme Modelling of Protein Digestion and L-Lysine Availability

M.B. Assoumani and N.P. Nguyen

Introduction

The evaluation of protein quality through measurement of protein digestion or of available lysine has been the subject of numerous studies on foods, especially those submitted to heat treatment, prolonged storage or other types of processing.

There is general agreement on the need for a method that could be used primarily by food manufacturers. Such a method would be simple, rapid, specific, accurate and precise to allow feed and food manufacturers to optimize their processes, notably heat processes, to achieve better protein quality (Hurrell and Carpenter, 1981; Coon, 1984; Finot and Hurrell, 1985; Sibbald, 1987). Ideally, the method could be used for on line quality control taking no more than a day (Anderson, 1978). Two categories of methods are in use:

1. protein *in vitro* digestibility methods with one or several enzymes (pepsin, trypsin or pepsin, pancreatin; pronase; trypsin, chymotrypsin, peptidase)
2. chemical methods for lysine availability measurement.

Lysine is interesting in that it is one of the two most limiting amino acids and is highly sensitive to Maillard reactions through its ε-amino group (Adrian, 1974; Mauron, 1981).

Numerous authors have discussed the advantages and disavantages of enzymatic methods for protein quality evaluation (Stahmann and Woldegiorgis, 1975; Hsu *et al.*, 1977; Bodwell and Marable, 1981).

Among the *in vitro* digestibility methods, that described by Hsu *et al.* (1977) emerged as being the most promising for the evaluation of heat treatment in the food and animal feed industries. The method is based on a combination of three mammalian enzymes: trypsin, chymotrypsin, and intestinal peptidase. It measures 10 min after the enzyme addition a rapid decline in pH due to the release of ionizable carboxyl groups of the peptide bonds. Hsu *et al.* correlated this decline in pH with apparent protein digestibiliy in rats.

The method has however been criticized for its sensitivity to the buffering capacity of the protein suspensions, pentosans, phenolic acids and other ionizable compounds (Hahn *et al.*, 1982; Pedersen and Eggum, 1983; Moughan *et al.*, 1989).

As an alternative to the method of Hsu *et al.* (1977), Pedersen and Eggum (1983) proposed a pH-stat procedure: the uptake of alkali provided a much more direct measure of the extent of proteolysis than the pH drop.

Moughan *et al.* (1989) compared three *in vitro* multienzymatic methods, those of Hsu *et al.* (1977), as modified by Satterlee *et al.* (1979), of Taverner and Farrell (1981) and of Metz and Van der Meer (1985) with meat and bone meals. They found that the best correlation with *in vivo* ileal protein digestibility was with pH measurement at 10 min. The original Hsu *et al.* method was shown to be a particularly precise assay in spite of the high buffering capacity of the meat and bone meals.

The effect of calcium ions on *in vitro* digestibility was evaluated by Pedersen and Eggum (1983) and by Rothenbuhler and Kinsella (1985). Pedersen and Eggum found that the method of Hsu *et al.* was significantly influenced by the calcium ion concentration of the suspension, with an optimum between 5 and 8 mg per sample. We found that results were affected by water quality, whether deionized, distilled or bidistilled (Assoumani and Jouannaux, unpublished) for Ca++ level. In our applications the best response was obtained with deionized water with a known resistivity greater than 5 MΩ. Optimum activation was achieved with 18 mM CaCl$_2$.

An interesting approach based on the use of immobilized enzymes has been proposed by Culver and Swaisgood (1989) and Chang *et al.* (1990). Their systems were based either on a single enzyme (pepsin) or multiple enzymes (trypsin, chymotrypsin, and peptidases) in biodigesters operated in a fluidized-bed mode that permitted analysis of samples containing insoluble materials. Results obtained with this system were well correlated with those from *in vivo* assays on rats (R=0.83; P< 0.001).

Other *in vitro* enzymatic methods combining protein digestion and essential amino acid determination have been reported. Mauron *et al* (1955) described a method based on the hydrolysis of the food with pepsin followed by pancreatin with simultaneous dialysis and determination of the liberated free amino acids by ion exchange chromatography. The values obtained on milk with this method were reported to be in excellent agreement with *in vivo* values for available lysine. These results were confirmed in an extensive study evaluating the impact of heat treatment on commercial milks (Bujard and Finot, 1978). The method appeared to be very sensitive and distinguished the different forms of available lysine in milk samples when chemical methods were less sensitive.

Hansen *et al.* (1975), assessing thermal processing of wheat flour, demonstrated that the enzymatic digestion rates of heat-treated flour proteins by pepsin and trypsin were decreased and the specific release of lysine and arginine by trypsin and carboxypeptidase-B was impaired.

Trypsin cleaves only lysyl or arginyl peptide bonds so that lysine or arginine

Table 6.1. Alternatives to the classic chemical method of amino acid analysis for the measurement of L-lysine.

Method	Advantages	Disadvantages
1- Chemical[1]		
1-Fluoro-2-4, Dinitrobenzene	-Estimation of available lysine (lysine with free amino groups)	-Interaction with carbohydrates -loss of DNP-lysine during acid digestion
2,4,6-Trinitrobenzene 1-sulfonic acid	-Estimation of available lysine -Time	-Lack of specificity
2- Dye binding[2]		
(Dye binding capacity with acid orange 12)	-Time	-Lack of specificity
(Dye binding L-lysine with azo	-Time	-Overestimates lysine content
dye acid orange 12) + propionic anhydride		-Difficult procedure
3- Microbiological[3]		
Tetrahymena pyriformis	-Values used to estimate availability	-Requires enzyme pretreatment
4- Enzyme electrodes[4]		
L-lysine decarboxylase + CO_2 electrode	-Specificity -Time of analysis (total time 1 min to 5-10 min)	-Necessity for co-enzymes -Lifetime of membranes -Interference with unidentified activators
L-lysine oxidase +O_2 electrode	-Specificity -Time (total time : 1 min)	Interference from levulinic acid in acid hydrolyzed samples

From: Booth (1971); Carpenter & Booth (1973); White & Guilbault (1978); Hurrell & Carpenter (1981); Bodwell & Marable (1981); Marshall *et al.* (1982); Tran *et al.* (1983); M.B. Assoumani & N.P. Nguyen, unpublished; Romette *et al.* (1983); Barlow *et al.* (1984); Assoumani *et al.* (1990)

Table 6.2. Examples of commercial biosensors using immobilized enzymes.

Company	Field of application	Apparatus	Substances	Electrode type
Kyoto Daiichi Kagaku	Clinical	GA-1110	Glucose	H_2O_2
Toyobo Co. Ltd. Omron Tateishi Electronics Co.	Clinical	HFR-100 Diagluca	Lactic acid Glucose Uric acid	H_2O_2
Toyo Jozo Co. Ltd.	Food industry Fermentation Chemistry	AD-300 AS-200 M-100	Glucose Alcohol Lactic acid Glycerol Lactose	O_2
Fuji Electric Co. Ltd.	Clinical Food industry Clinical Fermentation	Gluco-20A ZUP-10001 UA-300A	Glucose Glucose Uric Acid Alcohol	H_2O_2
Mitsubishi Chemical Industries Ltd.	Clinical	Gl-101	Glucose	H_2O_2
Toa Electronics Ltd.	Food industry	FGA1	Glucose	H_2O_2
Oriental Electronic Co. Ltd.	Fermentation Food industry	ST-1 KV-101	Glucose Fish freshness	O_2 O_2
Nikkiso Co. Ltd.	Clinical	SMG 11A	Glucose	H_2O_2
Toshiba Corporation	Clinical		Glucose	O_2
Yellow Springs Instruments	Food industry	Model 23A Model 27	Glucose Alcohol Lactose Galactose-Sucrose	O_2
ZWG	Clinical	GKM01	Glucose Uric acid	H_2O_2
Seres	Clinical	Enzymat	Glucose Choline L-lysine	H_2O_2
Laroche	Clinical	Lactate Analyser 640	L-lactate	H_2O_2

From Germain *et al.* (1988)

become terminal residues. Carboxypeptidase-B which is specific for C-terminal basic groups, then cleaves lysine or arginine. The release of lysine and arginine from flour proteins processed at 150°C and 174°C was less than from unheated flour proteins. The estimates of enzymically released lysine were closely correlated with PER for products treated at high temperatures (Hansen *et al.*, 1975).

Although essential for protein digestibility measurement and amino acid evaluation, these methods are time consuming (they require more than two days work) and expensive. For process optimization a single amino acid evaluation, for instance of lysine, seems easier to apply. However, the classic chemical method for amino acid determination is known to overestimate lysine (Hurrell and Carpenter, 1981).

Several *in vitro* methods were proposed as alternatives. Examples of some commonly used are listed in Table 6.1 and show the lack of agreement on a unique method which should be specific.

It was shown that chemical methods could not evaluate the availability of lysine when the proteins tested contain an inhibitor of one of the proteolytic enzymes tested. For example neither acid hydrolysis nor the Carpenter method detected an increase in available lysine after steaming of soyabean meals (Stahmann and Woldegiorgis, 1975).

Coon (1990) recently published an excellent review of the limitations of present methods for amino acid availability determination for poultry, pigs and non-ruminant animals. He showed that amino acid availabilty can be affected by factors other than Maillard reactions in poultry feed : protease inhibitors, sorghum tannins and barley β-glucans, for example.

In the 1970s there were major developments in the field of enzyme electrodes which appear to be highly promising in their specificity and rapidity. Enzyme electrodes are the combination of an electrochemical electrode with one or more enzymes immobilized at the electrochemically active surface. A number of authors have described different useful systems and their fields of application (Skogberg and Richardson, 1980; Carr and Bowers, 1980; Schaertel and Firstenberg-Eden, 1988; Guilbault and de Olivera, 1985). However 80 to 90% of applications are in the field of carbohydrates, mainly glucose determination with glucose oxidase. This point is confirmed by examining a list of the commercially available analytical apparatus (Table 6.2): there are few applications to amino acids and those do not meet the requirements of the food and feed industries. A specific protein hydrolysis method is a prerequisite for amino acid determination with enzyme electrodes.

For this reason, we investigated the potential use of L-lysine decarboxylase (from *Bacterium cadaveris*) as suggested by several authors (White and Guilbault, 1978; Machola'n, 1978; Skogberg and Richardson, 1979; Tran *et al.*, 1983). Working with the procedure developed by Tran *et al.* (1983) we found that the method was very rapid (less than one minute) but was limited by its requirement for pyridoxal 5'-phosphate as activator. This constituted a real problem as the membrane response depended on having the appropriate activator concentration which was achieved by storing the enzyme electrode jacket in a buffer with pyridoxal-phosphate. Interference from unidentified factors was noted, mainly with enzymatically hydrolyzed vegetable proteins (Assoumani and Nguyen, unpublished).

Work comparing the L-lysine oxidase electrode with the classic ion-exchange chromatography method on Maillard model reactions using soyabean meals and hydrolyzed samples (Assoumani *et al.*, 1990) showed the sensitivity of the enzyme electrode to Maillard reactions in addition to its precision. The standard 6 N HCl protein hydrolysis for total amino acid determination was adapted for lysine; it was able to discriminate heated products unlike the chemical method (unpublished data). The only limitation noted was the possibility of interference by levulinic acid, a degradation product of glucose formed during hydrolysis; its maximum interference was 10% with products rich in carbohydrates.

Extension of the enzyme electrode method to assay enzymically digested samples can only be achieved through the use of a reliable thermal modelling technique that is easy to handle.

In our view, microwaves with a monomodal cavity appear to be the best choice for two reasons :

1. applications of microwave heating are increasing and there is a need for valid thermal modelling;
2. microwave heating offers the possibility of easily conducted experiments to monitor the process with a microcomputer by measuring absorbed energy.

Table 6.3. Electromagnetic fields thermal modelling using a multimode cavity at 2450 MHz.

Measured parameters	References
Time (min)	Wing and Alexander (1971)
Time (min) temperature	Hafez *et al.* (1985)
-Temperature -e' : Dielectric constant -e" : Dielectric loss factor -E : Average field intensity -M E A (cal/g)	Pour-El *et al.* (1981)
- Temperature probe - Time (s) - E	Ofoli and Komolprasert (1988)

M E A - Minimum energy absorbed

91

Classical approaches in this area are based on multimode cavities used in microwave ovens for domestic and industrial applications. This is shown by the general use of domestic ovens for scientific experiments (Table 6.3) in thermal modelling. Such an approach as probe temperature measurement is of questionable validity and applicability: it is well known that dielectric properties (Table 6.4) are the only parameters that govern the behaviour of a material under an electromagnetic field (Mudgett, 1985). The monomodal cavity approach with energy measurement does not involve the thermal properties of foods (specific heat, latent heat vaporization of water), temperature measurement, heat transfer equations, dielectric loss factor (e") or product density.

Table 6.4. Relationship between structure and dielectric activity.

Constituents	Relative dielectric activity
Water, bound	Low
Water, free	High
Salts, associated	Low
Salts, dissociated	High
Colloidal solids	Low

From Mudgett (1985)

The fundamental equation for microwave power absorption per unit volume (Pa, W/cm^3) by a material has been set out by Goldblith (1967):

$$Pa = f\, \varepsilon o\, E^2\, \varepsilon'' \tag{6.1}$$

Where   f = microwave frequency (Hz)
           εo = dielectric constant of free space
           E^2 = square of the electric field strength (volts/cm)
           e" = dielectric loss factor (dimensionless)

The equation used in our application was based on power absorbed (Pa, joules/g)

$$Pa = K\, \frac{(Ui - Ur)^2}{P} \tag{6.2}$$

Where   Ui = incident energy (mV)
        Ur = reflected energy (mV)
        P = sample weight (g)
        K = waveguide efficiency (~ 1)

The objectives of our work were to develop an original concept using an α-L-lysine oxidase electrode to monitor early Maillard reactions. This concept was based on:

1. microwave process modelling with a monomodal cavity;
2. multienzymatic protein hydrolysis to release lysine;
3. acid protein hydrolysis;
4. lysine determination with a pO_2 electrode coupled to immobilized α-L-lysine oxidase.

Protein digestion was evaluated using the method of Hsu *et al.* (1977).

The experiments were conducted on whole soyabeans, but additional data were also obtained on other protein materials.

Material and Methods

Materials

Locally grown raw whole soyabeans were weighed precisely. The final weight is important for this type of cavity : the optimum for energy absorption is 20.0-30.4g.

Fig. 6.1. Energy field partition.

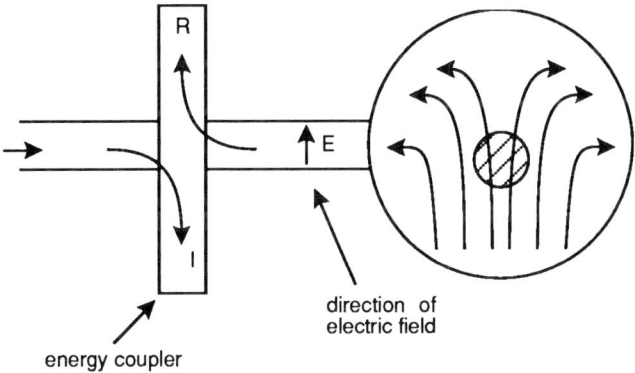

energy coupler

direction of
electric field

Microwave Monomodal Cavity

The apparatus, designed and constructed by S.P.E. (F 27540 Ivry La Bataille) was of Type TEo11 (cylindrical form), with a power consumption of 800 W operating at a frequency of 2.45 GHz. It was equipped with an energy coupler including two crystal detectors, one for measuring the incident energy and the other the reflected energy (Fig. 6.1). A complete description of the equipment, the hardware and software (SERATI - 37 Villa Alesia - F 75014 Paris) appeared in a previous paper (Assoumani and Nguyen, 1990).

Different sample batches were heated for 0, 5, 10, 20 and 27 seconds. During the microwave exposure, the samples were continuously rotated to obtain uniform heating.

Physical and Chemical Analysis

Humidity and protein (Kjeldahl) determinations were done according to E.E.C. methods (Bureau Interprofessionel d'Etudes Analytiques, 1976). Water activity (aw) was measured on ground soyabeans at 25°C with the JEL 20 Novasina with a BS/4 captor (Novasina A.G., Zürich, Switzerland). The *in vitro* method for protein digestibility was that of Hsu *et al.* (1977) with the addition of 18 mM calcium chloride to activate trypsin. Trypsin inhibitors were estimated by the American Oil Chemists' Society (1978) method.

A 7 h hydrolysis with 6 N HCl at 120°C and 1 bar pressure was used as previously (Assoumani *et al.*, 1990).

The multienzymatic protein hydrolysis for lysine release was partly based upon the approach of Hsu *et al.* (1977) to develop a two-stage method for lysine release and analysis taking less than 6 h (Assoumani, 1986). The basic principle involved hydrolysis with trypsin, chymotrypsin and peptidase at constant pH followed by filtration and treatment with carboxypeptidase-B at constant pH to liberate lysine.

L-Lysine Determination with the Immobilized α-L-lysine Oxidase Electrode

α-L-lysine oxidase was from *Trichoderma viride*, Y 244.2 (Yamassa Shoyi, Choshi, Chiba Japan) and L-lysine hydrochloride (99 %) was supplied by Merck (Darmstadt, FRG). The system used the Radiometer (Denmark, Copenhagen) pO_2 electrode model E5046 connected to a digital pO_2 meter interfaced to an Apple IIe. The lysine oxidase was immobilized on the electrode selective membrane (polypropylene) by copolymerization with gelatine and glutaraldehyde (Romette *et al.*, 1983).

The basic principle of the method was the measurement of oxygen consumption following the sample introduction and its oxidation:

$$\text{L-lysine} + O_2 + H_2O \xrightarrow{\text{L-lysine oxidase}} \alpha\text{-keto-}\varepsilon \text{ aminocaproate} + NH_3 + H_2O_2$$
$$\rightarrow \delta\text{-piperidine-2-carboxylate}$$

(Kusakabe *et al.*, 1980).

The oxygen consumption was followed dynamically by measuring the reaction slope (dpO_2/dt) at the inflection point of the acquisition curve. Total analysis time was 60 seconds.

The calibration curve was obtained with lysine concentrations varying from 0 to 0.06 g/l (Assoumani *et al.*, 1989).

Statistical Analysis

Data were analyzed using RS/1 (1986, BBN Software Products Corporation, Cambridge, MA, USA). A two-way analysis of covariance was used with pressure as the main effect at two levels and time of treatment as covariate.

For lysine, one analysis of variance and correlation was used to assess the differences between means for the different times of treatment.

Results and Discussion

Effect of Microwave Exposure Time and Pressure

One of the main objectives of this work was to show the applicability of equation (6.2) with a monomodal cavity for thermal modelling.

Table 6.5. Effect of microwave heating on whole soyabean protein.

Pressure	Treatment time (s)	0	5.1	10.1	20.1	27.3
Atmospheric	Absorbed energy (j/g)	0	8.12	38.2	147.04	250.16
	TIA (U/mg)	49.6	49.8	50.1	18.36	8.5
	Available lysine (% CP)	4.38	4.09	4.49	5.54	4.25
	Total lysine (% CP)	4.91	5.10	5.85	4.15	4.42
	in vitro digestibility	82.13	82.31	84.67	91.36	92.45
1 bar	Absorbed energy (j/g)	0	16.58	35.54	141.90	251.09
	TIA (U/mg)	49.6	47.1	44.8	14.9	9.9
	Available lysine (% CP)	4.38	3.95	4.84	4.96	4.81
	Total lysine (% CP)	4.91	5.35	4.44	5.08	4.67
	in vitro digestibility	82.13	85.03	86.84	91.72	91.54

The effects of microwave exposure on whole soyabeans are summarized in Table 6.5. At atmospheric pressure or at 1 bar there was an equivalent absorbed energy except at 5.1 seconds. For this time of exposure working at less than 1 bar increased by one fold the absorbed energy. One hypothesis to explain this phenomenon would be the effect of pressure in limiting evaporation. As a result, the dielectric constant ε'' which measures the material's ability to store electrical energy can be increased mainly through the material's water activity or free water (aw). However this hypothesis cannot explain the drop in lysine value at both pressures.

The absorbed energy was highly correlated ($r^2 = 0.95$; $P < 0.001$) with exposure time indicating the efficiency of the monomodal cavity with its captors.

These results agree with those of Ofoli and Komolprasert (1988) who showed that electric field strength is a very strong function of time but only relatively constant during the first 100 seconds of microwave exposure. However it must be noted that their experiments were conducted in a multimode cavity and temperature was measured with a fluoroptic sensor.

In work on whole soyabeans, Pour-El *et al.*(1981) demonstrated that absorbed energy was the best parameter to measure when experimenting with microwaves. The absorbed energy was termed minimum energy absorbed (MEA) and required for its calculation the use of such parameters as latent heat of vaporization of water, dry matter content and the specific heat of the soyabeans.

At atmospheric pressure, trypsin inhibitors (TI) remained constant during treatment for 5 and 10 seconds but were reduced by 63% after 20 seconds while digestibility was increased by 2.5 after 10 seconds. This can be seen as the beginning of protein denaturation allowing easy access to enzyme attack. This is consistent with the results of Rothenbuhler and Kinsella (1985); they estimated that protein denaturation accounted for about 60% of the increase in digestibility.

At 1 bar pressure there was a progressive increase in digestibility and a simultaneous decline in TI activity. Pressure obviously contributes to limiting dehydration of soyabean grains.

Trypsin inhibitors and *in vitro* digestibility correlated well with treatment time at atmospheric and at 1 bar pressure (r^2=0.90 and 0.93 respectively; P<0.001). We can see from these experiments that the method of Hsu *et al.* (1977) is highly sensitive and does not seem to be affected by fat content.

For lysine it was noted, with the exception of data obtained at 5 seconds that availability increased progressively to a maximum after about 20 seconds and then decreased. No correlation was observed for lysine, and overall pressure had no significant effect on any of the variables listed in Table 6.5.

Total lysine was poorly correlated with exposure time (r^2=0.489). The lysine released from whole soyabean by acid hydrolysis was very variable indicating possible Maillard reactions with the high fat content. The possible interference of levulinic acid does not explain such variation and is not in accord with extensive work on soyabean meals (Assoumani *et al.*, 1990).

Averaging the values obtained with the two pressures tested tends to show that the problem may be one of sampling. The average data are more consistent with our previous findings in showing that increased heat treatment of proteinaceous material resulted in a total lysine loss. We can see an indication of this at 20 and 27 seconds.

Effect of Absorbed Energy on the Digestibility of Lysine and Protein and on TIA

The calibration curve for lysine was fitted by least square following a second order polynomial (r^2 = 0.9994).

There was no correlation between lysine and treatment time. A one-way analysis of variance showed that the relationship between exposure time and lysine value did not follow a linear model ($r^2 = 0.80$; P< 0.05).

By fitting a least squares polynomial a high correlation ($r^2 = 0.98$) was obtained between lysine values and energy absorbed at atmospheric pressure (Fig.6.2) with the highest value of available lysine at 147 j/g (20 seconds). At 1 bar pressure (Fig.6.3) the highest value of available lysine was reached earlier at 35 j/g (10.1seconds) showing the contribution of steam pressure to the inactivation of trypsin inhibitors (Liener and Kakade, 1980).

Fig. 6.2. Microwave effect on available lysine and protein digestibility (atmospheric).

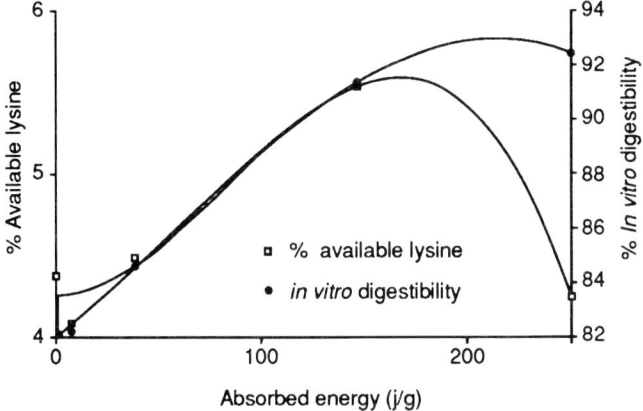

Fig. 6.3. Microwave effect on available lysine and protein digestibility (1 bar).

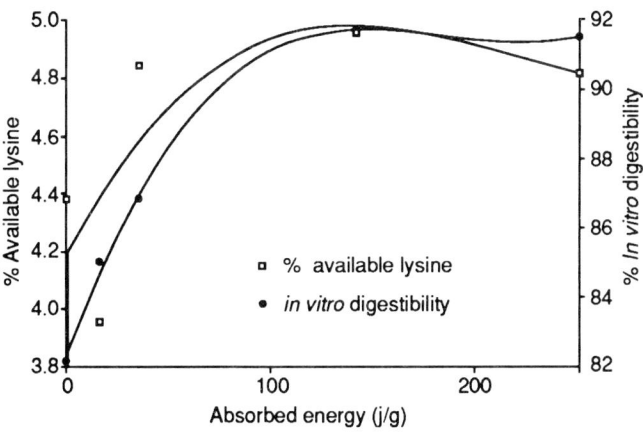

With this energy level available lysine was increased by 7.9%. The same trend was noted for digestibility with an increase of 2.6% and a reduction of 11.8% in trypsin inhibitors. However, while lysine was less affected by Maillard reactions,

97

there was a poor correlation ($r^2 = 0.75$) with energy. This could be the consequence of additional energy from the vaporized water maintained under pressure. In this case the total absorbed energy would be the sum of microwave-generated heat and heat transferred from vaporized water under pressure.

Fig. 6.4. Microwave effect on TIA and protein digestibility (atmospheric).

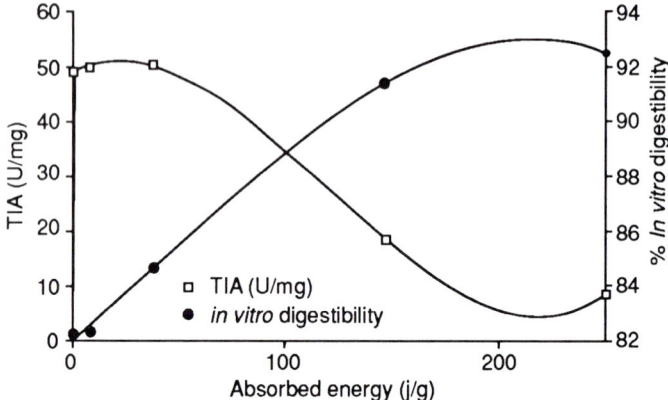

Fig. 6.5 Microwave effect on TIA and protein digestibility (1 bar).

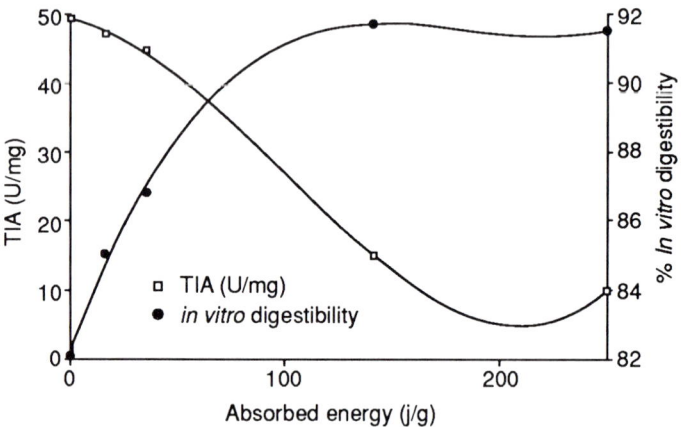

Digestibility and absorbed energy were highly correlated : $r^2 = 0.999$ atmospheric; 0.998 at 1 bar pressure.

It can be noted (Figs 6.2 and 6.3) that at atmospheric pressure the highest digestibility did not correspond to lysine availability. Digestibility continued to increase at atmospheric pressure but at 1 bar it started to decrease at 142 j/g.

The lysine loss corresponding to the highest digestibility was 23.2% showing the detrimental effect of Maillard reactions and the fact that protein digestibility and amino acid availability do not follow the same pattern. This agrees with previous publications (Knipfel, 1981; Hurrell and Finot, 1985; Tanksley and Knabe, 1985; Sibbald, 1987) and shows the importance of measuring available lysine in process optimization.

TIA was negatively correlated with digestibility (r^2 = 0.94 and 0.87) as shown in Figs 6.4 and 6.5. Pour-El *et al.* (1981) showed with unsoaked whole soyabeans (moisture content 7.6%) that the ideal mimimum energy absorbed (MEA) lay between 200 and 300 calories/g (837 and 1256 j/g) for 80 to 94% destruction of TIA. The apparent contradiction between these values and ours is principally due to the higher moisture contents and thus water activity of our soyabeans (13.3% and 0.714 respectively). This would result in a relatively high dielectric activity increasing the efficiency of the microwaves (Swami and Mudgett, 1981).

It must also be pointed out that MEA values were calculated on the basis of the specific heat of soyabeans at 7.6% moisture and the latent heat of vaporization of water. With a multimode cavity there are additional effects of reflected energy which contribute to the temperature increase.

Hafez *et al.* (1983) showed that the destruction of 79% or more of the TIA was sufficient to allow maximal growth of rats. In our case, on the basis of available lysine, the optimum microwave treatment corresponded to destruction of 63 and 70% of TIA.

These values can be considered as consistent with the findings of Rackis *et al.* (1975) based on *in vivo* trials and showing that 70-80% of the TIA needed to be destroyed in order to achieve maximal gains in weight and PER with rats. McNaughton and Reece (1980) reached similar conclusions from chick growth trials when investigating the effect of added moisture before heat treatment of whole soyabeans.

Applications to Commercial Products

Corn Gluten

This is protein obtained by wet milling corn. It does not contain any protease inhibitor. The six samples examined had a high protein digestibility (89.67%) and a high lysine availability (95.7%). Total lysine values (mean 0.933 g/16gN) were not affected by the acid hydrolysis in contrast to what was found for whole soyabeans. The total lysine data are consistent with published values. These samples can be considered as well processed.

Meat Meals

Five samples of different origin were evaluated on the basis of *in vitro* protein digestibility and total lysine. Digestibility values did not allow differentiation of

99

the samples, but total lysine values (mean 4.07 g/16 gN) did. Batterham *et al.* (1986) indicated that variability in lysine availability of meat meals is independent of the starting material and most probably reflects processing conditions. They also found a lack of agreement between pigs, rats and chicks for individual meals.

This raises questions about the applicability of an *in vitro* method until it has been tested *in vivo*, even though it is able to differentiate processed products.

The work undertaken here included three original approaches to show the potential use of an α-L-lysine oxidase electrode to monitor the impact of microwave heat treatment on early Maillard reactions in whole soyabeans. By this method the optimal exposure time was determined and it was shown that protein digestibility is not a suitable criterion of this.

References

Adrian, J. (1974) Nutritional and physiological consequences of the Maillard reaction. *World Review of Nutrition and Dietetics* 19, 71-122.

American Oil Chemists' Society (1978) *Official and Tentative Methods.* 3rd edn. A.O.C.S., Washington, D.C.

Anderson, R.H. (1978) Protein quality testing: Industry needs. *Food Technology* 12, 65 and 68.

Assoumani, M.B. (1986) Procédé pour doser un acide aminé, notamment essentiel, inclus dans une chaine protéique. French patent No. 86.09828.

Assoumani, M.B. and Nguyen, N.P. (1990) An enzyme probe: a future for analysis of amino acid availability. In : Roet, R. (ed.), *Trends and Developments in the Feed Industry.* Lannoo/Teilt, Belgium, pp. 49-57.

Assoumani, M.B., Nguyen, N. P., Lardinois, P. F., Van Bree, J., Baudichau, A., and Bruyer, D.C. (1990) Use of a lysine oxidase electrode for lysine determination in Maillard model reactions and in soyabean meals hydrolysates. *Lebensmittel Wissenchaft und Technologie* 23, 322-7.

Barlow, S.M., Collier, G.S., Jurtiz, J.M., Burt, J.R., Opstvedt, J. and Miller, E.L. (1984) Chemical and biological assay procedures for lysine in fish meals. *Journal of the Science of Food and Agriculture* 35, 154-64.

Batterham, E.S., Lowe, R.F. and Darnell, R.E. (1986) Availability of lysine in meat meal, meat and bone meal and blood meal as determined by the slope-ratio assay with growing pigs, rats and chicks and by chemical techniques. *British Journal of Nutrition* 55, 427-40.

Bodwell, C.E. and Marable, N.L. (1981) Effectiveness of methods for evaluating the nutritional quality of soyabean protein. *Journal of the American Oil Chemists' Society* 58, 475-83.

Booth, V.H. (1971) Problems in the determination of FDNB-available lysine. *Journal of the Science of Food and Agriculture* 22, 658-64.

Bujard, E. and Finot, P. A. (1978) Mesure de la disponibilité et du blocage de la lysine dans les laits industriels. *Annales de la Nutrition et de l'Alimentation.* 32, 291-305.

Bureau Interprofessionnel d'Etudes Analytiques - Gennevilliers France (1976) Recueil des médèanalyse des communautés européennes.

Carpenter, K.J. and Booth, V.H. (1973) Damage to lysine in food processing: its measurement and significance. *Nutrition Abstracts and Reviews* 43, 423-51.

Carr, P.W. and Bowers, L.D. (1980) Theory and applications of enzyme electrodes. In: Carr, P. W. and Bowers, L.D. (eds) *Immobilized Enzymes in Analytical and Clinical Chemistry. Fundamentals and Applications.* Wiley, New York, Vol. 56, pp. 197-310.

Chang, H.I., Caignani, G.L. and Swaisgood, H.E. (1990) Protein digestibility of alkali and fructose treated protein by rat true digestible assay and by the immobilized digestive enzyme assay system. *Journal of Agricultural and Food Chemistry* 38, 1016-18.

Coon, C.N. (1984) Assessing protein quality of protein rich feed ingredients. *Georgia Nutrition Conference for the Feed Industry* pp. 11-19.

Coon, C.N. (1990) Amino acids: how to get the most out of your raw materials. In: Roet, R. (ed.), *Trends and Developments in the Feed Industry.* Lannoo/Teilt, Belgium, pp. 21-37.

Culver, C.A. and Swaisgood, H.E. (1989) Changes in the digestibility of dried casein and glucose mixtures occurring during storage at different temperatures and water activities. *Journal of Dairy Science* 72, 2916-2920.

Finot, P.A. and Hurrell, R. F. (1985) *In vitro* methods to predict lysine availability. In: Finley, J. W. and Hopkins, D. T. (eds). *Digestibility and Amino Acid Availability in Cereals and Oilseeds* AACC, pp. 247-258.

Germain, P., Burteau, N. and Chrichton, R. (1988) Développement et applications des biosenseurs. *Chimie Nouvelle* 6, 662-7.

Goldblith, S.A. (1966) Basic principles of microwaves and recent developments. *Advances in Food Research* 15, 277-301.

Guilbault, G.G. and de Olivera Neto, G. (1985) Immobilised enzyme electrodes. In : Woodward, J. (ed.), *Immobilised Cells and Enzymes.* IRL Press, Oxford, pp. 55-74.

Hafez, Y.S., Singh, G., McLellan, M.E. and Monroe-Lord, L. (1983) Effects of microwave heating on nutritional quality of soyabeans. *Nutrition Reports International*, 28, 413-421.

Hafez, Y.S., Mohamed, A.I., Hewedy, F.M. and Singh, G. (1985) Effects of microwave heating on solubility, digestibility and metabolism of soy protein. *Journal of Food Science.* 50, 415-417, 423.

Hahn, D.H., Faubion, J.M., Ring, S.H., Doherty, C.A. and Rooney, L.W. (1982) Semiautomated *in vitro* analysis of sorghum protein availability via pronase

101

hydrolysis. *Cereal Chemistry* 59, 132-136.

Hansen, L.P., Johnston, P.H. and Ferrel, R.E. (1975) In: Friedman, M. (ed.), *Protein Nutritional Quality of Feeds Part 2*. Dekker, pp. 393-415.

Hsu, H.W., Vavak, D.L., Satterlee, L.D. and Miller, G.A. (1977) A multienzyme technique for estimating protein digestibility. *Journal of Food Science* 42, 1269-1273.

Hurrell, R. F. and Carpenter, K.J. (1981) The estimation of available lysine in foodstuffs after Maillard reactions. *Progress in Food and Nutrition Science*, 159-176.

Hurrell, R.F. and Finot, P.A. (1985) Effects of food processing on protein digestibility and amino acid availability. In: Finley, J. W. and Hopkins, D. T. (eds). *Digestibility and Amino Acid Availability in Cereals and Oilseeds*. AACC, pp. 233-246.

Knipfel, J.E. (1981) Nitrogen and energy availabilities in foods and feeds subjected to heating. *Progress in Food and Nutrition Science*, 5, 177-192.

Kusakabe, H., Kodama, K., Kuninaka, A., Yoshino, H., Misono, H. and Soda, K. (1980) A new antitumor enzyme, L-lysine oxidase from *Trichoderma viride*. Purification and enzymological properties. *Journal of Biological Chemistry* 255, 976-81.

Liener, I.E. and Kakade, M.L. (1980) Protease inhibitors. In: Liener, I.E. (ed.). *Toxic Constituents of Plant Foodstuffs Academic Press*, pp. 7-71.

Machola'n, L. (1978) Rapid determination of L-lysine and L-arginine by oxygen electrode with membrane attached amino acid decarboxylasediamine oxidase system. *Collection of Czechoslovak Chemical Communications* 43, 1811-1817.

McNaughton, J. L. and Reece, F. N. (1980) Effect of moisture content and cooking time on soyabean meal urease index, trypsin inhibitor content and broiler growth. *Poultry Science* 59, 2300-2306.

Mauron, J. (1981) The Maillard reaction in food; a critical review from the nutritional standpoint. *Progress in Food and Nutrition Science* 5, 5-35.

Mauron, J., Mottu, F., Bugard, E. and Egli, R.II. (1955) The availability of lysine, methionine and tryptophan in condensed milk and milk powder. *In vitro* digestion studies. *Archives of Biochemistry and Biophysics* 59, 433-451.

Metz, S.H.M. and Van der Meer, J.M. (1985) Nylon bag and *in vitro* techniques to predict *in vivo* digestibility of organic matter in feedstuffs for pigs. In: Just, A., Jorgensen, II., and Fernandez, J. A. (ed.). *Proceedings of the 3rd International Seminar on digestive physiology in the pig*. National Institute of Animal Science, Copenhagen, pp. 373-376.

Moughan, P. J., Schrama, J., Skilton, G. A. and Smith, W. C. (1989) *In vitro* determination of nitrogen digestibility and lysine availability in meat and bone meals and comparison with *in vivo* ileal digestibility estimates. *Journal of the Science of Food and Agriculture*, 4, 281-292.

Mudgett, R.E. (1985) Dielectric properties of foods. In: Decareau, R.V. (ed.),

Microwaves in the Food Processing Industry. Academic Press, Inc. pp. 15-37.

Ofoli, R.Y. and Komolprasert, V. (1988) On the thermal modelling of foods in electromagnetic fields. *Journal of Food Processing and Preservation* 12, 219-241.

Pedersen, B. and Eggum, B. O. (1983) Prediction of protein digestibility by an *in vitro* enzymatic pH-stat procedure. *Zeitschrift für Tierphysiologie, Tiernährung und Futtermittelkunde* 49, 265-277.

Pour-El, A., Nelson, S.O., Peck, E.E., Tjhio, B. and Stetson, L.E. (1981) Biological properties of VHF and microwave heated soyabeans. *Journal of Food Science* 46, 880-885, 895.

Rackis, J.J., McGhee, J.E. and Booth, A.N. (1975) Biological threshold levels of soybean trypsin inhibitors by rat bioassay. *Cereal Chemistry* 52, 85-93.

Romette, J.L., Yang, J.S., Kusakabe, H. and Thomas, D. (1983) Enzyme electrode for specific determination of L-lysine. *Biotechnology and Bioengineering* 25, 2557-2566.

Rothenbuhler, E. and Kinsella, J.E. (1985) The pH stat method for assessing protein digestibility: an evaluation. *Journal of Agricultural and Food Chemistry* 33, 433-438.

Satterlee, L.D., Marshall, H.F. and Tennyson, J.M. (1979) Methods of measuring protein quality. *Journal of the American Oil Chemists' Society* 56, 103-109.

Schaertel, B.J. and Firstenberg-Eden, R. (1988) Biosensors in the food industry: present and future. *Journal of Food Protection* 51, 811-820.

Sibbald, I.R. (1987) Estimation of bioavailable amino acids in feedingstuffs for poultry and pigs: a review with emphasis on balance experiments. *Canadian Journal of Animal Science* 67, 221-300.

Skogberg, D. and Richardson, T. (1979) Preparation and use of an enzyme electrode for specific analysis of L-lysine in cereal grains. *Cereal Chemistry* 56, 147-152.

Skogberg, D. and Richardson, T. (1980) Enzyme electrodes for the food industry. *Journal of Food Protection* 43, 808-819.

Stahmann, M. A. and Woldegiorgis, W. (1975) Enzymatic methods for protein quality determination. In: Friedel, M. (ed.), *Protein Nutritional Quality of Foods and Feeds Part 1*, Dekker, pp. 211-234.

Swami, S. and Mudgett, R.E. (1981) Effect of moisture and salt contents on the dielectric behaviour of liquid and semi-solid foods. Paper presented at Symp. Int. Microwave Power Inst., Toronto, Canada. 16, 48.

Tanksley, T.D. and Knabe, D.A. (1985) Direct measurements of amino acid digestibility in swine. In: Finlay, J.W. and Hopkins, D.T. (eds), *Digestibility and Amino Acid Availability in Cereals and Oilseeds*. AACC. pp. 259-73.

Taverner, M.R. and Farrell, D.J. (1981) Availability to pigs of amino acids in cereal grains. 3. A comparison of ileal availability values with faecal, chemical and enzymic estimates. *British Journal of Nutrition* 46, 173-180.

M.B. Assoumani and N.P. Nguyen

Tran, N.D., Romette, J.L. and Thomas, D. (1983) An enzyme electrode for specific determination of L-lysine: a real time control sensor. *Biotechnology and Bioengineering* 25, 329-340.

White, W.C. and Guilbault, G.G. (1978) Lysine specific enzyme electrode for determination of lysine in grain foodstuffs. *Analytical Chemistry* 50, 1484-1486.

Wing, R.W. and Alexander, J.C. (1971) The heating of soybean meals by microwave radiations. *Nutrition Reports International* 4, 387-396.

Chapter 7

Use of Pepsin Digestibility, Multienzyme pH Change and Protein Solubility Assays to Predict *In Vivo* Protein Quality of Feedstuffs

C.M. Parsons

Introduction

There has been much research during the last ten years on the amino acid availability or digestibility of feedstuffs. Much of this work has been performed using ileally-cannulated pigs (Tanksley and Knabe, 1984; Sauer and Ozimek, 1986) or conventional or caecectomized chickens in the precision-fed cockerel assay (Sibbald, 1986; Green, 1987; Parsons, 1990). This research has led to the publication of tables containing amino acid digestibility coefficients for a wide variety of commonly used feedstuffs such as that in *Nutrient Requirements of Swine* (National Research Council, 1988). A similar table for poultry will be forthcoming in the 9th Revised Edition of *Nutrient Requirements of Poultry* (National Research Council, 1991; in press). Although such tables provide important information on relative differences in quality among feedstuffs, the large variation often observed among different samples of the same feedstuff (Parsons, 1990) is of concern and illustrates the need for simple *in vitro* assays that accurately predict *in vivo* availability of amino acids in feed ingredients. Some of the recent research conducted in our laboratory and others with three *in vitro* assays is summarized in this paper.

Pepsin Digestibility

Digestibility of nitrogen (N) by pepsin has been used for evaluation of animal protein feedstuffs for many years. The primary limitation of this assay seems to be that the 0.2% pepsin concentration recommended by the Association of Official Analytical Chemists (1984) is excessive and can almost completely digest proteins of poor quality. Thus, the assay is not sensitive enough to assess differences in quality among ingredient samples. Johnston and Coon (1979a) showed that even when the pepsin concentration was decreased by 10-fold to 0.02%, the digestible N values for nine meat meals were almost identical to those obtained with 0.2% pepsin. When the pepsin concentration was reduced to 0.002%, however, the digestible N values were substantially reduced, and the difference or range in values among meat meal samples increased markedly. Similar results were obtained for six feather meals. The 0.002% pepsin digestible N values for the meat meals and feather meals were also found to be highly correlated with estimates of protein efficiency ratio and net protein utilization (Johnston and Coon, 1979b).

Research has been conducted in our laboratory during the last four years to evaluate further the effect of pepsin concentration on digestible N values of animal protein feedstuffs and to determine whether or not these values indicate differences in amino acid digestibility. Digestible N values for 14 meat meals, eight feather meals and nine poultry by-product meals were lower when determined with 0.002% pepsin than when determined with 0.2% pepsin, particularly for the feather meals (Table 7.1). Digestible N values for meat meal were reduced further by decreasing the pepsin concentration to 0.0002%. The range in values among samples of the same feedstuff were much larger at the lower pepsin concentrations.

Table 7.1. Effect of pepsin concentration on *in vitro* digestibility of nitrogen (%) in 14 meat meals, 8 feather meals and 9 poultry by-product meals.

Pepsin conc. (%)	Meat meal			Feather meal			Poultry meal		
	Mean	Min	Max	Mean	Min	Max	Mean	Min	Max
0.2	86	83	89	76	70	81	85	80	92
0.002	72	54	83	32	17	49	75	58	89
0.0002	42	29	69	-	-	-	-	-	-

C. M. Parsons (unpublished)

The pepsin digestible N values were correlated with *in vivo* lysine digestibility values determined on caecectomized cockerels by the precision-fed cockerel assay (Table 7.2). Digestible N values for the feather and meat meals determined with 0.002% pepsin were more highly correlated with lysine digestibility values than were those determined with 0.2% pepsin. However, with poultry by-product meal, both 0.2% and 0.002% pepsin digestible N values were very highly correlated with lysine digestibility values. Reducing the pepsin concentration to 0.0002% did not improve the correlation with lysine digestibility for the meat meals.

The results of these studies indicate that the 0.002% pepsin assay is superior to the 0.2% pepsin assay in predicting *in vivo* protein and amino acid quality of meat meals and feather meals.

Multienzyme pH Change Assay

Many of the *in vitro* protein digestibility methods based on enzymatic digestion were reviewed by Hsu *et al.* (1977). The authors concluded that these methods had not been widely accepted because no corresponding *in vivo* data were presented for comparison or because the procedures were too complicated and time consuming for routine use. Consequently, Hsu *et al.* (1977) conducted research to develop a reliable *in vitro* enzymatic method that could determine protein digestibility within an hour. The resulting assay is commonly known as the multienzyme pH change assay and is a modification of the assay used by Maga *et al.* (1973). The multienzyme assay consists of incubating test ingredients in an aqueous suspension with a combination of trypsin, chymotrypsin and peptidase. The pH of the solution is initially adjusted to pH 8.0. As the proteolytic enzymes digest the protein and break the peptide bonds in the proteins' primary structures, the liberated carboxyl groups release hydrogen ions (H+) which lower the pH of the protein suspension. The pH usually decreases rapidly during the first few minutes of incubation and then gradually stabilizes by about 10 minutes. The study by Hsu *et al.* (1977) indicated that the pH of the protein suspension following 10 min digestion was highly correlated with *in vivo* apparent protein digestibility in rats. Regression analyses on the latter two parameters for 23 samples of ingredients yielded a correlation coefficient of 0.90. It was also found that the multienzyme assay was sensitive to the presence of trypsin inhibitors and the effects of heat treatment on protein digestibility. Buffering effects of feedstuffs did not substantially affect the assay. This procedure has subsequently been modified for use in predicting *in vivo* protein efficiency ratio (Satterlee *et al.*, 1977; 1982).

Table 7.2. Correlation between pepsin digestible nitrogen and *in vivo* lysine digestibility for animal protein meals.

Feed ingredient	Pepsin conc.	Correlation with lysine digestibility[1]
Feather meal	0.2%	0.23
	0.002%	0.68*
Meat meal:	0.2%	0.17
	0.002%	0.67*
	0.0002%	0.63*
Poultry by-product meal	0.2%	0.98*
	0.002%	0.95*

Results from the author's laboratory

[1] Values are Pearson correlation coefficients for 7 samples of feather meal, 14 samples of meat meal and 9 samples of poultry by-product meal. Lysine digestibility was determined with the precision-fed cockerel assay.

* $P < 0.05$

C.M. Parsons

University of Illinois Research

Research has been conducted recently to evaluate the multienzyme assay for prediction of *in vivo* amino acid digestibility for poultry and swine (Bellaver, 1989; Parsons *et al.*, unpublished). In the first series of experiments, multienzyme pH change, true digestibility of amino acids using caecectomized cockerels and apparent digestibility of amino acids using ileally cannulated pigs were determined for various high-protein feedstuffs. The results are summarized in Table 7.3. In general, the multienzyme pH change values were positively correlated with *in vivo* lysine digestibility. This relationship was particularly strong for true lysine digestibility in poultry with a correlation between multienzyme pH change and lysine digestibility of 0.90.

Table 7.3. Multienzyme pH change values and *in vivo* lysine digestibility values for various high-protein feedstuffs.

Feed ingredient	Multienzyme pH change (units)[1]	True lysine digestibility(%)[2]	Apparent lysine digestibility (%)[3]
Casein	2.36	99	-
Soyabean meal	1.52	92	86
Meat meal	1.39	85	76
Poulty by-product meal	1.37	84	78
Cottonseed meal	1.23	72	60
Feather meal	0.90	68	-

Bellaver (1989) and C.M. Parsons (unpublished).
[1] pH change after 10 min. of incubation with a mixture of peptidase, trypsin and chymotrypsin.
[2] Determined with caecectomized cockerels.
[3] Determined with ileally cannulated pigs.

In the second series of experiments, the multienzyme assay was evaluated for its ability to detect differences in protein quality and amino acid digestibility among samples of feather meals and meat meals varying markedly in quality obtained from commercial suppliers. These were evaluated in chick growth assays (protein efficiency ratio and amino acid bioavailability); amino acid digestibility assays were conducted on caecectomized cockerels (Parsons, 1988). The multienzyme assay was then conducted on the samples of lowest and highest quality and the values compared to *in vivo* lysine digestibility and protein efficiency ratio (PER). There were large differences in lysine digestibility and PER between the low and high quality meals (Table 7.4). However, there was no consistent relationship between multienzyme pH change values and *in vivo* lysine digestibility or PER. It seems that the multienzyme assay is sensitive in detecting differences in amino acid digestibility between feedstuffs that differ greatly in composition but seems to be of limited use in predicting *in vivo* quality among different samples of the same animal protein meal.

Table 7.4. Multienzyme pH change and *in vivo* lysine digestibility values for feather meals and meat meals varying in quality.

Ingredient	Multienzyme pH change[1] (units)	Lysine digestibility[2](%)	Protein efficiency ratio[3]
High-quality feather meal 1	0.83	73	1.2
High-quality feather meal 2	0.94	73	1.2
Low-quality feather meal 1	0.96	67	0.80
Low-quality feather meal 2	0.85	58	0.82
High-quality meat meal 1	0.85	90	2.8
High-quality meat meal 2	0.92	85	2.5
Low-quality meat meal 1	0.92	73	1.1
Low-quality meat meal 2	0.93	69	1.1

From Parsons (1988) and C. M. Parsons (unpublished)
[1] pH change after 10 min. of incubation with a mixture of peptidase, trypsin and chymotrypsin.
[2] Determined with caecectomized cockerels.
[3] Weight gain (g) per g of protein consumed. Determined with chicks given diets containing 9% protein provided solely by the animal protein meal.

C.M. Parsons

Protein Solubility in Potassium Hydroxide

It is well known that many plant protein feedstuffs such as soyabeans must be properly processed by cooking to destroy endogenous antinutritional factors (Ham *et al.*, 1945; Birk *et al.*, 1963) and to denature the protein (Liener, 1976). Either under-cooking or over-cooking can be detrimental to the nutritional value of soyabean meal (SBM) for animal growth (McNaughton *et al.*, 1981).

The measurement of urease activity based on change in pH is one of the most commonly used *in vitro* tests for assessing quality of SBM. This assay, however, is useful only for detecting under-cooking of SBM because the urease activity rapidly decreases to zero as SBM is heated (Balloun *et al.*, 1953) and SBM containing no urease activity may not have reduced protein quality due to over-cooking (McNaughton *et al.*, 1981; Araba and Dale, 1990). An *in vitro* assay is needed to indicate over-processing of SBM and other plant protein.

Evans and St. John (1945) reported that as raw SBM was cooked for increasing lengths of time the amount of SBM protein soluble in 0.2% KOH decreased. Araba and Dale (1990) from the University of Georgia recently concluded from an initial study that this assay could detect reduced SBM protein quality for chicks. We have recently conducted research with both chicks and pigs to evaluate the assay further as an indicator of reduced SBM protein quality associated with either under- or over-processing.

Analytical Procedure for Protein Solubility

The procedure used was similar to that described previously by Araba and Dale (1990). Approximately 1.5 g of soyabeans or SBM were placed in a 250ml beaker and 75 ml of 0.2% KOH (w/v; 0.036N) were added. The mixture was stirred for 20 min at 22°C. Approximately 50 ml of the liquid were then collected and centrifuged at 1250 X g for 10 min. A 15 ml aliquot of the supernatant was collected and analysed for N content by the Kjeldahl method. Soluble protein was then calculated as a percentage of the total protein in the original sample of soyabeans or SBM. Urease activity was also assessed using the urease index which is based on pH change (Association of Official Analytical Chemists, 1980).

Over-processing of Soyabean Meal

Experiments with Chicks

The results of two experiments conducted in our laboratory and two conducted by Araba and Dale (1990) are summarized in Table 7.5. Commercial dehulled solvent-extracted SBM was heated for increasing lengths of time at 120°C in a small laboratory autoclave. The autoclaved SBM samples were then given to chicks as the sole protein source in a 23% protein diet (Parsons *et al.*, 1989) or as the primary

110

source of protein in an 18% protein diet deficient in lysine (Araba and Dale, 1990). Growth performance was measured for two to three weeks. Urease activity in the control SBM (0 min) was very low in both studies and decreased to zero within five min of autoclaving whereas protein solubility continued to decrease as autoclaving time increased. Rate and efficiency of weight gain of chicks fed SBM with protein solubility less than 64% (versus 50%) was significantly depressed in our study (Parsons *et al.*, 1989), whereas growth performance of chicks fed SBM with protein solubility less than 70% (versus 63%) was significantly depressed in the study of Araba and Dale (1990). The higher critical protein solubility level suggested by the study of Araba and Dale (1990) compared to ours may be primarily associated with the type of diet in which the over-processed SBMs were evaluated. In the Georgia study chicks were given a lysine-deficient diet whereas in our study the diet was adequate in all amino acids. Further work in our laboratory indicated that over-cooking the SBM reduced the digestibility of lysine much more than that of the other amino acids. Moreover, the measured concentration of lysine in SBM was decreased by approximately 15% by autoclaving for 40 min. These results indicate that protein solubility is a sensitive index of *in vivo* SBM protein quality for poultry and that protein solubility values below 70% are suggestive of reduced protein quality.

Table 7.5. Effect of autoclaving on protein solubility in 0.2% KOH and protein quality of commercial dehulled soyabean meal for chicks[1.]

Autoclaving time at 121°C (min.)	Parsons *et al.* (1989)[2]				Araba and Dale (1990)[3]			
	Urease index (pH change)	Protein solubility (%)	Weight gain (g)	Gain: feed ratio	Urease Index (pH change)	Protein solubility (%)	Weight gain (g)	Gain: feed ratio
0	.07	84[a]	161[a]	.697[a]	.01	84[a]	436[a]	.494[a]
5	0	72[b]	155[a]	.696[a]	.01	74[b]	448[a]	.501[a]
10	0	64[c]	156[a]	.677[a]	0	70[c]	434[a]	.491[a]
20	0	50[d]	131[b]	.630[b]	0	63[d]	399[b]	.471[b]
40	0	36[e]	78[c]	.452[c]	0	47[e]	236[c]	.431[c]

[a-e] Means within a column bearing no common superscripts are significantly different (P < 0.05).

[1] Results are averages of two experiments within each study.

[2] Growth performance of crossbred male chicks from 8 to 17 days of age.

[3] Growth performance of commercial male broiler chicks from 1 to 18 or 21 days of age.

C.M. Parsons

Experiments with Pigs

An experiment similar to those described above has been conducted with pigs (Parsons *et al.*, 1989). Commercial solvent-extracted hulled SBM (43% protein) was cooked for increasing lengths of time at 121°C in a large industrial autoclave. It was given to Landrace-Duroc-Yorkshire crossbred pigs from 33 to 46 days of age as the primary source of protein in a 20% protein diet. Protein solubility was reduced from 89 to 71, 66 and 56% by autoclaving the SBM for 0, 10, 20 and 40 min, respectively. Weight gain was significantly reduced when protein solubility was less than 71%, and feed efficiency was depressed when protein solubility was less than 66%. The decrease in growth rate was primarily due to reduced feed intake, suggesting that the autoclaving may have reduced the palatability of the SBM. These results indicate that the protein solubility test is also a good test of SBM quality for pigs.

Fig. 7.1. Effect of autoclaving on protein solubility of raw full-fat soyabeans.

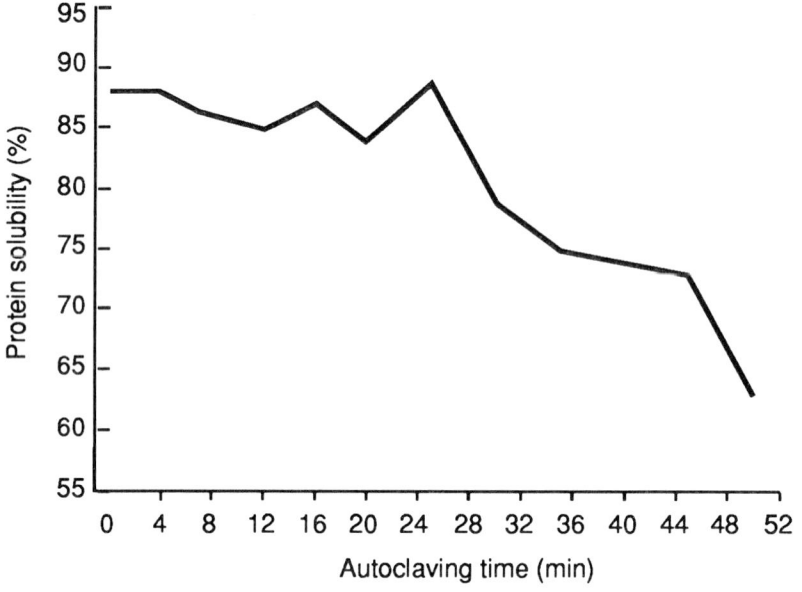

Under-processing of Soyabean Meal

Experiments with Chicks

We have recently conducted experiments to evaluate the protein solubility assay for detecting under-processing of SBM (C. M. Parsons, unpublished). Raw full-fat soyabeans were autoclaved for 0, 3, 6, 9, 12, 15 or 18 min in a laboratory autoclave as described previously and given to chicks as the sole source of dietary protein.

Growth performance of the chicks increased progressively as the autoclaving time increased from 0 to 15 min. The performance of chicks given soyabeans autoclaved for 15 or 18 min was similar. Urease activity of the raw soyabeans was high and was unaffected by autoclaving times between 0 and 9 min. Urease activity of soyabeans autoclaved for 12 min decreased to 0.21 units of pH change and decreased only slightly thereafter. Protein solubility of the raw uncooked soyabeans was 90% and did not change consistently as the autoclaving time increased to 18 min. Thus, the protein solubility assay does not seem to provide a sensitive index of variation in SBM protein quality associated with under-processing. Further results to support this hypothesis are given in Fig. 7.1. Protein solubility did not change consistently as raw soyabeans were autoclaved for 0 to 24 min. However, as autoclaving time increased beyond 24 min protein solubility decreased markedly, indicating that changes in protein solubility are greatest when SBM is heated for excessive periods of time.

Table 7.6. Effect of sample particle size on the protein solubility of dehulled soyabean meal in 0.2% potassium hydroxide.

Mean particle size[1] (μm)	Protein solubility[2] (%)
184	90
251	83
299	82
556	79
599	77
707	76
831	74
939	70

Parsons, *et al.* (1989).

[1] Various particle sizes produced using a coffee grinder or Wiley Mill with different screen sizes.

[2] Linear decrease as a function of increased particle size ($P < 0.0001$). Equation relating protein solubility to mean particle size was: $y = 91.6 - 0.0206 (\pm 0.0017)x$; $r = 0.94$.

Effect of Sample Particle Size on Protein Solubility

Initial cooperative work with Dr Nick Dale's group at the University of Georgia suggested that sample particle size may influence protein solubility values. To test this hypothesis, a sample of dehulled SBM was ground to eight different particle sizes using a coffee grinder and analytical mills. Mean particle size was determined by passing the samples through a series of sieves ranging in size from 75 to 1400 μm in diameter. The results are shown in Table 7.6. As the mean sample particle size increased from 184 to 939 μm, protein solubility decreased from 90% to 70%.

These results clearly show that sample particle size has a large effect on protein solubility values and that it is necessary for labs to grind SBM samples to a consistent small particle size to obtain repeatable results with the KOH protein solubility test.

In addition to standardizing particle size, length of stirring should also be kept constant since this variable can also affect solubility (C. M. Parsons, unpublished). Oil content of the SBM does not affect solubility values, although high-fat soyabean or SBM samples tend to clump when the KOH is added and care is needed to achieve proper mixing and stirring (Dale, 1990).

References

Araba, M. and Dale, N.M. (1990) Evaluation of protein solubility as an indicator of overprocessing of soybean meal. *Poultry Science* 69, 76-83.

Association of Official Analytical Chemists (1984) *Official Methods of Analysis*, 14th. edn AOAC, Washington, DC.

Balloun, S.L., Johnston, E. and Arnold, L.K. (1953) Laboratory estimation of the nutritive value of soybean meals. *Poultry Science* 32, 517-27.

Bellaver, C. (1989) *Estimation of Amino Acid Digestibility and its Usefulness in Swine Feed Formulation*. Ph.D. thesis, University of Illinois, Urbana, Illinois.

Birk, Y., Gertler, A. and Khalef, S. (1963) A pure trypsin inhibitor from soya beans. *Biochemical Journal* 87, 281-4.

Dale, N.M. (1990) Protein solubility as an indicator of optimum processing of soybean meal. *Proceedings of Guelph Nutrition Conference*, University of Guelph, Guelph, Ontario, Canada, pp. 42-52.

Evans, R.J. and St. John, J.L. (1945) Estimation of the relative nutritive value of vegetable proteins by two chemical methods. *Journal of Nutrition* 30, 209-17.

Green, S. (1987) *Digestibilities of Amino Acids in Foodstuffs for Poultry and Pigs*. A.E.C. - Rhône Poulenc Nutrition Laboratories, Commentry, France.

Ham, W.E., Sandstedt, R.M. and Mussehl, F.E. (1945) The proteolytic inhibiting substance in the extract from unheated soybean meal and its effect upon growth in chicks. *Journal of Biological Chemistry* 161, 635-42.

Hsu, H.W., Vavak, D.L., Satterlee, L.D. and Miller, G.A. (1977) A multienzyme technique for estimating protein digestibility. *Journal of Food Science* 42, 1269-73.

Johnston, J. and Coon, C.N. (1979a) The use of varying levels of pepsin for pepsin digestion studies with animal proteins. *Poultry Science* 58, 1271-3.

Johnston, J. and Coon, C.N. (1979b) A comparison of six protein quality assays using commercially available protein meals. *Poultry Science* 58, 919-27.

Liener, I.E. (1976) Problems with endogenous toxic factors in oilseed residues. *Proceedings of Georgia Nutrition Conference*. University of Georgia, Athens, Georgia, pp. 3-21.

McNaughton, J.M., Reece, F.N. and Deaton, J.W. (1981) Relationships between color, trypsin inhibitor contents, urease index of soybean meal and effects on broiler performance. *Poultry Science* 60, 393-400.

Maga, J.A., Lorenz, K. and Onayemi, O. (1973). Digestive acceptability of proteins as measured by the initial rate of *in vitro* proteolysis. *Journal of Food Science* 38, 173-4.

National Research Council (1988) *Nutrient Requirements of Swine*, 9th edn. National Academy Press, Washington, D.C. p. 62.

Parsons, C.M. (1988) Amino acid digestibility and metabolizable energy of animal protein feedstuffs. *Proceedings of Arkansas Nutrition Conference*, University of Arkansas, Fayetteville, Arkansas, pp. 18-25.

Parsons, C.M. (1990) Digestibility of amino acids in feedstuffs for poultry. *Proceedings of Maryland Nutrition Conference for Feed Manufacturers*, University of Maryland, College Park, Maryland, pp. 22-9.

Parsons, C.M., Hashimoto, K., Wedekind, K.J. and Baker, D.H. (1989) Soybean protein solubility in KOH as *in vitro* test of *in vivo* protein quality: effects of particle size and overprocessing. *Poultry Science* 68(Suppl. 1), 110.

Satterlee, L.D., Kendrick, J.G. and Miller, G.A. (1977) Rapid *in vitro* assays for estimating protein quality. *Food Technology* June, 1977, pp. 78-82.

Satterlee, L.D., Kendrick, J.G., Marshall, H. F., Jewell, D. K., Ali, R. A., Heckman, M. M., Steinke, H. F., Larson, P., Phillips, D., Sarwar, G., and Slump, P. (1982) *In vitro* assay for predicting protein efficiency ratio as measured by rat bioassay: collaborative study. *Journal of the Association of Official Analytical Chemists* 65, 798-809.

Sauer, W.C., and Ozimek, L. (1986) Digestibility of amino acids in swine: results and their practical applications. A review. *Livestock Production Science* 15, 367-88.

Sibbald, I. R. (1986) The T. M. E. system of feed evaluation: methodology, feed composition data and bibliography. *Animal Research Centre Contribution* 85-19, Animal Research Centre, Ottawa, Ontario, Canada.

Tanksley, T. D., Jr. and Knabe, D. A. (1984) Ileal digestibility of amino acids in pig feeds and their use in formulating diets. In: Haresign, W. and Cole, D. J. A. (eds), *Recent Advances in Animal Nutrition*, Butterworth, London.

Chapter 8

Estimation of True Ileal Digestibility of Amino Acids With Pigs by an *In Vitro* Method Using Intestinal Fluid

S. Furuya

Introduction

In order to improve the accuracy of diet formulation for pigs, it is important to estimate the levels of digestibility rather than total amino acid contents of feedstuffs. Although amino acid digestibility values have generally been determined by the ileal analysis method, the determination is not only tedious and time-consuming but also requires a large quantity of feed. For feed evaluation in a laboratory that does not maintain surgically modified animals, an *in vitro* assay could provide an acceptable method for estimating amino acid digestibility.

In recent years several *in vitro* methods have been developed for assessing protein digestibility in simple-stomached animals, using pig intestinal fluid (Furuya *et al.*, 1979; Clunies and Leeson, 1984), duodenal and ileal digesta and faeces from pigs as inocula for incubations (Löwgren *et al.*, 1989) and pepsin-pancreatin (Gauthier *et al.*, 1982; Dierick *et al.*, 1985; Cave, 1988; Drake, 1990). There appear to be few reports of the use of an *in vitro* method for estimating amino acid digestibility in which results are compared with the ileal amino acid digestibility values obtained with pigs. In these comparisons, as indicated by Dierick *et al.* (1985) and Vachon *et al.* (1987), the *in vitro* digestibility should be compared with the *in vivo* true digestibility because the apparent amino acid digestibility is significantly affected by the endogenous amino acids (Furuya and Kaji, 1989), which are not present *in vitro*.

The objective of this study was to compare the *in vivo* procedure with the *in vitro* method using intestinal fluid of pigs for the prediction of the true ileal digestibility (TID) of amino acids with pigs.

Materials and Methods

A total of 15 feedstuffs including protein supplements, cereal grains and cereal by-products was studied (Table 8.1). The naked barley was a new variety with high lysine. For the *in vitro* studies feedstuffs were ground through a laboratory mill using screen sizes of 1 mm or 0.5 mm.

Determination of True Ileal Amino Acid Digestibility with Pigs

The true ileal amino acid digestibility of these 15 feedstuffs, determined with pigs fitted with a simple T cannula, was reported earlier (Furuya *et al.*, 1986, for casein, cottonseed meal, fish meal and soyabean meal; Furuya and Kaji, 1987, for barley, maize, naked barley, rice and wheat; Furuya *et al.*, 1988, for feather meal, meat and bone meal, rapeseed meal, grain sorghum, defatted rice bran and wheat bran). For the protein supplements except feather meal, meat and bone meal and rapeseed meal, TID of amino acids was determined by a regression method (Furuya *et al.*, 1986), which eliminates the determination of the endogenous ileal amino acid output. A maize-maize starch basal diet containing 53 g crude protein (nitrogen x 6.25, CP) /kg and diets in which each feed was incorporated into the basal diet to provide three levels of CP at the expense of maize starch, were used. For the other feedstuffs, a maize-starch basal diet containing 34 g CP per kg, and diets in which each feed was also incorporated into the basal diet at the expense of starch, were fed and TID was determined by a difference method. Further details were given by Furuya *et al.* (1986) and Furuya and Kaji (1987).

Collection and Preparation of Intestinal Fluid

A three month old female crossbred pig (Large White x Landrace) weighing approximately 30 kg was fitted with a simple T cannula in the upper jejunum as described previously (Furuya *et al.*, 1979). The pig was fed at 0900 hours with 1.2 kg daily of a conventional pig diet, mixed with an equal weight of water. The diet contained (g/kg air-dry basis): 220 each of barley, maize and sorghum grain, 121.5 of wheat bran, 90 of soyabean meal, 40 each of defatted rice bran and white fish meal, 25 of lucerne meal and 23.5 of a vitamin and mineral supplement (for further details see Furuya *et al.*, 1979). Drinking water was freely available except during the collection of digesta. Approximately 500 g of the intestinal digesta were collected between 0930 and 1030 hours through the cannula and centrifuged for 10 min at 1250 g. The supernatant fraction (intestinal fluid) was stored at -20°C for *in vitro* digestion experiments.

Determination of In vitro CP Digestibility

The *in vitro* CP digestibility was determined using feedstuffs of two particle sizes by a method based on the procedure described previously (Furuya *et al.*, 1979). In the first stage, 0.50 g duplicate samples of each feed were mixed with 20 mg of pepsin in 10 ml 0.075N hydrochloric acid, and the mixture was incubated for 4 h at 37°C. Then, 2 ml of 0.20N Tris-buffer were added and this mixture was neutralized with 0.10N sodium hydroxide, instead of 0.20N sodium hydroxide in the original method (Furuya *et al.*, 1979), following modification of Clunies and Leeson (1984). In the second stage, 10 ml of intestinal fluid were added and the digestion mixtures were incubated for an additional 4 h at 37°C. At the

Table 8.1. Composition (lysine and crude protein), true ileal digestibility (*in vivo* with pigs) and *in vitro* CP digestibility and digestible lysine in the feedstuffs studied*.

| | Composition (g/kg DM) | | Digestibility(%) | | | | Digestible lysine (g/kg DM) | | |
| | | | *In vivo* | | *In vitro* CP | | *In vivo* | *In vitro*[†] | |
	Lysine	CP	Lysine	Average of EAA	1 mm	0.5 mm		1 mm	0.5 mm
Protein supplements									
Casein (CASEIN)	77.1	942	100	98	99	100	77.1	76.3	77.1
Cottonseed meal (COTTON)	15.8	390	73	80	69	75	11.5	10.9	11.9
Feather meal (FEATHER)	22.3	914	67	78	64	82	14.9	14.3	18.3
Fish meal (FISH)	60.9	734	98	96	92	93	59.7	56.0	56.6
Meat and bone meal (M & B)	24.0	544	74	74	73	81	17.8	17.5	19.4
Rapeseed meal (RAPE)	17.6	430	77	82	80	87	13.6	14.1	15.3
Soyabean meal (SOYA)	30.8	501	86	86	91	95	26.5	28.0	29.3

Cereal grains									
Barley (BARLEY)	3.0	106	84	85	81	85	2.5	2.4	2.6
Grain sorghum									
(SORGH)	3.0	122	83	82	66	78	2.5	2.0	2.3
Maize (MAIZE)	2.5	93	89	87	73	83	2.2	1.8	2.1
Naked barley									
(NAKED B)	6.2	134	89	87	84	92	5.5	5.2	5.7
Rice (RICE)	3.9	103	81	87	84	93	3.2	3.3	3.6
Wheat (WHEAT)	3.7	131	88	90	90	91	3.3	3.3	3.4
Cereal by-products									
Defatted rice bran									
(RICE B)	10.5	209	71	70	66	75	7.5	6.9	7.9
Wheat bran									
(WHEAT B)	7.9	175	86	85	78	80	6.8	6.2	6.3

DM = dry matter, CP = crude protein (N x 6.25), EAA = essential amino acids

*Samples of feedstuffs for the *in vitro* method were ground to pass through 1.0 or 0.5 mm screen.

†Digestible lysine contents for the *in vitro* assay were obtained by multipling the lysine content of each feedstuff by the *in vitro* CP digestibility.

completion of the second incubation the contents of the flask were centrifuged at 1250 g for 10 min and the supernatant was discarded; the undigested precipitate was washed with water, recentrifuged, and the supernatant again discarded. The undigested precipitate was then transferred to a filter paper for CP determination. The *in vitro* CP digestibility was calculated as follows.

$$(1 - \frac{R}{S}) \times 100 \tag{8.1}$$

where R is the weight of CP in the residue and S is the weight of CP in 0.50 g sample.

Chemical and Statistical Analysis

Crude protein in the feedstuffs and the filter paper containing the residue was determined by the method of the Association of Official Analytical Chemists (1975). Data were analysed by regression analysis according to the method of Snedecor and Cochran (1967). Residual standard deviation (RSD) of the regression of *in vitro* CP digestibility on TID was mainly used to measure the accuracy of prediction.

Results and Discussion

The lysine and CP contents and the digestibility values of the feedstuffs studied are given in Table 8.1, together with the digestible lysine contents calculated from the TID of lysine and the *in vitro* CP digestibility.

The TID values of lysine ranged from 67 to 100 %, being lowest in feather meal and highest in casein. The TID values for cereal grains were in a relatively narrow range, 81% for rice to 89% for maize and naked barley. The average TID values of essential amino acids (EAA) were similar to those of lysine in each feedstuff except for feather meal, cottonseed meal, rice and rapeseed meal. The low ileal digestibility of lysine in feather meal and cottonseed meal has also been reported by Tanksley *et al.* (1981) and Knabe *et al.* (1989). The low digestibility of lysine in cottonseed meal is thought to be due to the formation of an indigestible complex between lysine and gossypol during processing (Tanksley *et al.*, 1981). The *in vitro* CP digestibility values for 1 mm and 0.5 mm grinding treatments were in the range of 64 (feather meal) to 99% (casein) and 75 (cottonseed meal and defatted rice bran) to 100% (casein), respectively. Applied to the 15 feedstuffs, the digestibility with 0.5 mm grinding was on average 7 percentage units higher than that obtained with 1 mm grinding. However, the difference varied with the feedstuffs. The *in vitro* CP digestibility for feather meal and grain sorghum was markedly improved by 0.5 mm grinding, 18 and 12 percentage units, respectively. In casein, fish meal, wheat and wheat bran there was little change in *in vitro* digestibility with finer grinding: this is assumed to be due to the high initial digestibility or to the ease with which these feedstuffs can be comminuted.

Fig. 8.1. Relationship between the true ileal digestibility of lysine and *in vitro* crude protein (CP) digestibility for 15 feedstuffs, including protein supplements (●), cereal grains (▲) and cereal by-products (■); (a) 1mm grinding treatment and (b) 0.5 mm grinding treatment. For key to abbreviations see Table 8.1.

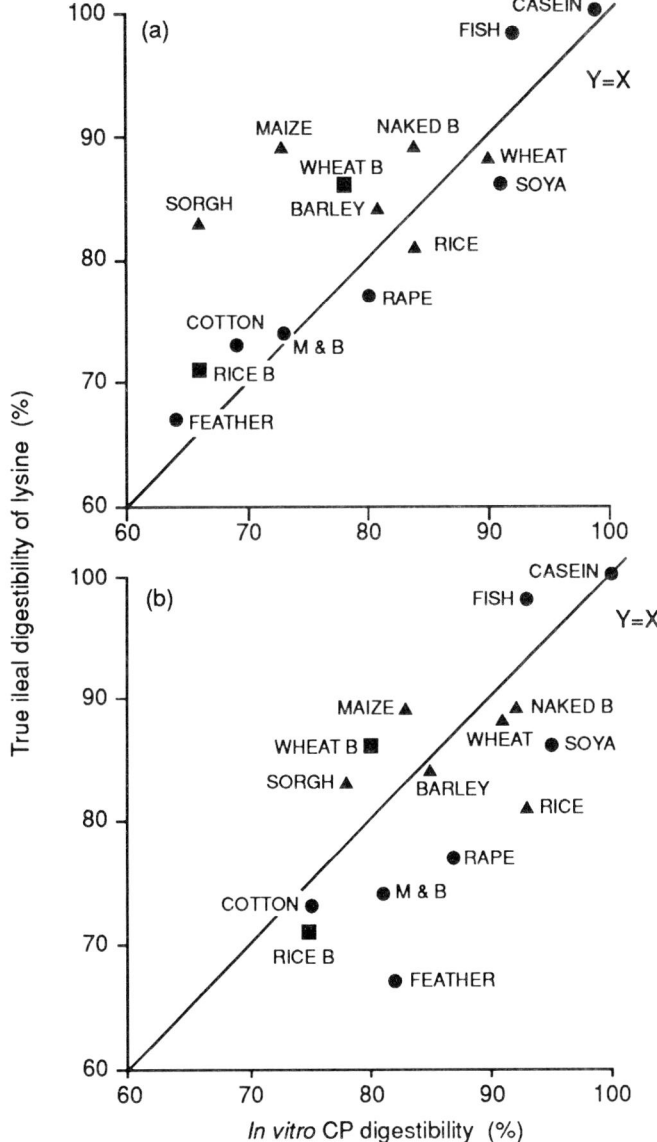

Fig. 8.2. Relationship of average of true ileal digestibility of essential amino acids to *in vitro* crude protein (CP) digestibility for 15 feedstuffs, including protein supplements (●), cereal grains (▲) and cereal by-products (■); (a) 1mm grinding treatment and (b) 0.5 mm grinding treatment. For key to abbreviations see Table 8.1.

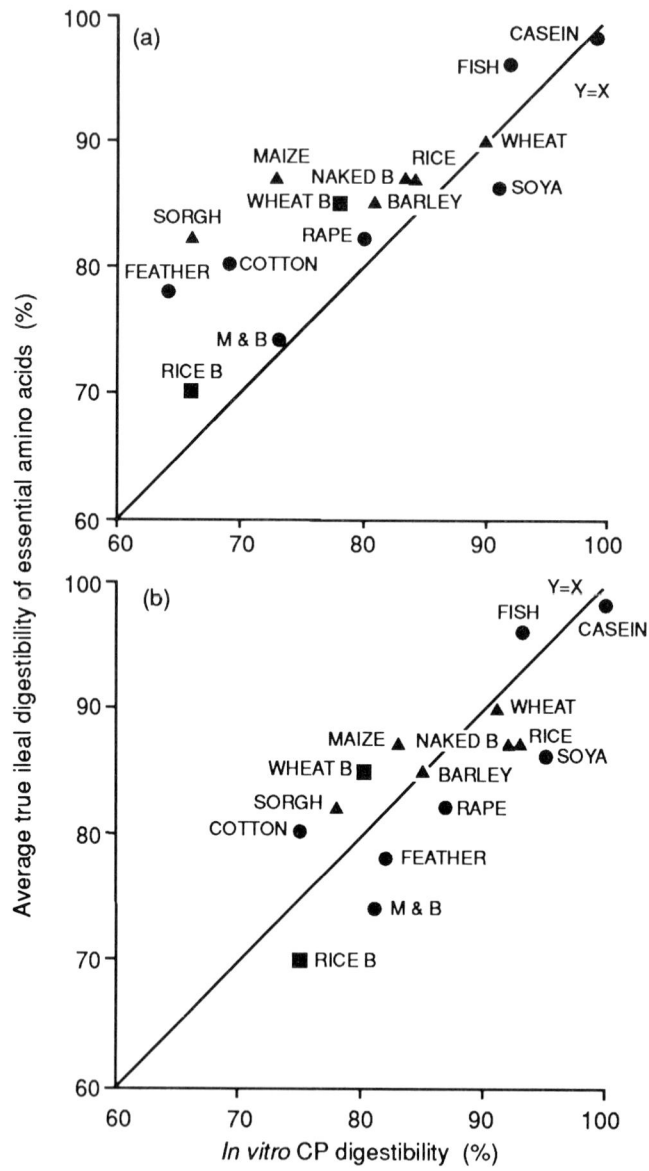

Figures 8.1 and 8.2 show the relationships between *in vitro* CP digestibility values and TID values of lysine and EAA, respectively, for all feedstuffs studied. Precision of prediction from samples of 1 mm grinding treatment (RSD= 5.8 for lysine and 4.2 for EAA) was slightly better than that obtained from samples of 0.5 mm grinding treatment (RSD= 6.9 for lysine and 4.6 for EAA) as shown in Table 8.2.

Table 8.2. Relationships between true ileal digestibility (%) of lysine (LYS) and the average of essential amino acids (EAA) and *in vitro* crude protein digestibility (%) determined with samples ground to pass through 1.0 (VITCP1.0) or 0.5 (VITCP0.5) mm screen.

Regression equation	r	RSD
All feedstuffs (n=15)		
LYS = 27 + 0.71 VITCP1.0	0.81	5.8
LYS = 8 + 0.87 VITCP0.5	0.71	6.9
EAA = 39 + 0.57 VITCP1.0	0.84	4.2
EAA = 18 + 0.77 VITCP0.5	0.80	4.6
Protein supplements (n=7)		
LYS = 7 + 0.93 VITCP1.0	0.96	4.1
LYS = -28 + 1.26 VITCP0.5	0.87	7.0
EAA = 35 + 0.61 VITCP1.0	0.88	4.6
EAA = 10 + 0.86 VITCP0.5	0.84	5.4
Cereal grains (n=6)		
LYS = 79 + 0.08 VITCP1.0	0.20	3.8
LYS = 80 + 0.07 VITCP0.5	0.12	3.8
EAA = 66 + 0.26 VITCP1.0	0.84	1.6
EAA = 57 + 0.34 VITCP0.5	0.77	1.9
Cereal grains and cereal by-products (n=8)		
LYS = 55 + 0.38 VITCP1.0	0.55	5.4
LYS = 45 + 0.47 VITCP0.5	0.53	5.5
EAA = 42 + 0.54 VITCP1.0	0.76	4.3
EAA = 26 + 0.69 VITCP0.5	0.76	4.3

The scatter diagram shown in Fig. 8.1(a) indicates the presence of two isolated scatter points at lower in vitro CP digestibility, which are maize and grain sorghum. If these two feedstuffs are excluded, the RSD value is reduced from 5.8 to 3.9 and the correlation coefficient is improved from 0.81 to 0.93. Hence,

123

separate regression analyses were carried out with each type of feedstuff. The results of these analyses are also given in Table 8.2. No regression equation for cereal by-products is available because of limited numbers of samples. Comparisons of RSD indicate that the predictability of TID depends on the type of feedstuffs and on grinding treatment. Although the correlation coefficients related to the TID of lysine in protein supplements were high (r=0.96 and 0.87 for 1 and 0.5 mm grinding treatment, respectively), the RSD values remained high, especially for 0.5 mm grinding treatment (7.0). For cereal grains the correlation coefficients for the TID of lysine were surprisingly low for both 1 and 0.5 mm grinding treatments (r= 0.20 and 0.12, respectively) but with smaller RSDs (3.8 for both grinding treatments) than those for protein supplements. The samples of cereal grains examined in this study had a narrow range in TID of lysine (from 81 to 89%), which may be a reason for the low correlation observed. Furthermore, the RSD values for the average TID of EAA were small with cereal grains: 1.6 and 1.9 with 1 and 0.5 mm grinding treatments, respectively, a correlation coefficient of around 0.8. It is interesting to note that for cereal grains significant reductions in RSD were seen with no improvement of correlation coefficient. This suggests that RSD rather than correlation coefficient should be used as a measure of the error of prediction for comparing *in vitro* procedures. The fact that the RSD values were smaller when similar types of feedstuffs were grouped together suggests that, to improve the accuracy of prediction of TID, a different regression equation is needed for each grouping of feedstuffs.

A small RSD value of 1.2 for the regression equation relating *in vivo* overall CP digestibility with pigs and the *in vitro* CP digestibility was achieved when samples of mixed feeds were ground with 1 mm screen before the *in vitro* assay (Furuya *et al.*, 1979). A similarly low RSD of 0.8 was reported for chickens by Sakamoto *et al.*, (1980) and of 1.6 by Clunies and Leeson (1984) also using mixed feeds. These values are smaller than those obtained from TID data in the present study, in which single feedstuffs rather than mixed feeds were examined. The better precision observed for *in vivo* digestibility with mixed feeds (Furuya *et al.*, 1979; Sakamoto *et al.*, 1980; Clunies and Leeson, 1984) probably results from the fact that the errors of estimation of the components usually compensate for each other when mixed diets are used as test samples, as suggested by Aufrère and Michalet-Doreau (1988).

The particle size of feedstuffs affects digestibility both *in vitro* and *in vivo*. In the present study, *in vitro* digestibility values for some feedstuffs, for example feather meal and grain sorghum, were markedly improved by decreasing particle size (Table 8.1). Improvement in ileal digestibility with decreasing particle size has been reported for wheat (Sauer *et al.*, 1977), grain sorghum (Owsley *et al.*, 1981) and rice (Furuya and Kaji, 1987), although the improvement *in vivo* is smaller than that *in vitro*. Data on the effects of particle size on ileal digestibility are very scarce; however this is a very important factor and further study on it is required.

The *in vitro* method used in the present study measures protein solubilization and not protein digestion. For more accurate simulation of *in vivo* digestion, it is necessary to distinguish undigested protein from that which would be absorbable *in vivo*. It has been customary to use acid precipitation, using, for example sulphosalicylic or trichloroacetic acid to separate digested from undigested protein (e.g. Greenberg and Shipe, 1979). However, using precipitation methods to separate digested protein will produce product sizes that depend on the substrate and are not necessarily analogous to the products produced *in vivo* that can be absorbed, as mentioned by Drake (1990). Recently, attention has turned to the use of *in vitro* enzymatic hydrolysis with simultaneous dialysis to control the size of the released products (Gauthier *et al.*, 1982; Savoie and Gauthier, 1986; Drake, 1990). The *in vitro* procedure with simultaneous dialysis would be expected to more closely predict the TID of amino acids than that used in the present study, although the dialysis procedure requires special equipment and longer assay time, which may be a drawback for an assay to be used routinely in the feed mill.

Drake (1990) compared the TID of essential amino acids (Y, %) with the digestibility of essential amino acids after 13 hours *in vitro* dialysis (X, %) with six feedstuffs including protein supplements and cereal grains. The linear regression equation was as follows.

$$Y = 65.36 + 0.1421X, \qquad (8.2)$$
$$r = 0.229, RSD = 8.70$$

It was suggested that this rather low precision was due to very low estimates of TID of some amino acids (Drake, 1990). This strongly suggests that further study on the TID determination as well as *in vitro* procedures is required to improve accuracy of predicting TID.

Formulation of diets on a digestible amino acid basis should be more accurate than formulations on a total amino acid basis especially when feedstuffs of varying amino acid digestibility values are used. In Table 8.1 the true ileal digestible lysine contents are compared with the values obtained in *in vitro* assays with samples ground with 1 and 0.5 mm screens. The relationships between *in vivo* (Y) and *in vitro* (X) digestible lysine contents (g/kg dry matter) of feedstuffs were:

$$Y = 0.06 + 1.02X \qquad (8.3)$$
$$r = 1.00, RSD = 1.01, \text{ for 1mm grinding}$$

$$Y = -0.72 + 1.01X \qquad (8.4)$$
$$r = 1.00, RSD = 1.52, \text{ for 0.5 mm grinding}$$

The relationship between *in vivo* digestible lysine (Y) and total lysine (X) (g/kg dry matter) is given as follows:

$$Y = -2.20 + 0.99X \qquad (8.5)$$
$$r = 0.99, RSD = 2.47$$

S. Furuya

Judging from the RSD, prediction of the true ileal digestible lysine contents from *in vitro* CP digestibility seems to be more accurate than total lysine. This suggests that use of the *in vitro* CP digestibility data improves the precision of diet formulation when feedstuffs with different digestibility values are fed. In practical diet formulation, the *in vitro* CP digestibility values should be standardized with samples of known TID as similar as possible to those being tested.

References

Association of Official Analytical Chemists (1975) *Official Methods of Analysis*, 12th edn. Association of Official Analytical Chemists, Washington, DC, p.16.

Aufrere, J. and Michalet-Doreau, B. (1988) Comparison of methods for predicting digestibility of feeds. *Animal Feed Science and Technology* 20, 203-18.

Cave, N.A. (1988) Bioavailability of amino acids in plant feedstuffs determined by *in vitro* digestion, chick growth assay, and true amino acid availability methods. *Poultry Science* 67, 78-87.

Clunies, M. and Leeson, S. (1984) *In vitro* estimation of dry matter and crude protein digestibility. *Poultry Science* 63, 89-96.

Dierick, N., Vervaeke, I., Decuypere, J. and Henderickx, H. (1985) Protein digestion in pigs measured *in vivo* and *in vitro*. In: Just, A., Jørgensen, H. and Fernandez, J.A. (eds), *Proceedings of the 3rd International Seminar on Digestive Physiology in the Pig*, 16-18 May 1985, at Copenhagen, pp. 329-32.

Drake, A.P. (1990) The development of an *in vitro* system for predicting nutrient digestibility in feeds for pigs, Unpublished PhD thesis, University of Aberdeen.

Furuya, S. and Kaji, Y. (1987) Ileal digestibilities of amino acids in corn, rice, barley, naked barley and wheat for growing pigs. *Japanese Journal of Zootechnical Science* 58, 228-35.

Furuya, S. and Kaji, Y. (1989) Estimation of the true ileal digestibility of amino acids and nitrogen from their apparent values for growing pigs. *Animal Feed Science and Technology* 26, 271-85.

Furuya, S., Sakamoto, K. and Takahashi, S. (1979) A new *in vitro* method for the estimation of digestibility using the intestinal fluid of the pig. *British Journal of Nutrition* 41, 511-20.

Furuya, S., Nagano, R. and Kaji, Y. (1986) True ileal digestibility of crude protein and amino acids in protein sources as determined by a regression method for growing pigs. *Japanese Journal of Zootechnical Science* 57, 859-70.

Furuya, S., Kaji, Y., Asano, T. and Murayama, T. (1988) Ileal digestibilities of amino acids in wheat bran, rice bran, rapeseed meal, grain sorghum, meat and bone meal and feather meal for growing pigs. *Japanese Journal of Zootechnical Science* 59, 407-13.

Gauthier, S.F., Vachon, C., Jones, J.D. and Savoie, L. (1982) Assessment of protein digestibility by *in vitro* enzymatic Hydrolysis with simultaneous dialysis. *Journal of Nutrition* 112, 1718-25.

Greenberg, N.A. and Shipe, W.F. (1979) Comparison of the abilities of trichloroacetic, picric, sulfosalicylic, and tungstic acids to precipitate protein hydrolysates and proteins. *Journal of Food Science* 44, 735-7.

Knabe, D.A., LaRue, D.C., Gregg, E.J., Martinez, G.M. and Tanksley, T.D., Jr. (1989) Apparent digestibility of nitrogen and amino acids in protein feedstuffs by growing pigs. *Journal of Animal Science* 67, 441-58.

Löwgren, W., Graham, H. and Åman, P. (1989) An *in vitro* method for studying digestion in the pig. 1. Simulating digestion in the different compartments of the intestine. *British Journal of Nutrition* 61, 673-87.

Owsley, W.F., Knabe, D.A. and Tanksley, T.D., Jr. (1981) Effect of sorghum particle size on digestibility of nutrients at the terminal ileum and over the total digestive tract of growing-finishing pigs. *Journal of Animal Science* 52, 557-66.

Sakamoto, K., Asano, T., Furuya, S. and Takahashi, S. (1980) Estimation of *in vivo* digestibility with the laying hen by an *in vitro* method using the intestinal fluid of the pig. *British Journal of Nutrition* 43, 389-91.

Sauer, W.C., Stothers, S.C. and Phillips, G.D. (1977) Apparent availabilities of amino acids in corn, wheat and barley for growing pigs. *Canadian Journal of Animal Science* 57, 585-97.

Savoie, L. and Gauthier, S.F. (1986) Dialysis cell for the *in vitro* measurement of protein digestibility. *Journal of Food Science* 51, 494-8.

Snedecor, G.W. and Cochran, W.G. (1967) *Statistical Methods*. 6th edn. Iowa State University Press, Ames, IA.

Tanksley, T.D., Jr., Knabe, D.A., Purser, K., Zebrowska, T. and Corley, J.R. (1981) Apparent digestibility of amino acids and nitrogen in three cottonseed meals and one soyabean meal. *Journal of Animal Science* 52, 769-77.

Vachon, C., Gauthier, S., Charbonneau, R. and Savoie, L. (1987) Relationship between *in vitro* digestion of proteins and *in vivo* assessment of their nutritional quality. *Reproduction, Nutrition et Developpement* 27, 659-72.

Chapter 9

Prediction of the Energy Value of Non-ruminant Feeds Using *In Vitro* Digestion with Intestinal Fluid and Other Chemical Methods

H. Graham and W. Löwgren

Introduction

The determination of digestibility by conventional methods requires large quantities of feed, a number of animals and considerable expenditure on equipment and manpower. In ruminant studies several chemical, *in vitro* and *in sacco* methods are widely used to predict nutritive values of feeds, but no such methods were available for the evaluation of non-ruminant feeds. However, in recent years several methods have been proposed for this purpose, including *in vitro* and *in sacco* techniques. During the past five years a research project at the Swedish University of Agricultural Sciences has concentrated on developing techniques which could be applied to predicting the nutritive value of non-ruminant feeds. The aim was to develop methods which could be used in research or in a commercial environment, and attention was focussed on three approaches:

1. complete chemical analysis of the feed;
2. *in sacco* methods;
3. *in vitro* methods.

Methods

Chemical Analysis

Classical analytical methods were employed for the analysis of ash, crude protein (Kjeldahl N x 6.25) and crude fat (including acid pre-hydrolysis). Free sugars were extracted with water and analysed by HPLC or enzymic methods; however, as they only contribute 2-4% of most feeds, soluble sugars were often omitted from the analytical procedure. Starch was analysed by an enzymic method employing thermostable amylases (Åman and Hesselman, 1984). Dietary fibre was estimated as the sum of Klason lignin, determined gravimetrically, neutral non-starch polysaccharide residues, determined by GLC as alditol acetates, and uronic acids, determined by decarboxylation (Theander and Åman, 1979). In common feeds the fibre content can be estimated with sufficient accuracy as the undetermined fraction after analysis of ash, sugars, protein, fat and starch (Åman and Hesselman, 1984).

In Sacco Method

The *in sacco* method employed was essentially that already in use in a number of research institutes. Basically a sample (0.5 g) of the ground feed was enclosed in a small (40 x 25 mm) nylon bag with a pore size of 20 microns. The bag was introduced into the intestinal tract of a pig through a duodenal cannula and recovered in the faeces (Graham *et al.*, 1985). The bag and contents were carefully washed in water after recovery. It was possible to run over 50 samples per day through each available pig.

In Vitro Method

The *in vitro* method was also based on previously published techniques and used equipment available from *in vitro* ruminant studies. Basically this involved incubation of a small sample (0.5 g) of a ground feed with 50 ml of buffered (pH 6.9) inoculum from the pig duodenum, ileum or faeces (Lowgren *et al.*, 1989). The inoculum was filtered and diluted 1:4 with buffer prior to addition. After incubation, which lasted from 30 minutes up to 96 hours, the residues were washed with water and dried. Up to 250 samples could easily be run simultaneously with this method.

In Sacco Prediction of Digestibility of Pig Feeds

Initial studies on the *in sacco* method established that pre-incubation with proteases or using bags with pore sizes from 10 to 36 microns did not influence results obtained (Graham *et al.*, 1985). The method was shown to have a low coefficient of variation, varying from 1% for barley to 2% for whole crop peas. The time taken for bags to pass through the pig varied from 23 to 69 hours, and they were not recovered in the order in which they had been placed in the animal. The mean retention time of bags introduced in the morning (37 h) was less than that of those introduced in the afternoon (44 h), and there was a correlation between retention time and dry matter disappearance. Eleven samples of known organic matter (55-89%) and crude protein (47-80%) *in vivo* apparent digestibility were tested with the *in sacco* method. *In sacco* organic matter disappearance exceeded *in vivo* organic matter disappearance by 1-10%, and these two parameters were closely correlated (Table 9.1). For crude protein, *in sacco* disappearance was 14-41% greater than *in vivo* apparent digestibility, and the latter was more closely correlated to *in sacco* organic matter disappearance than to *in sacco* protein disappearance. However, both *in vivo* parameters could be predicted from dietary neutral detergent fibre content.

Although the *in sacco* method was reasonably successful in predicting the *in vivo* organic matter digestibility of the pig feeds, this method requires access to duodenally cannulated animals. Further, since the animals were not fitted with re-entrant ileal cannulae, no data were obtained on the rate of digestion of different components. It also proved difficult to prevent re-ingestion of the bags immediately on defecation! Thus, although of interest for research purposes and special investigations, this method was judged to be unsuitable for widespread commercial use.

Table 9.1. First order regression analysis between *in vivo* organic matter (IVOM) and crude protein (IVCP) digestibilities (%) and *in sacco* organic matter (SAOM) and crude protein (SACP) disappearances (%) and dietary neutral detergent fibre (NDF) content.

Independent variable	Dependent variable	Intercept	Coefficient of regression	Coefficient of determination
IVOM	SAOM	8	0.97	0.95
IVOM	NDF	100	-1.01	0.82
IVCP	SACP	85	0.13	0.50
IVCP	SAOM	13	0.97	0.76
IVCP	NDF	104	-1.14	0.78

(Graham *et al.*, 1985)

Chemical and *In Vitro* Prediction of Metabolizable Energy in Feeds

Pigs

Initial studies established that the *in vitro* method was applicable to animal feeds, and that a short incubation time could be used to predict readily available nutrients and a longer time less readily available nutrients (Lowgren *et al.*, 1989). It was also apparent that degradations by duodenal, ileal and faecal inocula differed in rate but little in pattern; i.e. all three inocula degraded the individual feed components in approximately the same order. There was, however, a lower apparent digestibility of crude protein when using faecal inocula, and ileal and faecal inocula tended to degrade fibre somewhat earlier than duodenal inocula. Subsequent studies indicated that a 12 h incubation with a duodenal inoculum could be used to predict ileal apparent digestibility of starch and crude protein while a 48 h incubation with an ileal or a faecal inoculum could predict faecal apparent digestibility of fibre (Graham *et al.*, 1989). The pattern of degradation of individual fibre residues was also similar.

A study was then initiated including 13 feeds or feedstuffs characterized by both chemical methods and ileal *in vitro* disappearance. These samples included barley, rapeseed meal, lupins, seven diets based on these feedstuffs and three triticales; *in vivo* work was carried out by Dr S. Raj, at the Polish Academy of Sciences, Institute of Animal Physiology and Nutrition, Jablonna. The ME contents of the samples ranged from 12.3 to 15.5 MJ/kg, with crude protein contents of 12-49%, starch contents of 1-66% and dietary fibre contents of 10-30%. *In vitro* disappearance of the samples using ileal inocula was 85-94%.

It was established that rapeseed meal (Figure 9.1, sample 8) and lupin meal (Figure 9.1, sample 10) were outliers, and these samples were excluded from any further statistical analysis. The lupin meal, for example, had an *in vitro* disappearance much higher than would be predicted from its ME content and a ME greater than would be expected from its chemical analysis. This was presumably due to its high content of degradable fibre, particularly galactans. This, together with the divergence of the rapeseed meal, indicates that it will probably prove necessary to group feedstuffs according to composition.

Fig. 9.1. Relationship between ME (MJ/kg) and dietary fibre (%) and *in vitro* dissappearance (IVD; %) for 13 pig feeds.

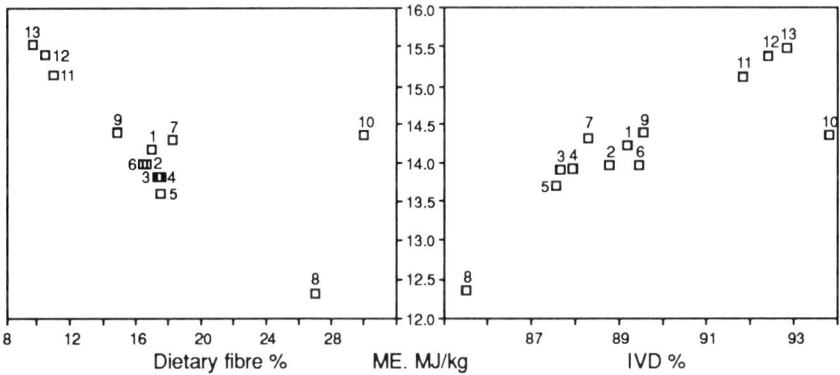

Regression analysis established that starch content was negatively correlated (r = -0.90 to -0.76) to crude protein, dietary fibre, ash and crude fat (Table 9.2). The last four named were also positively correlated to each other (r = 0.46 to 0.91). Such relationships make it rather difficult to interpret any further correlation data on nutritive value, and such data must be treated with care. However starch content was closely correlated to ME (r = 0.80) and ileal *in vitro* disappearance (r = 0.86), not surprisingly as starch was the predominant dietary component. Of the other main nutrients, dietary fibre and ash gave the closest relationships (for fibre, r = -0.95 vs ME and -0.98 vs *in vitro*; for ash r = -0.93 vs ME and -0.91 vs *in vitro*). Ileal *in vitro* disappearance was also closely correlated to ME content (r = 0.97).

Table 9.2. Correlation coefficients between content of chemical components, ME content and ileal *in vitro* dry matter disappearance (IVD) of the pig feeds (n = 11).

	Protein	Ash	Fibre	Fat	IVD	ME
Starch	-0.88	-0.76	-0.86	-0.90	0.86	0.80
Protein		0.46	0.55	0.69	-0.57	-0.47
Ash			0.86	0.71	-0.91	-0.93
Fibre				0.91	-0.98	-0.95
Fat					-0.87	-0.81
IVD						0.97

Single and multiple regression analysis of ME on *in vitro* disappearance and chemical composition are presented in Table 9.3. Ileal *in vitro* disappearance explained 94% of the variation in ME, while including dietary fibre, starch and protein improved this marginally to 98%. Regression including the two 'non-nutrients' in the feeds, ash and dietary fibre, explained 95% of the variation in ME, with the intercept, perhaps rather fortuitously, approaching the gross energy. It was also appropriate that the coefficient of determination was greater for ash than for the partly degradable fibre. A similar regression, which included the main nutrients, starch, crude protein and crude fat, explained 93% of the variation in ME, and again the intercept passed conveniently close to zero. The reason for the higher coefficient of determination for protein than for starch is not clear, although the diets were somewhat limiting in protein content.

Table 9.3. Multiple and single regression of *in vitro* ileal disappearance (IVD) and chemical components on ME for pig feeds (n = 11).

Intercept Slope/regressor	R^2
ME = -14.1 + 0.32 IVD	0.94
17.0 - 0.27 Ash - 0.11 Fib	0.95
-1.0 + 0.18 Sta + 0.32 CPr + 0.39 Fat	0.93
-25.0 + 0.33 IVD + 0.10 Fib + 0.09 Sta + 0.20 CPr	0.98

Fib = dietary fibre; Sta = starch; CPr = crude protein

Poultry

Eleven barley-based diets with ME contents, corrected to zero nitrogen retention, for broiler chicks of 11.3 - 12.7 MJ/kg were employed in this study. The diets were also fed with and without supplementation with β-glucanase. The diets varied in crude protein content from 22-25%, in starch content from 33-38%, in non-starch polysaccharide content from 13-16% and in mixed-linked β-glucan contents from 2.0-3.6%. Slurry viscosities of the diets varied from 12-70 mPa.s. *In vitro* disappearance with faecal inocula from pigs varied from 85% to 91%.

Multiple regression analysis was used to fit a prediction equation for ME, with chemical components, viscosity and *in vitro* disappearance as independent variables. For the diets not supplemented with β-glucanase the best fit simple equation ($R^2 = 0.70$; $P<0.01$) had only non-starch polysaccharides as dependent variable (equation 9.1). For the enzyme-supplemented diets the ME was correlated ($R^2 = 0.82$; $P<0.01$) with β-glucans (β-G) and again with NSP (equation 9.2). The significance of β-glucans in the latter equation could possibly have been due to the close correlation between the content of this component and that of crude protein.

a. without β-glucanase

$$ME = 24.4 - 0.38 \text{ NSP} \tag{9.1}$$

b. with β-glucanase

$$ME = 15.2 + 0.22 \text{ β-G} - 0.25 \text{ NSP} \tag{9.2}$$

This experiment again showed that chemical and *in vitro* methods, alone or together, may be employed to predict the nutritive value of similar feeds.

Conclusions

Three methods, *in sacco*, *in vitro* and chemical analysis, have been tested for predicting the nutritive value of pig and poultry feeds. While the *in sacco* and *in vitro* methods were successful in predicting nutritive value, the former gives no data on the rate or site of digestion of dietary components and requires access to cannulated animals. The *in vitro* method, on the other hand, can be used to study the processes of digestion and, if faecal inocula are employed, does not require cannulated animals. However, these methods have the disadvantage that it takes at least 2-3 days before an answer is available, which is no restraint in research but could disqualify both from use in commercial practice. Further, both methods demand the ability to differentiate accurately and consistently between feed residues which weigh only a few milligrams. *In vitro* and *in sacco* methods could, however, be easily standardized by using universal standard feeds and dried inocula or enzymes.

Chemical analysis could also be used to predict nutritive value, with starch and dietary fibre, often the predominant constituents, of particular interest. Although the methods of analysis used in these studies were quite laborious, it is only a matter of time before methods, such as NMR, NIR and NIT, are developed for the quick and accurate analysis of these components. The prospect of on-line analysis of incoming feedstuffs coupled directly to diet formulation programs in feed mills is rather exciting, and may well be the way forward for the feed industry.

H. Graham and W. Löwgren

References

Åman, P. and Hesselman, K. (1984) Analysis of starch and other main constituents of cereal grains. *Swedish Journal of Agricultural Research* 14, 135-9.

Graham, H., Åman, P., Newman, R.K. and Newman, C.W. (1985) Use of a nylon-bag technique for pig feed digestibility studies. *British Journal of Nutrition 54*, 719-26.

Graham, H., Lowgren, W. and Åman, P. (1989) An in vitro method for studying digestion in the pig. 2. Comparison with in vivo ileal and faecal digestibilities. *British Journal of Nutrition* 61, 689-98.

Lowgren, W., Graham, H. and Åman, P. (1989) An in vitro method for studying digestion in the pig. 1. Simulating digestion in different compartments of the intestine. *British Journal of Nutrition* 61, 673-87.

Theander, O. and Åman, P. (1979) Studies on dietary fibre. 1. Analysis and chemical characterization of water-soluble and water-insoluble dietary fibres. *Swedish Journal of Agricultural Research* 9, 97-106.

Chapter 10

A Model for Feed Evaluation Based on *In Vitro* Digestible Dry Matter and Protein

S. Boisen

Introduction

Optimal feed formulations for non-ruminants require a precise knowledge of the contents of digestible amino acids and energy in the feedstuffs. This requires chemical analyses of amino acids and energy combined with measurements of digestibility.

An *in vitro* method for estimation of true protein digestibility in pig feeds has recently been developed (Boisen, unpublished). This method was further developed to estimate the net digestibility of amino acids and energy in the small intestine as well as the fermentability of energy in the hindgut (Boisen *et al.*, unpublished).

The present work gives a description of the final *in vitro* system and a model for feed evaluation based on *in vitro* measurements is proposed.

Materials and Methods

Feeds

Samples of eight common feedstuffs (barley, rye, wheat, oats, soyabean meal, rapeseed meal, sunflower meal, and grass meal) were analysed *in vitro*. All samples were representative aliquots from experimental diets used in previous trials with ileum-fistulated pigs. The samples were stored in a deep-freeze from preparation until the *in vitro* assays were performed. All *in vitro* data are mean values of two measurements made on two different days.

The *in vivo* digestibility trials were performed with pigs of about 50 kg as described by Just *et al.* (1985). Cereals were given as the only feedstuff while the protein sources were given together with a protein-free basal diet containing (g/kg): maize starch 660, potato starch 165, cellulose 75, animal fat 100. All *in vivo* data are mean values ± SD from five digestibility trials.

S. Boisen

In Vitro Technique

Simulating Digestion in Stomach and Small Intestine

The *in vitro* incubation conditions simulating the digestion processes in the stomach and small intestine with pepsin followed by pancreatin were a modification of the dietary fibre method of Asp *et al.* (1983). This method was modified to measure *in vitro* protein digestibility by changing enzyme concentrations, incubation time and pH in the incubation mixture.

Step 1. A series of 20 samples with about 1 g of finely ground material (ground to pass a screen with a mesh size of 1 mm) were weighed to an accuracy of ± 0.1 mg in 100 ml conical flasks. In each series a blank was included. A small magnetic rod and 25 ml of phosphate buffer (0.1 M, pH 6.0) were added to each flask and the sample and buffer were mixed carefully by gentle magnetic stirring. To this mixture were added 10 ml 0.2 M HCl and the pH was adjusted to pH 2 with a 1 M HCl (or a 1 M NaOH solution). Then 1 ml of a freshly prepared pepsin solution was added, containing 10 mg porcine pepsin (2000 FIP-U/g, Merck no 7190). In order to prevent bacterial growth, especially during the second incubation step, 0.5 ml of a chloramphenicol solution (0.5 g/100 ml ethanol) was added. Then the flasks were closed with a rubber stopper and the samples were incubated in a water bath at 39°C for 6 hours with repeated gentle magnetic stirring.

Step 2. To the mixture was added 10 ml of a phosphate buffer (0.2 M, pH 6.8) + 5 ml of a 0.6 M NaOH solution. The pH was adjusted to 6.8 with 1 M HCl or 1 M NaOH. The slurry was then carefully mixed with 1 ml of freshly prepared pancreatin solution containing 50 mg porcine pancreatin (grade IV, Sigma no P-1790). After closing with a rubber stopper, the flasks were placed in a water bath at 39°C for incubation overnight (18 hours).

To all samples were added 5 ml of 20% sulphosalicylic acid. The solubilized but undigested proteins were precipitated during 30 minutes' incubation at room temperature. The undigested residues were then collected in a filtration unit for crude fibre determination (Fibertec System M, Tecator, Sweden) by using dried and preweighed glass filter crucibles (dia 3 cm, pore size 40-90 µm) containing about 0.5 g Celite as a filter aid. All material was transferred with 1% sulphosalicylic acid to the crucible, and the samples were dried at 80°C overnight. Then Celite and undigested material were wrapped in a piece of nitrogen-free paper and undigested nitrogen was measured by the Kjeldahl method in an automatic Kjelfoss apparatus (Foss Electric, Denmark).

In vitro digestibilities of dry matter (DMI) and protein, respectively, were calculated from DM and N in the sample and in undigested residues after correction for DM and N in the blank. The results were very reproducible. All values are means from two measurements performed on two different days.

136

Simulating Digestion in the Whole Gastro-intestinal Tract

The *in vitro* incubation simulating the whole gastro-intestinal tract was performed by adding an additional incubation step. The incubations in step 1 and step 2 with pepsin and pancreatin, respectively, were performed as described in procedure A, but were shortened to 2 and 4 hours, respectively. This had no influence on the final dry matter digestibility and allowed the two *in vitro* procedures to be performed in parallel.

Furthermore, no sulphosalicylic acid was used for protein precipitation after step 2, and undigested materials were collected in the filtration unit by transferring to crucibles (see above) with water. The crucibles were closed at the bottom with a rubber stopper, and the undigested material was incubated with 20 ml of a freshly prepared solution of fibre-degrading enzymes containing 0.4 g Viscozyme (120L, Novo, Bagsværd, Denmark) in 0.1 M acetate buffer, pH 5. The enzyme solution was thoroughly mixed with the undigested material (and Celite) and then the crucibles were placed in an oven at 40°C for incubation overnight (18 hours).

Fig. 10.1. Chemical analyses and flow diagram of *in vitro* incubations for predicting ileal digestibility of dry matter (DM-1) and protein (N-1) and faecal digestibility of dry matter (DM-2) as a basis for a new feed evaluation system.

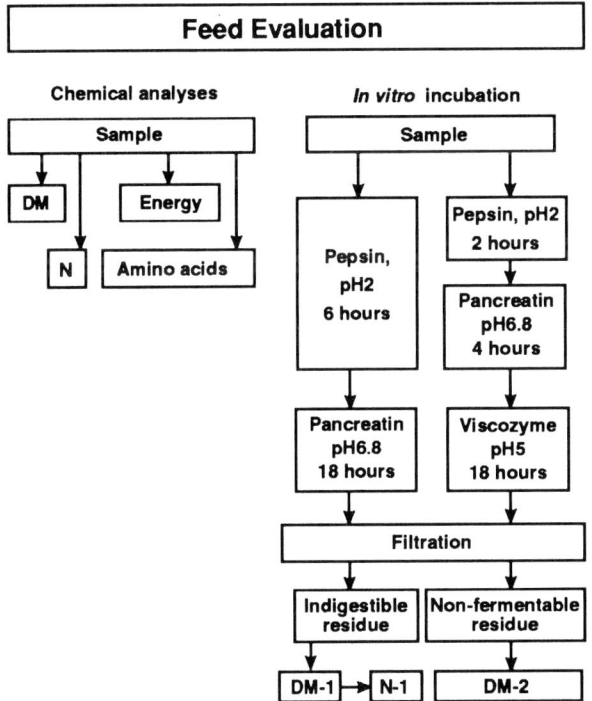

137

S. Boisen

After incubation the rubber stopper was removed and the crucibles were placed in the filtration unit. After filtration and washing with water, the residue was dried at 80°C overnight, and undigested dry matter (DM 2) was measured as described in procedure A. The two *in vitro* procedures were run in parallel. The principles of the method are illustrated in Fig. 10.1.

Results and Discussion

In Vitro Measurements

In vitro digestibilities of dry matter (DM 1 and DM 2) by the two procedures were found to correspond closely to ileal and faecal digestibilities of dry matter. As digestibility values of dry matter and energy are closely correlated to each other (Lekule *et al.*, 1990), the *in vitro* dry matter digestibility values also correspond closely to ileal and faecal energy digestibility (E1 and E2) in the eight feedstuffs investigated (Table 10.1). The only exception was rye which had a significantly higher digestibility *in vitro* than *in vivo*. This may be due partly to a relatively high content of soluble pentosans, but also antinutritional compounds may reduce its digestion *in vivo*. The incubation step 3 with Viscozyme in procedure B corresponds to fermentation in the hindgut, although the fermentation of some feedstuffs may be slightly overestimated, especially that of grass meal and other fibre-rich feedstuffs.

Table 10.1. *In vitro* digestibility of protein (N) and dry matter (DM) compared with *in vivo* values of apparent ileal digestibility of protein and energy (E1), respectively, and apparent faecal digestibility of energy (E2) as measured in pigs fed eight common feedstuffs.

| | N in Feed | Digestibility (%) | | | | | |
| | | *in vitro* | | | *in vivo* | | |
	(g/kg DM)	N	DM1	DM2	N	E1	E2
Barley	19.0	85	70	82	70	72	81
Rye	18.2	87	80	89	65	70	82
Wheat	23.2	91	72	89	74	73	85
Oats	18.2	89	68	68	61	68	67
Soyabean meal[1]	29.1	92	69	87	78	69	88
Rapeseed meal[1]	31.2	83	62	79	69	63	76
Sunflower meal[1]	31.4	90	58	74	73	60	72
Grass meal[1]	14.2	74	57	73	35	54	66

[1] in N-free diet.

In vitro values of protein digestibility were in general much higher than *in vivo* values of apparent ileal digestibility (Table 10.1). However, *in vitro* values correspond to true digestibility (Boisen, unpublished). Chemical analyses and flow diagram of *in vitro* incubations for predicting ileal digestibility of dry matter (DM-1) and protein (N-1) and faecal digestibility of dry matter (DM-2) as a basis for a new feed evaluation system.), and the differences therefore, reflect the endogenous losses of protein in the stomach and small intestine. Calculations of these losses indicate a great variation dependent on feed composition. However, a close correlation between crude fibre intake and endogenous loss of protein could be demonstrated (Boisen *et al.*, unpublished), in good agreement with the observations of Taverner *et al.*, 1981.

Consequently, the endogenous loss of N (g/kg DM intake, y) is also correlated with ileal undigested dry matter (g/g intake, x). A simple linear relationship (y = 13.2x) was proposed for calculating the endogenous loss of N on the basis of ileal undigested energy (Fig. 10.2) or *in vitro* undigested dry matter (UDM 1).

Fig. 10.2. Relationship between calculated endogenous loss of N and ileal undigested energy in pigs fed eight common feedstuffs.

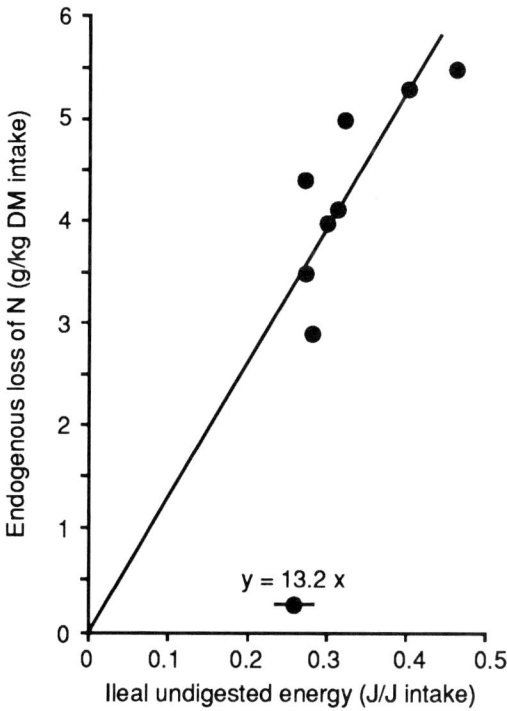

Net digestible N (DNNET, g/kg DM) was then calculated from *in vitro* (true) digestibility of N (NDIV) corrected for endogenous loss of N by the equation:

$$DNNET = N \text{ intake} * NDIV - 13.2 * UDM \qquad (10.1)$$

where N intake is as g/kg DM and UDM as g/g intake

In vitro (true) digestibilities of amino acids were also investigated by using procedure A. The digestibilities of the individual amino acids were in general similar to each other and also to the digestibilities of N (Tables 10.1 and 10.2). This is in contrast to the apparent ileal digestibility values which are generally higher for amino acids than for N; furthermore, the digestibility of individual amino acids may vary considerably (Table 10.2). The apparent ileal digestibilities of cystine and threonine were generally significantly lower than those of the other essential amino acids.

Table 10.2. *In vitro* digestibility of essential amino acids compared with *in vivo* values of apparent ileal digestibility as measured in pigs fed eight common feedstuffs.

	lys	met	cys	thr	ile	leu	his	phe	tyr	val
In vitro										
Barley	84	87	85	85	88	88	86	88	90	86
Rye	87	90	87	87	90	90	87	90	88	88
Wheat	90	90	93	91	92	92	92	93	94	89
Oats	90	90	90	89	91	92	91	91	93	90
Soyabean meal	93	95	85	91	90	89	92	89	92	89
Rapeseed meal	86	88	87	81	79	82	86	81	84	80
Sunflower meal	92	92	86	89	89	89	92	91	92	90
Grass meal	80	74	73	80	74	78	73	74	77	77
In vivo										
Barley	76	81	76	66	78	79	81	80	81	76
Rye	68	75	72	57	72	73	72	74	73	69
Wheat	76	82	77	63	81	83	86	84	86	76
Oats	70	79	64	55	73	75	79	77	73	72
Soyabean meal	88	87	76	75	84	84	88	81	85	81
Rapeseed meal	73	82	77	66	73	76	82	71	69	71
Sunflower meal	78	85	69	70	67	77	77	75	76	75
Grass meal	62	68	15	47	64	67	64	54	54	62

Calculations of the endogenous losses of individual amino acids showed an influence of ileal undigested dry matter similar to that observed for protein (Boisen *et al.*, unpublished). Consequently, the endogenous protein loss was found to be relatively constant in amino acid composition. The mean composition is shown in

Table 10.3. Literature values of the amino acid composition of endogenous protein measured *in vivo* vary considerably. Much of this variation may be due to different techniques and to experimental error. However, the mean composition, calculated from literature data collected and evaluated by Wünsche *et al.* (1987) is in very good agreement with the mean composition obtained in this study (Table 10.3).

Table 10.3. Amino acid composition (g/160 g N) of endogenous protein calculated from differences between *in vitro* and *in vivo* digestibilities compared with direct *in vivo* measurements.

	lys	met	cys	thr	ile	leu	his	phe	tyr	val
In vitro/in vivo	28	8	16	40	23	35	10	28	22	33
In vivo[1]	27	7	15	37	18	36	13	23	18	29

[1] calculated from Wünsche *et al.* (1987)

Therefore, the endogenous losses of individual amino acids were calculated from the endogenous loss of N by using individual conversion factors for the amino acids, e.g. lysine: 28/160 = 0.175 (see Table 10.3). Assuming that the *in vitro* digestibilities of amino acids and N are identical within the same feed, the net digestible amino acid can be calculated from the *in vitro* digestibility of N and undigested dry matter by an equation, e.g. for lysine:

$$DlysNET = lys\ intake * NDIV - 13.2 * 0.175 * UDM \qquad (10.2)$$

where DlysNET and lys intake are in g/kg DM and UDM is as g/g intake.

Protein Evaluation

The protein value of the digested feed depends on the relationship between net digestible amino acids and the animal's requirements for essential amino acids. The requirements for all the essential amino acids relative to N corresponds to the amino acid composition of ideal protein as proposed by the Agricultural Research Council (1981) or as estimated by Wang and Fuller (1989).

However, the latter ideal protein corresponds to the requirements for true digestible amino acids which include the net requirements for the digestive processes in the stomach and small intestine. Comparisons of the amino acid composition in endogenous protein and ideal protein (Tables 10.3 and 10.4) reveal characteristic differences: except for threonine and cystine, all essential amino acids contribute much less to endogenous protein than to ideal protein. As the calculated endogenous losses of protein typically amount to about 20% of the protein intake (Table 10.1 and Fig. 10. 2) it follows that the requirements for threonine and sulphur-containing amino acids should be relatively lower when based on net digestible amino acids than when true digestible amino acids are considered.

141

S. Boisen

Feed formulations should preferably be based on the animal's requirements for net (or apparent ileal) digestible amino acids as these are independent of the variable endogenous losses in the stomach and small intestine.

The amino acid composition of protein determined in 32 samples of sows' milk was found to be very constant and is supposed to be ideal for piglets (Boisen *et al.*, 1988). As milk is highly digestible, minimal amounts of undigested dry matter from milk will pass into the large intestine. Consequently, endogenous losses of protein should also be minimal and thus, true digestible amino acids should be close to net digestible amino acids in sows' milk.

Fig. 10.3. Model for a protein evaluation system based on *in vitro* incubations for predicting ileal digestibility of nitrogen and dry matter.

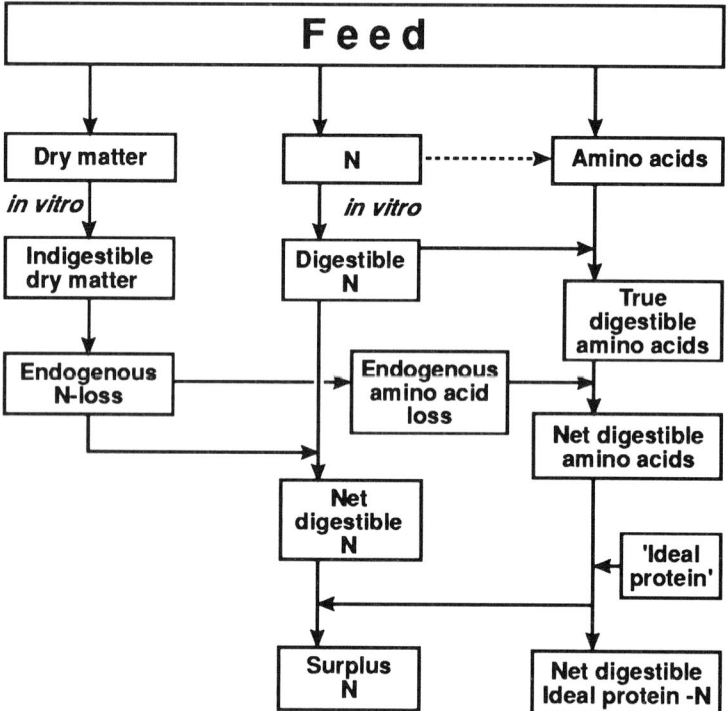

In agreement with this, contents of threonine and sulphur-containing amino acids are relatively lower in sows' milk than literature values for ideal protein, whereas contents of all other essential amino acids are higher (Table 10.4). It is therefore suggested that the amino acid composition of sows' milk corresponds to the relative requirements of net digestible amino acids. Taking these results and

142

conclusions into account, a model for protein evaluation based on *in vitro* measurements is outlined in Fig. 10.3. In this model the quality of net digested protein is defined by the contribution of N in ideal protein-N and N which is not utilized for protein synthesis (surplus N). The amount of ideal protein-N is the lowest value obtained when the amount of each essential amino acid is calculated using individual conversion factors, e.g. for lysine: 160/71 = 2.25 (see Table 10.4).

The amount of surplus-N has a negative effect on the energy value, as this has to be excreted in the urine after synthesis to urea, which requires energy.

Fig. 10.4. Model for an energy evaluation system based on *in vitro* incubations for predicting ileal and faecal digestibility of dry matter.

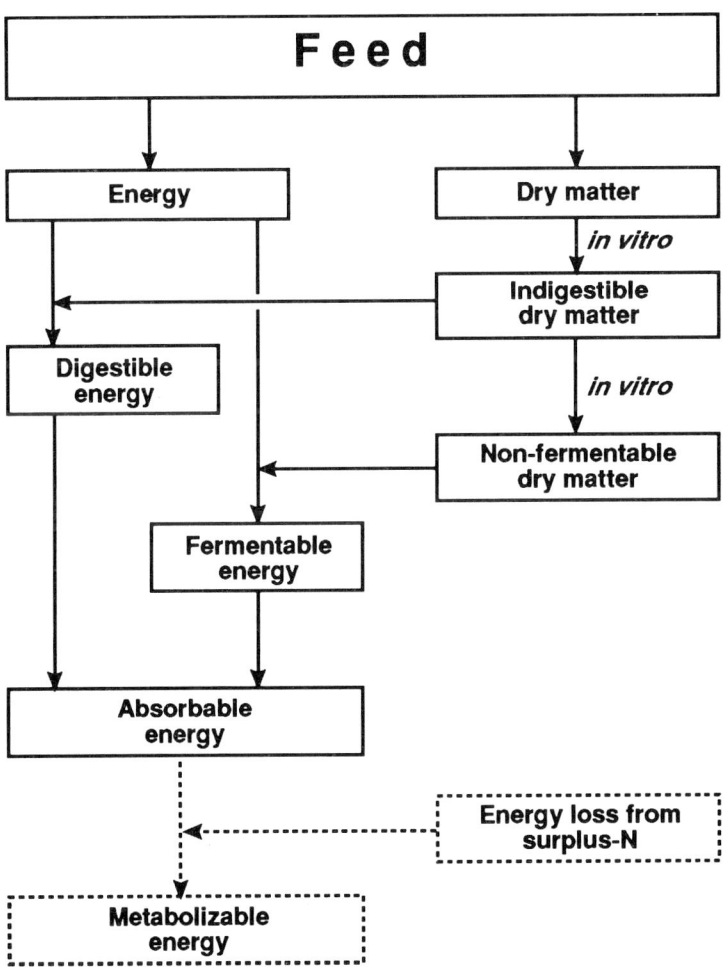

Table 10.4. Amino acid composition (g/160 g N) of ideal protein in sows' milk and literature values.

		met +						phe +	
	lys	met	cys	thr	ile	leu	his	phe	tyr	val
Sow's milk[1]	71	18	31	39	41	81	25	39	81	54
Literature[2]	70	-	35	42	38	70	23	-	67	49
Literature[3]	65	-	41	47	39	72	-	-	78	49

[1]Boisen *et al.* (1987); [2]Agricultural Research Council (1981); [3]Wang and Fuller (1989).

Energy Evaluation

Predictions of the energy values of feeds are usually based on faecal digestibility values. However, the *in vitro* method introduced here makes it possible to take into account the reduced utilization of that part which is fermented in the hindgut. A schematic model for energy evaluation based on *in vitro* measurements of digestible and fermentable energy is outlined in Fig. 10.4. As indicated, metabolizable energy may also be calculated after correction for the energy loss from surplus N. However, this parameter is not a constant, but depends on the relative requirements of amino acids and energy, which decrease during growth from birth to slaughter.

Further investigations are in progress with the aim of integrating the proposed feed evaluation model into a growth model for use in practical pig feeding.

References

Agricultural Research Council (1981) *The Nutrient Requirements of Pigs*. Agricultural Research Council, London.

Asp, N.G., Johansen, C.G., Hallmer, H., and Siljeström, M. (1983) Rapid enzymatic assay of insoluble and soluble dietary fiber. *Journal of Agricultural and Food Chemistry* 31, 476-82.

Boisen, S., Bech-Andersen, S., and Danielsen, V. (1988) Amino acid contents in sows milk in relation to official requirements. *National Institute of Animal Science, Foulum, Denmark, Communication* no. 712

Boisen, S. (1991) *In vitro* estimation of true protein digestibility in pig feeds. (unpublished)

Boisen, S., Fernandez, J.A., and Bech-Andersen, S. (1991) *In vitro* estimation of net digestibility of amino acids and energy in pig feeds. (unpublished)

Just, A., Jørgensen, H., and Fernandez, J.A. (1985) Correlations of protein deposited in growing female pigs to ileal and faecal protein and amino acids. *Livestock Production Science* 12, 145-59.

Lekule, F.P., Jørgensen, H., Fernandez, J.A., and Just, A. (1990) Nutritive value of some tropical feedstuffs for pigs. Chemical composition, digestibility and metabolizable energy content. *Animal Feed Science and Technology* 28, 91-101.

Taverner, M.R., Hume, I.D., and Farrell, D.J. (1981) Availability to pigs of amino acids in cereal grains. 1. Endogenous levels in digesta and faeces of pigs given cereal diets. *British Journal of Nutrition* 46, 149-58.

Wang, T.C. and Fuller, M.F. (1989) The optimum dietary amino acid pattern for growing pigs. 1. Experiments by amino acid deletion *British Journal of Nutrition* 62, 77-89.

Wünsche, J., Herrmann, U., Meinl, M., Hennig, U., Kreienbring, F. and Zwierz, P. (1987) Einfluss exogener Faktoren auf die präzäkal Aminosäurenresorption, ermittelt an Schweinen mit Ileo-Rektal-Anastomosen. *Archives of Animal Nutrition* 37, 745-64.

Chapter 11

In Vitro Simulation of Protein Digestion: an Integrated Approach

L. Savoie

Introduction

The complexity of food protein processing by the body before proper utilization arises from the nature of the substrate, the type of degradation reactions and the conditions in which they occur. For practical reasons, protein digestion is most often considered overall and is evaluated by a single measurement of the disappearance of a food constituent between input and output in the digestive tract. The great dependence of animals on the process of digestion arises from the fact that protein synthesis is an all or none phenomenon. All amino acids, in the right proportion, must be present in various organs at the same time for efficient protein synthesis.

Fig. 11.1. Schematic description of biochemical and physiological events involved in food protein utilization.

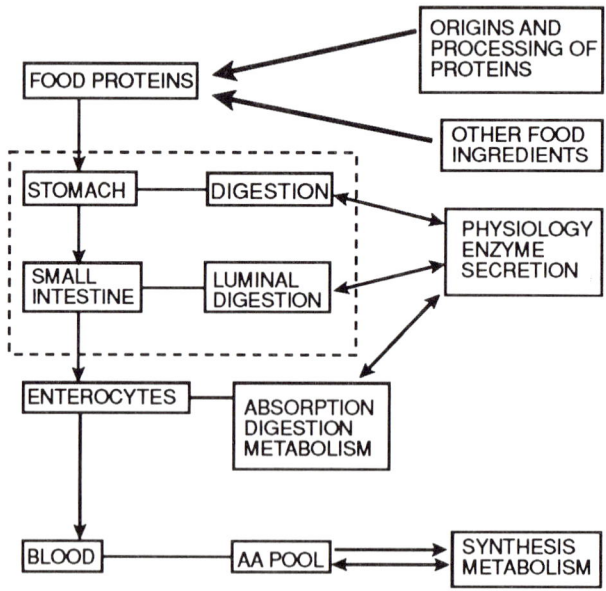

Numerous tissue proteins are in a constant state of synthesis and degradation. The free amino acid blood pool is greatly increased by amino acids arising from intestinal hydrolysis of food proteins, enhancing their availability for synthesis. Since the essential amino acids not involved in active protein synthesis are readily catabolized, the timing of amino acid arrival is important.

Digestion of Proteins: Conceptual Aspects

The utilization of proteins is affected by many factors acting even before the food is eaten, such as their origin, their degree of processing and the simultaneous presence of other food ingredients (Fig. 11.1). The hydrolytic processes take place in the stomach and small intestine in the presence of various enzymes. The transit of digesta affects the degree and the nature of the products of hydrolysis; on the other hand, the physiology of the intestine as well as the secretion of enzymes are governed by the nature of the end products. At the brush border level, extra- and intra-enterocytic digestion will continue the degradation of proteins and peptides as fast as they are absorbed. Amino acids appearing in the blood have been further modified by the metabolism of enterocyte and mixed with the existing amino acid pool.

Table 11.1. Factors influencing digestion of food proteins.

	Variables	Factors
Substrate	Nature	Origin of food protein; protein structure; food matrix; endogenous proteins
Enzyme	Nature	Number, origin, specificity
	Conditions of milieu	Various organs; various pH; various E:S
	Mode of operation	Endo- or exo-peptidases; limited, simultaneous or sequential action; variable substrate
Reaction products	Absorption	Hydrolysis kinetics; amino acid composition; transport system; distribution

As summarized in Table 11.1, protein hydrolysis cannot be considered as a single irreversible enzymatic reaction which splits peptide bonds, liberating amino acids. Proteins may be poorly accessible to enzymes. For example, the relative indigestibility of zein seems to be largely due to its insolubility in the gastric and intestinal juices (Rolls *et al.*, 1972). The structure of proteins, either naturally occurring proteins such as soyabean globulins or as a consequence of food processing, may also be unfavourable to the attack by proteolytic enzymes (Kakade *et al.*, 1973). Moreover, food proteins are often included in a complex food matrix (cell walls, links with sugars, fibres, lipids). Endogenous proteins, which account for a variable but important fraction of the substrate to be hydrolyzed, influence the nature of the reaction products. The hydrolysis of proteins is performed by a battery of enzymes whose specificity is either narrow (trypsin) or broad (elastase, pepsin; Darcy, 1984). They are either endo- or exopeptidases, and may be free or bound. The hydrolysis is performed in various organs in which solubility, pH, concentration and time differ. The proteolytic action of enzymes may be exclusive, as for pepsin in the stomach, or simultaneous, as for most other enzymes in the small intestine. These factors control the mode of action of enzymes. Hence, the hydrolysis kinetics of each enzyme are quite complex and different from the usual models. The action of some enzymes such as pepsin is limited by the time food stays in the stomach. Strictly, the only sequential hydrolysis is that performed by pancreatic enzymes following the action of pepsin. The subsequent proteolytic processes in the gut are mostly simultaneous. As hydrolysis proceeds, enzymes, mainly endopeptidases, are constantly in the presence of a different substrate, varying from complex proteins to oligopeptides of smaller and smaller sizes. Kinetics of the reaction are favoured if reaction products are removed from the medium. The brush border membranes of the intestinal epithelium clear the products of protein digestion from the gut lumen by three independent mechanisms (Adibi, 1985). The free amino acids are taken up by amino acid carrier systems; dipeptides and tripeptides are taken up by the peptide carrier systems, and oligopeptides with more than three amino acid residues are further hydrolysed to absorbable products (free AA or dipeptides) by the brush border enzymes. The distribution of these absorption systems along the entire length of the small intestine is not linear and amino acids are in competition for a carrier system.

A deficiency in any of these interdependent processes (transit, enzyme hydrolysis and absorption) or their inadequate chronology, leads to a reduced digestibility or metabolic utilization of nutrients. In order to understand the process completely, it is thus necessary to know when after a meal, where in the gut and in which form amino acids are released from food proteins.

In Vitro Digestion with Simultaneous Dialysis

Description of the Technique

To measure systematically the sequence and form of release of amino acids during digestion, while eliminating the interference of products from endogenous nitrogen, the *in vitro* technique must simulate as closely as possible *in vivo* conditions. Thus, the use of gut enzymes in their natural sequence and environment is a

Fig. 11. 2. Graphic representation of different parts of the digestion cell.

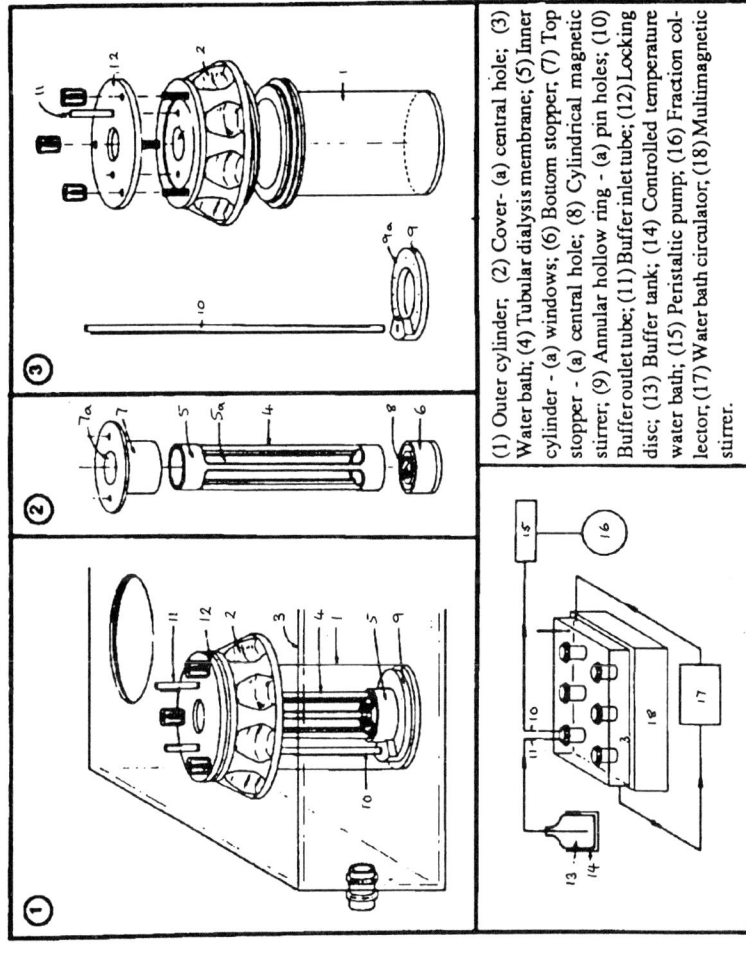

(1) Outer cylinder; (2) Cover - (a) central hole; (3) Water bath; (4) Tubular dialysis membrane; (5) Inner cylinder - (a) windows; (6) Bottom stopper; (7) Top stopper - (a) central hole; (8) Cylindrical magnetic stirrer; (9) Annular hollow ring - (a) pin holes; (10) Buffer outlet tube; (11) Buffer inlet tube; (12) Locking disc; (13) Buffer tank; (14) Controlled temperature water bath; (15) Peristaltic pump; (16) Fraction collector; (17) Water bath circulator; (18) Multimagnetic stirrer.

Adapted from Savoie and Gauthier, 1986

prerequisite. Furthermore, a device that can select digestion products as they are generated will allow the measurement of the kinetics of release of amino acids in the form in which they appear in the lumen of the gut.

The technique developed by our group (Savoie and Gauthier, 1986; Gauthier *et al.*, 1986) consists of a predigestion of the protein source with pepsin, at pH 1.9 for 30 min. The mixture is made alkaline and poured into a dialysis tube with a molecular weight cut off of 1000 Daltons where it is treated with pancreatin. The products released diffuse through the membrane and are collected by the circulation of a sodium phosphate buffer. The dialysate (a mixture of free amino acids and low molecular weight peptides) is then fractionated on Cu-Sephadex G-25 (Savoie and Parent, 1987).

The apparatus developed to perform the pancreatic digestion, called a digestion cell (Fig. 11.2), is made of two concentric compartments. The enzymatic reaction takes place in the inner cylinder surrounded by the membrane; mixing is provided by a magnetic stirrer. Circulation of the buffer in the outer cylinder proceeds from the top to the bottom without disturbance of the gradient of materials diffusing through the membrane. Digested products are thus continously collected from the bottom through an annular collector. The entire system lies in a water bath maintained at constant temperature and includes six independent digestion cells. Preheated buffer is circulated by a multi-channel peristaltic pump and digestion products are collected into a fraction collector.

A comparative *in vitro* and *in vivo* study was performed with two different protein sources, casein (86.6% protein) and rapeseed protein concentrate (51.2% protein).

In Vitro Assay

Protein aliquots were submitted in four replicates to a 24 h pancreatin hydrolysis in the digestion cell, after a 30 min pepsin predigestion. The composition of the digesta was determined every three hours.

Throughout the experimental period, casein had a higher cumulative digestibility than rapeseed (Fig. 11.3). After 24 h of proteolysis, casein was almost totally digested (97%), while rapeseed digestibility reached 83%. Differences in the cumulative values were mostly due to the high rate of digestion (31%) of casein during the first three hours.

Individual amino acids followed various patterns of digestion (Table 11.2). After three hours of proteolysis more than 40% of the arginine, tyrosine, lysine, methionine, leucine and phenylalanine of casein was released; after 12h more than 95% of three of these, arginine, tyrosine and methionine, was released. Threonine, serine, glutamic acid and proline were released much more slowly. The amino acids of rapeseed protein were released more gradually and they varied less in their individual rates of release. Arginine and cystine were much less rapidly released

150

from rapeseed than from casein (P<0.01). Lysine also was not preferentially hydrolysed from rapeseed. In contrast to what was noted with casein, only two essential amino acids in rapeseed (tyrosine and methionine) were more than 95% released by the end of the 24h proteolysis.

In the first three hours of *in vitro* digestion of both proteins, the digestion products consisted of about 60% low molecular weight peptides (Table 11.3). Differences were observed in the distribution of amino acids within peptide fractions. For casein, isoleucine, phenylalanine and especially threonine were mostly found in peptides, whereas arginine and lysine were mostly released as free amino acids. Non-essential amino acids were preferentially released as peptides. With rapeseed, leucine, phenylalanine and tyrosine were mostly released in the free form, whereas histidine, threonine, valine and methionine were found in the peptide fractions. Methionine was preferentially released in peptides. The total picture was modified as the digestion proceeded. Between 9 and 12 hours, the total proportion of amino acids released as peptides increased to 70% and the only difference between the two proteins was that with casein a higher proportion of tyrosine and phenylalanine were in peptides and less histidine.

Fig. 11.3. Time-course of dialysis of nitrogen released during casein and rapeseed *in vitro* digestion with pancreatin. Means of four assays ± SD.

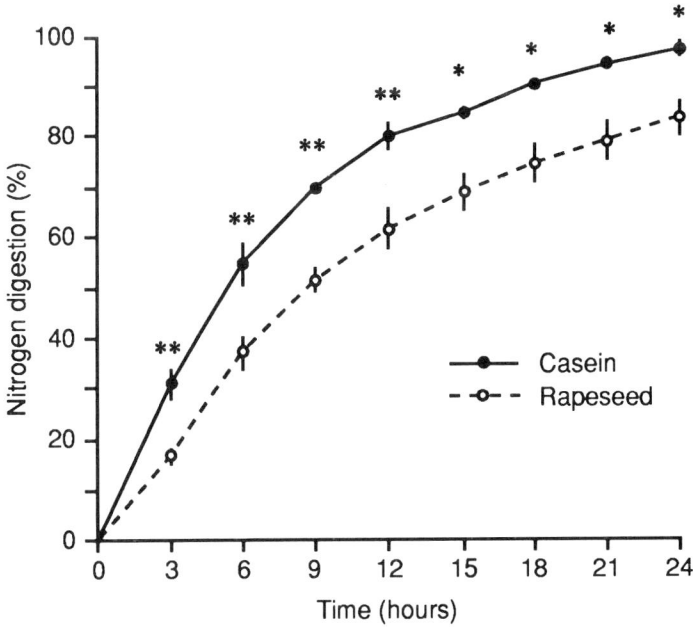

Savoie *et al.*, 1988.

Table 11.2. Cumulative *in vitro* amino acid digestibility (%).

Amino acid	Duration of digestion (hours)					
	3	6	9	12	18	24
			Casein			
Arg	54	81	93	>95	>95	>95
His	31	55	72	82	91	>95
Ile	27	51	67	78	91	>95
Leu	41	68	84	93	>95	>95
Lys	43	67	81	90	>95	>95
Met	42	73	92	>95	>95	>05
Cys	22	45	63	80	>95	>95
Phe	41	66	81	90	>95	>95
Thr	25	47	62	75	86	94
Tyr	48	76	91	>95	>95	>95
Val	28	52	69	81	94	>95
Ala	34	59	74	86	>95	>95
Asp	24	46	61	74	88	>95
Glu	25	47	61	72	83	92
Gly	35	62	80	94	>95	>95
Pro	21	41	56	71	85	91
Ser	25	44	58	69	80	91
			Rapeseed			
Arg	21	41	53	59	71	80
His	17	40	56	59	77	86
Ile	18	40	55	66	79	89
Leu	20	42	57	67	76	82
Lys	15	34	51	61	77	87
Met	25	61	86	>95	>95	>95
Cys	4	13	22	34	57	85
Phe	28	53	69	77	84	87
Thr	17	35	49	58	71	81
Tyr	34	68	88	>95	>95	>95
Val	18	39	54	66	80	90
Ala	20	42	56	64	76	86
Asp	18	37	51	61	77	90
Glu	14	35	50	61	74	83
Gly	16	36	52	64	81	92
Pro	9	22	34	43	58	69
Ser	17	37	52	63	76	86

Savoie *et al.*, 1989.

As shown by r values (Table 11.4), there was, with both proteins during the first three hours of digestion, a significant negative correlation between the release of individual amino acids and the percentage of their release in peptide form. Thus, for that period, the amino acids which were released to the least extent tended to be found mostly in peptides. With rapeseed protein this relationship continued as digestion proceeded up to 9 h, but with casein was already lost by the second interval.

Table 11.3. Distribution (%) of amino acids and total nitrogen in the peptide fraction of the dialysate.

	Periods of digestion					
Amino acid	0-3 h			9-12 h		
	Casein	Rapeseed	$P*$	Casein	Rapeseed	$P*$
Arg	17	32	<0.01	31	50	NS
His	53	54	NS	47	72	<0.05
Ile	70	47	<0.05	79	60	NS
Leu	43	35	NS	49	46	NS
Lys	34	49	<0.01	33	56	NS
Met	50	63	NS	61	37	NS
Phe	31	22	<0.05	56	36	<0.05
Thr	100	75	<0.01	73	88	NS
Tyr	42	29	NS	49	25	<0.05
Val	72	59	NS	76	59	<0.05
Ala	73	69	NS	71	88	NS
Asp	85	79	NS	82	96	NS
Glu	81	79	NS	86	88	NS
Gly	93	82	NS	82	88	NS
Pro	100	97	NS	77	100	NS
Ser	70	83	NS	77	87	NS
N	61	58	NS	70	71	NS

Adapted from Savoie *et al.*, 1989.
* Statistical significance of the difference between the two protein groups, as assessed by student's t test.

In Vivo Assay

Six pigs were fitted with catheters in the portal vein and the carotid artery, and with an electromagnetic flow probe around the portal vein (Rérat *et al.*, 1980). They received 800 g test meals containing 12% of either protein. Measurements were made every hour for eight hours. With the casein diet, differences in the net appearance rates began to be observed one h after ingestion (Table 11.5). By 4 h, isoleucine was the slowest appearing amino acid, while lysine and histidine were among the fastest. After 8 h, more than 80% of the dietary content of every essential amino acid had appeared in the portal blood, with histidine the highest. With the rapeseed diet, fewer significant differences were found between essential amino acids in the kinetics of their appearance owing in part to a greater variability in results. All essential amino acids were well transported, having more than 75% of their dietary content taken up into the portal blood 7 h after the meal. A significant difference was noticed only at 8 h, with histidine having a higher level of appearance than leucine and arginine.

Table 11.4. Correlation (r, n=16) between the digestibility of amino acids (%) and their proportions as peptides (%) in the digestion products.

Period of digestion	Casein	Rapeseed
0 - 3 h	-0.85***	-0.72**
0 - 6 h	-0.29	-0.64*
6 - 12 h	-0.21	-0.51*
9 - 12 h	0.03	0.10

*P<0.05; **P<0.01;***P<0.001. Source: Savoie *et al.*, 1988.

Correlation Between Release in Vitro and in Vivo

Table 11.6 shows the correlation coefficients obtained when comparing *in vivo* profiles to free and peptide-bound amino acids *in vitro*. With casein, only the *in vitro* EAA pattern measured up to the fifth interval was significantly correlated with the *in vivo* pattern up to 7 h. The strongest correspondence was seen with the *in vivo* patterns of the first 4 postprandial intervals. With rapeseed proteins, the EAA pattern of the early *in vitro* intervals was poorly correlated with the *in vivo* patterns. In contrast to casein, the subsequent patterns of EAA release from the digesta were significantly correlated with most *in vivo* patterns. However, from 7-8 h, as with casein, no correspondence was noted between *in vitro* patterns and the patterns of EAA released in the portal blood of pigs after the rapeseed protein meal.

In the case of casein, when only the EAA released as peptides in the *in vitro* digesta were taken into account (Table 11.7), the pattern in one interval (0-3 h) bore some resemblance to the EAA patterns measured *in vivo* in the portal blood of pigs. On the other hand, with rapeseed proteins, strong correlations were noted for all intervals *in vitro*. Particularly, peptides of the *in vitro* digesta collected between 0 and 3 h had an EAA composition which was very similar to those measured *in vivo* from 2-7 h after the meal, while, when EAA from total digestion products of this *in vitro* interval were considered, low correlations had been observed.

Table 11.5. Cumulative appearance (%) of individual essential amino acids in pigs.

Time (h)	Thr	Val	Met	Ile	Leu	Phe	Lys	His	Arg
Casein diet									
0.5	5.9[a]	6.0[a]	5.8[a]	5.6[a]	5.9[a]	5.3[a]	7.0[a]	5.7[a]	5.2[a]
1	19.3[b]	16.4[ab]	13.5[ab]	14.2[ab]	14.5[ab]	12.7[a]	17.0[ab]	15.3[ab]	14.1[ab]
2	30.9[a]	27.4[a]	26.3[a]	24.4[a]	25.5[a]	25.5[a]	29.0[a]	27.1[a]	26.4[a]
3	44.7[a]	39.6[a]	44.2[a]	37.6[a]	39.4[a]	39.2[a]	45.5[a]	46.6[a]	39.9[a]
4	57.4[abc]	54.7[abc]	56.9[abc]	47.8[a]	50.4[ab]	49.3[ab]	60.1[bc]	61.8[c]	55.9[abc]
5	65.0[ab]	59.6[ab]	63.8[ab]	57.1[a]	56.2[a]	56.7[a]	69.2[ab]	72.2[b]	67.2[ab]
6	77.8[abc]	65.9[ab]	71.4[ab]	68.2[ab]	64.9[a]	67.7[ab]	81.7[bc]	85.0[c]	78.9[abc]
7	89.1[abc]	72.4[a]	78.5[ab]	76.6[ab]	73.8[ab]	78.0[ab]	92.6[bc]	107.2[c]	88.7[abc]
8	96.7[a]	82.8[a]	88.7[a]	82.5[a]	80.1[a]	84.2[a]	100.0[a]	133.9[b]	97.2[a]
Rapeseed diet									
0.5	2.4[a]	3.0[abc]	3.5[abc]	2.7[ab]	3.2[abc]	3.2[abc]	3.5[abc]	4.0[bc]	4.2[c]
1	8.7[a]	8.5[a]	10.4[a]	8.1[a]	9.0[a]	9.7[a]	9.2[a]	8.7[a]	10.2[a]
2	22.2[a]	20.7[a]	22.0[a]	19.4[a]	19.6[a]	23.3[a]	22.1[a]	19.8[a]	20.9[a]
3	30.3[ab]	29.0[ab]	33.6[b]	28.3[a]	28.7[ab]	33.5[ab]	31.7[ab]	29.7[ab]	32.0[ab]
4	39.89[ab]	38.6[ab]	45.6[b]	36.8[a]	36.4[a]	43.6[ab]	41.8[ab]	42.0[ab]	43.5[ab]
5	47.5[abc]	47.8[abc]	57.4[c]	45.3[ab]	45.0[a]	52.9[abc]	51.7[abc]	55.7[bc]	54.3[abc]
6	56.1[ab]	58.1[abc]	67.8[bc]	54.2[a]	53.9[a]	60.7[abc]	61.8[abc]	69.2[c]	64.9[abc]
7	63.0[ab]	66.3[ab]	75.7[b]	61.7[a]	61.3[a]	68.9[ab]	70.7[ab]	75.8[b]	74.2[ab]
8	66.7[a]	73.2[ab]	83.6[b]	68.5[ab]	68.3[ab]	77.0[ab]	79.4[ab]	78.7[ab]	82.4[b]

Adapted from Galibois et al., 1989a. Each value represents the mean of 6 animals. Within a row, values followed by the same superscript letter are not significantly different ($P<0.05$).

155

Table 11.6. Correlations between EAA profiles of in vitro digesta and profiles of EAA absorbed in vivo following a 12% protein meal in the pig.

in vitro / in vivo	03-3 h	3-6 h	6-9 h	9-12 h	12-15 h	15-18 h	18-21 h	21-24 h
				r^1				
Casein								
0-1h	0.83**	0.92***	0.94***	0.93***	0.77**	0.61	0.58	0.29
1-2h	0.93***	0.98***	0.95***	0.88***	0.65*	0.48	0.44	0.13
2-3h	0.91***	0.93***	0.90***	0.82**	0.56	0.34	0.33	0.04
3-4h	0.81**	0.86**	0.84**	0.81**	0.67*	0.50	0.43	0.33
4-5h	0.81**	0.76*	0.65*	0.54	0.36	0.20	0.18	0.23
5-6h	0.85**	0.83**	0.75*	0.68*	0.45	0.27	0.28	0.11
6-7h	0.74*	0.74*	0.67*	0.58	0.30	0.13	0.17	-0.05
7-8h	0.25	0.34	0.40	0.39	0.34	0.22	0.22	0.04
Rapeseed								
0-1h	0.81**	0.91***	0.95***	0.90***	0.91***	0.86**	0.85**	0.82**
1-2h	0.69*	0.86**	0.94***	0.91***	0.85**	0.76*	0.76*	0.73*
2-3h	0.56	0.72*	0.83**	0.87**	0.88**	0.81**	0.84**	0.82**
3-4h	0.55	0.71*	0.84**	0.90**	0.94***	0.88***	0.92***	0.84***
4-5h	0.56	0.69*	0.79**	0.82**	0.88***	0.81***	0.84***	0.81**
5-6h	0.53	0.71*	0.86**	0.91***	0.90***	0.83***	0.84***	0.76*
6-7h	0.42	0.57	0.73*	0.78**	0.86**	0.82**	0.82**	0.80**
7-8h	0.16	0.28	0.41	0.41	0.54	0.56	0.48	0.56

Adapted from Galibois et al., 1989b.
[1] Coefficient of correlation, n=9   * $P<0.05$, ** $P<0.01$, *** $P<0.001$

This very large number of highly significant correlations gave a first indication that luminal digestion is indeed a determinant of EAA availability. However, the patterns *in vitro* and *in vivo* were not similarly distributed with time of digestion, and varied with the protein studied.

Table 11.7. Correlation (r) between profiles of EAA found in peptide fractions in the *in vitro* digesta and profiles of EAA absorbed *in vivo* following ingestion of 12% protein meals in the pig.

in vitro *in vivo*	0-3h	3-6h	6-9h	9-12h
Casein				
0-1h	0.87**	0.75*	0.66	0.59
1-2h	0.76**	0.62	0.52	0.46
2-3h	0.74*	0.56	0.44	0.36
3-4h	0.71*	0.57	0.49	0.44
4-5h	0.45	0.28	0.16	0.10
5-6h	0.63	0.44	0.30	0.22
6-7h	0.60	0.36	0.20	0.11
7-8h	0.40	0.29	0.26	0.21
Rapeseed				
0-1h	0.68*	0.71*	0.71*	0.66
1-2h	0.67*	0.71*	0.72*	0.69*
2-3h	0.95***	0.94***	0.93***	0.93***
3-4h	0.89**	0.90***	0.91***	0.89**
4-5h	0.88**	0.91***	0.88**	0.84**
5-6h	0.80**	0.85**	0.90***	0.85**
6-7h	0.80**	0.87**	0.89***	0.83**
7-8h	0.31	0.48	0.52	0.44

Adapted from Galibois *et al.* (1989b)   n=9   *$P<0.05$, ** $P<0.01$, *** $P<0.001$

Discussion and Conclusion

The fundamental difference between the two methods of measurement should be pointed out. During *in vitro* digestion, the protein substrate was in continuous contact with the enzyme mixture and the kinetics of release were measured for each amino acid until the substrate was exhausted. *In vivo*, the protein meal stayed in the stomach for a relatively long period, and was only gradually released into the duodenum, when it was in progressively greater contact with the enzymes.

As the digestion proceeded, there was a continuous mixing of the protein from the meal, and also a dilution with protein from endogenous sources (Laplace *et al.*, 1985). As the measure of absorption was made in the portal vein, it was not possible to distinguish between the amino acids arising from the proximal part and those from the distal part of the digestive tract.

With a rapidly hydrolysed protein such as casein, significant correlations appeared mostly between EAA patterns measured during the first intervals *in vitro* and *in vivo*. Later on, in the animal, the absorbed material became more and more diluted with amino acids from endogenous proteins, and displayed EAA compositions different from those of the last three periods *in vitro*. On the other hand, the rapeseed proteins were digested more gradually, and the correspondence between *in vitro* and *in vivo* patterns of release was sustained over longer periods of measurement.

Table 11.8. Increase (%) in pancreatin amino acid hydrolysis (digestibility/min) by brush border peptidases in the first period (30 to 180 min) of kinetics.

Amino acid	Casein	Rapeseed
Asp	134***	97**
Thr	114***	94**
Ser	91***	91*
Glu	108**	97*
Pro	158***	162**
Gly	145***	138**
Ala	152***	92**
Val	147***	94**
Met	120***	82*
Ile	151***	86**
Leu	67***	34*
Tyr	59***	16 NS
Phe	72***	18 NS
His	116***	71*
Lys	38*	93*
Arg	25*	68*
Cys	142**	94*
N	89**	75***

Adapted from Savoie *et al.*, 1990
Statistical significance of the increase by Student's t-test ***$P<0.001$, **$P<0.01$, *$P<0.05$

In this form, the technique may present some drawbacks: for instance, it cannot take into account the important role that peptidases from the intestinal brush-border and from enterocytes play in the digestion of proteins (Silk *et al.*, 1985).

In a preliminary experiment (Table 11.8), brush border vesicles isolated from pigs fed either a casein or a rapeseed diet were mixed with pancreatin in the digestion cell. They were shown to increase from 75 to 90% the rapidity of protein hydrolysis. The increase in the release of amino acids was not only specific to each amino acid but also related to its protein of origin, resulting in a change in the amino acid pattern available for absorption. Corrections were particularly important for proline, glycine and acidic amino acids.

Fig. 11.4. Schematic representation of an integrated approach to measure amino acid bioavailability.

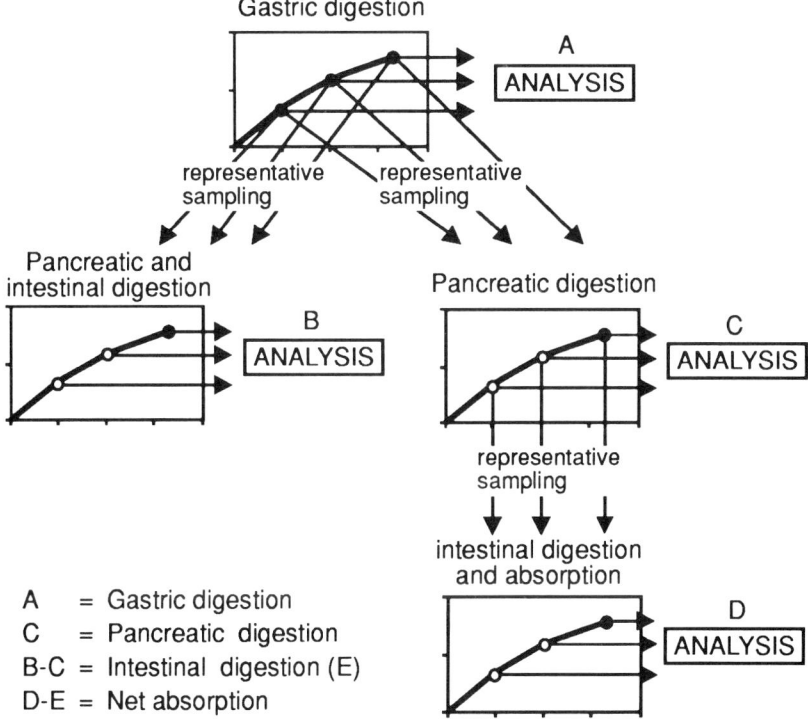

It is difficult to conceive a unique model that will continuously integrate all the interdependent events occurring *in vivo*. The number of samples and the analyses needed would be prohibitive. It seems more worthwhile to develop different techniques which work independently and allow, on the one hand, measurement of the contribution of each kinetic parameter (transit, enzymatic hydrolysis, absorption) and, on the other hand, integrates them together (Fig. 11.4). From a pepsin digestion (A) in a closed system, samples should be taken at regular intervals for analysis and measurement of the kinetics of hydrolysis. From these data, representative samples should be used for the next step according to two approaches. The first consists of a digestion with pancreatin and with enzymes from brush borders (B) with a device that would allow continuous collection of the digestion products. The analysis of samples at various intervals should allow measurement of the kinetics of release of absorbable products. The second uses a digestion with pancreatin with continuous dialysis of digestion products (C). The analysis of samples should give the kinetics of release of digestion products by pancreatic enzymes. By difference with the results obtained in B, the specific role of brush border enzymes could be evaluated. Representative samples of the mixture of free amino acids and oligopeptides obtained by pancreatin digestion (C) could then be transferred to a modified Ussing Chamber (Grass and Sweetana, 1988) where it should be possible to measure the kinetics of absorption of amino acids in relation to the substrate (food protein) and intestinal site (level of intestinal epithelium taken).

The procedure described is far too complex to be used in routine testing. However, by giving insight into the various steps of the digestion process, it should be possible to evaluate the respective importance of each and eventually to derive simpler prediction equations or tests.

Acknowledgements

Support by NSERC Grants N° OGP0018095 and N° STR0045632, Grant FCAR EQ-1188 from the Ministère de l'Education du Québec, and a grant from the France-Québec collaboration in biotechnology.

References

Adibi, S.A. (1984) Absorption of products of protein digestion. In: Finley, J.W. and Hopkins, D.T. (eds), *Digestibility and Amino Acid Availability in Cereals and Oilseeds.* AACC, St.Paul, Minn. pp. 285-93.

Darcy, B. (1985) Availability of amino acids in monogastric animals. Variations of digestive origin. *Diabete et Metabolism,* 10, 121-33.

Galibois, I., Simoes Nunes, C., Rérat, A. and Savoie, L. (1989a) Net appearance of amino acids in portal blood during the digestion of casein or rapeseed proteins in the pig. *Canadian Journal of Physiology and Pharmacology* 67, 1409-17.

Galibois, I., Savoie, L., Simoes Nunes, C. and Rérat, A. (1989b) Relation between *in vitro* and *in vivo* assessment of amino acid availability. *Reproduction, Nutrition et Developpement* 29, 495-508.

Gauthier, S., Vachon, C. and Savoie, L. (1986) Enzymatic conditions of an *in vitro* method to study protein digestion. *Journal of Food Science* 51, 960-64.

Grass, G.M. and Sweetana S.A. (1988) *In vitro* measurement of gastrointestinal tissue permeability using a new diffusion cell. *Pharmaceutical Research* 5, 372-6.

Kakade, M.L., Hoffa, D.E., Liener, I.E. (1973)   Contribution of trypsin inhibitors to the deleterious effects of unheated soybeans fed to rats. *Journal of Nutrition* 103, 17-8.

Laplace, J.P., Darcy-Vrillon, B., Duval-Iflan, X. and Raibaud, P. (1985) Proteins in the digesta of the pig: amino acid composition of endogenous, bacterial and fecal fractions. *Reproduction, Nutrition et Developpement* 25, 1083-99.

Rérat, A., Vaugelade, P. and Villiers, P. (1980) A new method for measuring the absorption of nutrients in the pig: critical examination. In: Low, A.G. and Partridge, I.G. (eds), *Current Concepts of Digestion and Absorption in the Pig.* NIRD, Reading, UK pp. 177-214.

Rolls, B.A., Porter, J.W.G. and Westgarth, D.R. (1972) The course of digestion of different food proteins in the rat. *British Journal of Nutrition* 28, 283-93.

Savoie, L. and Gauthier, S. (1986) Dialysis cell for the *in vitro* measurement of protein digestibility. *Journal of Food Science* 51, 494-8.

Savoie, L. and Parent, G. (1987) Characterization of protein *in vitro* digestion products by Copper-Sephadex Chromatography. *Nutrition Reports International* 35, 783-91.

Savoie, L., Galibois, I., Parent, G. and Charbonneau, R. (1988) Sequential release of amino acids and peptides during *in vitro* digestion of casein and rapeseed proteins. *Nutrition Research* 8, 1319-26.

Savoie, L., Galibois, I., Parent, G. and Charbonneau, R. (1989) Sequential release of amino acids and peptides during *in vitro* digestion of casein and rapeseed proteins. *Nutrition Research* 9, 696-8.

Savoie, L., Poullain, M.G., Parent, G. and Cezard, J.P. (1990) Role of brush border enzymes on the kinetics of hydrolyses of food proteins. *Federation Proceedings,* Abstract N° 3116.

Silk, D.B.A., Grimble, G.R. and Rees, R.G. (1985) Protein digestion and amino acid and peptide absorption. *Proceeding of the Nutrition Society* 44, 63-72.

Chapter 12

Simultaneous Estimations of Precaecal Protein and Carbohydrate Digestion in the Pig

A.P. Drake , M.F. Fuller and A. Chesson

Introduction

The aim of this project was to develop a rapid *in vitro* assay that could predict ileal digestibility of feedstuffs used in the formulation of diets for pigs.

Since the turn of the century and the introduction of the first pepsin digestion assay (Wedermeyer,1899), scientists have been trying to assess the nutritive values of foods by *in vitro* methods. Until the 1970s development of *in vitro* techniques involved simulation of the digestion processes that were known to be present in the animal. In the case of protein, straightforward pepsin digestions were superseded by two-step multi-enzyme digestions (Akeson and Stahmann, 1964; Ford and Salter,1966; Saunders *et al.*,1973) which take into account the wide range of enzyme activities that exist in the gut. However, such classical techniques became increasingly laborious and this stimulated interest in the development of very quick assays such as the 'pH drop' method of Hsu *et al.* (1977) which were shown to be efficient in ranking proteins but were open to criticism because of inaccuracies when analysing foods of strong buffering capacity (O'Hare *et al.*,1984; Pedersen and Eggum,1981) and because of their inability to cope with a wide range of feedstuffs (Satterlee *et al.*,1982). More recent research (Gauthier *et al.*,1982; Savoie *et al.*,1989; Cave,1988; Kennedy *et al.*,1989) has returned to the idea of producing a closer simulation of the *in vivo* system with the use of a dialysis membrane to separate continuously digestion products from undigested residues, eliminating the possibility of product inhibition of the enzyme reaction (Robbins, 1978).

Until recently most of the workers developing *in vitro* methods failed to relate their estimates to suitable *in vivo* standards. If an *in vitro* technique is to be judged by its ability to simulate *in vivo* digestion it is essential to define the *in vivo* measures that are to be simulated. To be of use to nutritionists these measures must reflect available knowledge of nutrient availability and use the most accurate *in vivo* techniques. If improvements in *in vitro* technology are to be achieved the *in vivo* processes involved must be identified and understood to improve the simulation *in vitro*.

The protein and starch fractions of a feedstuff are quantitatively of greatest importance in pig diets. In addition, when considering the digestion of, for example, particles of grain; the relative digestion of one fraction is likely to affect the digestion of another. This paper will describe some of the significant steps taken in the development of an assay to predict both protein and carbohydrate digestion, up to the terminal ileum, in which the development was centred on improving the simulation of the *in vivo* processes.

In Vivo Ileal Digestibility Standard Values

Ileal digestibility values for five feedstuffs were obtained using T-cannulas placed at the terminal ileum. An estimate of endogenous nitrogen flow was made from collections made whilst feeding protein-free diets with two levels of fibre so as to allow true crude protein and amino acid digestibility values to be calculated.

The particle sizes of the feedstuffs, classified using the modulus of fineness (American Society of Agricultural Engineers, 1967) were as follows: soyabean meal, 244.5; sunflower meal, 256.0; rapeseed meal, 237.1; maize (3mm mesh), 296.9; wheat(S) (3mm mesh), 238.0; and wheat(L) (5mm mesh), 315.5.

Many of the previously reported assays required that the feed under test be finely ground before analysis (Hahn *et al.,*1982; Clunies and Leeson,1984; Cave, 1988). Particle size has been shown to affect *in vivo* digestibility (e.g. Sauer *et al.,* 1977a) and therefore an *in vitro* technique would be of greater use if it could differentiate between particle sizes. Unless otherwise stated the feedstuffs in all the experiments described in this paper were used without regrinding (i.e. as fed).

Assay Development

The development of the assay began with a simple, two-stage pepsin + pancreatin digestion. Through a methodical sequence of trials, we first investigated the effects of changes in reaction conditions on the assay's ability to predict *in vivo* digestibility values. We then added further digestion stages, incorporating additional aspects of the *in vivo* system. Once a satisfactory prediction of *in vivo* digestion of starch and crude protein prior to the terminal ileum had been achieved, the assay was tested for its ability to predict amino acid digestibility.

The basic assay chosen was as follows: A sample of feedstuff containing a standard amount of nitrogen (17.96mg as contained in 1g wheat) was weighed into a boiling tube. An acid/pepsin (EC 3.4.23.1 550 units/mg, supplied by Sigma Chemical Company Ltd.) solution (pH 1.9) was added and the tube was incubated at 39°C for the required test time. Subsequently the pH was adjusted to 7.5, a pancreatin solution (4X U.S.P. supplied by Sigma Chemical Company, Ltd.) was added and the mixture was transferred to a 10cm length of dialysis tubing clipped at the bottom. Additional buffer was used to ensure the transfer of all the residue.

A.P. Drake, M.F. Fuller, and A. Chesson

The tube was then sealed at the top and immersed in 1 litre of buffer (pH 7.5) in a 2 litre glass beaker. The beaker was capped and incubated in a water bath at 39°C for the test period. The concentrations of glucose, amino acids or nitrogen in a hydrolysed buffer sample from the beaker were used to calculate starch, protein or crude protein digestibility respectively over a sequence of dialysis times so as to construct a time course digestion curve. The first series of trials was designed to determine the optimum concentrations of acid/pepsin and pancreatin, the optimum times for the pepsin incubation and for the dialysis step and the effect of pH on the reaction. In addition, the effects of enzyme co-factors and antimicrobial agents in the incubating buffer were evaluated. Finally, the effects of supplementing the pancreatin enzyme mixture with additional protease and amylase activity were assessed.

Table 12.1. Fractional crude protein digestion with pepsin (10mg/assay)+ pancreatin (40 or 80mg/assay) compared with digestion *in vivo*. Means of two replicates.

Treatment		Dialysis time (h)					*in vivo*	
Substrate	(mg pancreatin)	10	12	14	16	18	App.	True
Rape							0.59	0.66
	40	0.58	0.61	0.63	0.64	0.65		
	80	0.58	0.64	0.70	0.74	0.77		
Soya							0.74	0.78
	40	0.70	0.75	0.79	0.82	0.85		
	80	0.74	0.79	0.82	0.85	0.87		
Sunflower							0.70	0.75
	40	0.64	0.70	0.74	0.77	0.80		
	80	0.67	0.72	0.75	0.77	0.79		
Wheat(s)							0.69	0.75
	40	0.51	0.56	0.60	0.63	0.66		
	80	0.54	0.60	0.64	0.67	0.70		
Maize							0.59	0.64
	40	0.32	0.36	0.39	0.41	0.43		
	80	0.36	0.42	0.47	0.51	0.56		

In Table 12.1 the crude protein digestion for the test feedstuffs, in two pepsin pancreatin assays over dialysis times of 10 to 18 hours are compared to apparent and true crude protein digestibility measured *in vivo*. The procedure using the higher concentration of pancreatin could accurately predict apparent *in vivo* crude protein digestibility for the protein meals over 10 hours' dialysis. 'True' crude protein digestibility was not so consistently predicted. However, over 18 hours dialysis the system failed to predict crude protein digestibility for cereals and levels of starch digestion achieved for the cereals were considerably below those *in vivo;* suggesting that perhaps the presence of undigested starch was restricting access of the proteases to some of the cereal protein.

A question of particular interest was whether an acid/pepsin predigestion stage was necessary, considering the range of enzyme activities that were to follow with the addition of pancreatin. Several workers have previously indicated that a degree of pepsin action is necessary for efficient digestion by pancreatin (Sheffner *et al.,*1956; Camus and Laporte,1980; Gauthier *et al.,*1986).

In an experiment to investigate the optimum pepsin/pancreatin ratio it was noticed that the presence of a low concentration of pepsin, compared to a control lacking pepsin activity, enhanced the starch digestion of wheat (Table 12.2) although no effect was seen when the wheat was first freeze-milled. The presence of pepsin appeared to be of no benefit to the starch digestion of maize, perhaps reflecting the difference in protein-starch relationships between the two grains (Hinton, 1953; Miflin *et al.* 1981).

Table 12.2. The effect of a pepsin (Pep, 0 or 10mg/assay) predigestion on fractional starch digestion both with and without freeze milling (FM). Values are means of two replicates.

Treatment		Dialysis time (h)								
		3	4	5	6	7	8	9	11	18
Wheat(S)										
	+Pep	0.13	0.14	0.20	0.25	0.27	0.27	0.30	0.33	0.44
	-Pep	0.09	0.09	0.08	0.13	0.13	0.13	0.17	0.22	0.33
FM	+Pep	0.18	0.19	0.21	0.24	0.24	0.29	0.38	0.33	0.64
FM	-Pep	0.21	0.23	0.24	0.29	0.30	0.32	0.33	0.44	0.60
Maize										
	+Pep	0.19	0.22	0.26	0.33	0.34	0.34	0.33	0.42	0.56
	-Pep	0.16	0.19	0.22	0.25	0.20	0.34	0.32	0.42	0.52
FM	+Pep	0.23	0.32	0.30	0.45	0.40	0.46	0.56	0.64	0.72
FM	-Pep	0.25	0.28	0.28	0.40	0.41	0.49	0.55	0.58	0.72

The appearance of glucose in the blood after feeding a starch meal is often used to assess the rate of starch digestion *in vivo*. Holm *et al.* (1985) showed that the inclusion of a protease step in an *in vitro* starch digestion assay improved the correlation with the glycaemic reponse *in vivo*. Similarly, removal of gluten from wheat flour has been shown to increase the rate of amylolytic digestion *in vitro* and increase glycaemic response *in vivo* (Jenkins *et al.*,1987). It would appear that if the protein matrix is not disrupted by pepsin attack the subsequent amylase digestion is greatly inhibited.

An experiment in which the pancreatin was replaced by individual protease activities demonstrated that pronase E (EC 3.4.24.4.) from *Streptomyces griseus* would digest the protein of the feedstuffs more efficiently than the pancreatin. Table 12.3 shows the results of an experiment to supplement the pancreatin with additional protease activity. Addition of pronase significantly improved crude protein digestion of wheat. However, pronase is not a natural mammalian enzyme. It shows no sequence specificity for hydrolysis, releasing amino acids from both the carboxyl- and amino-terminals of peptides (Barker, 1971). Therefore, pronase was not used further as it is likely that the amino acid profile produced by digesting a protein with pronase would be very different from that achieved using mammalian proteases.

Table 12.3. The effect of supplementing pancreatin with extra protease activities on crude protein digestion of wheat after 12 hours' dialysis. This followed a digestion with acid/pepsin at pH 1.9. Values are means of four replicates.

Treatment (Pep 10 Pan 40)	
1. Control	0.57
2. +5mg Trypsin	0.57 n.s
3. +5mg Chymotrypsin	0.55 n.s
4. +2mg Elastase	0.60 n.s
5. +3mg Pronase E	0.67 ***
	s.e.d = 0.020

*** = significantly ($P<0.001$) different from control.

The general conclusion from the first set of experiments was that the low protein digestibility of cereals was probably due to the inaccessibility of the protein to the enzyme. Grinding the cereals was shown to increase the digestibility of both crude protein and starch as shown in Table 12.4. In addition, the difference in crude protein and starch digestibility values between the wheat of different particle sizes was greater *in vitro* than *in vivo* suggesting the animal's digestive tract is more efficient in reducing the effect of particle size than the conditions employed *in vitro*.

The presence of large amounts of undigested starch is likely to reduce accessibility of the grain protein. In the normal course of digestion *in vivo* starch digestion is initiated by amylase in the saliva. Although the significance of starch digestion by salivary amylase is often debated it seems plausible that the rise in stomach pH immediately after feeding (Braude *et al.*, 1976), dependent on the buffering capacity of the food, would provide sufficient time for some starch digestion to take place. As a means of increasing the rate of starch digestion in the *in vitro* assay an initial amylase incubation was added to the assay in addition to amylase supplementation of the pancreatin stage. For this purpose, Termamyl, a heat-stable amylase (α-1,4-glucan-glucanohydrolase) from *Bacillus licheniformis* was used. The feedstuff was incubated with Termamyl and buffer for 1 hour at 60°C before cooling and acidifying prior to the pepsin incubation. As Termamyl is heat-stable the higher temperature was used to increase the rate of starch digestion. Table 12.5 shows the time course of digestion of wheat and maize using Termamyl in both the preincubation and in the pancreatin stages.

Table 12.4. The effect of cereal particle size (S, small; L, large) on starch and crude protein digestibility. Pancreatin was included at 160 mg/assay. Values are means of two replicates, except where otherwise indicated.

Crude protein		
Dialysis time (h)	11.75	19
Wheat		
Freeze milled	0.72	0.81
Ground	0.63	0.75
As fed (S)	0.59	0.74
As fed (L)	0.56	0.68
Dialysis time (h)	12.25	20
Maize		
Freeze milled	0.66	0.71
Ground	0.47	0.61
As fed	0.49	0.63

Starch					
Dialysis time (h)	9.5	11.5	14.5	19	
Wheat					
Freeze milled	0.60 (4)	0.72 (4)	0.80 (2)	0.89 (2)	
Ground	0.55 (4)	0.65 (4)	0.79 (2)	0.79 (2)	
As fed (S)	0.51 (4)	0.65 (4)	0.71 (2)	0.81 (2)	
As fed (L)	0.44 (4)	0.52 (4)	0.58 (2)	0.65 (2)	
Dialysis time (h)	10	12	14	16	20
Maize					
Freeze milled	0.71 (4)	0.79 (4)	0.79 (2)	0.85 (2)	0.94 (2)
Ground	0.66 (4)	0.75 (4)	0.76 (4)	0.86 (2)	0.87 (2)
As fed	0.56 (4)	0.64 (4)	0.68 (4)	0.76 (2)	0.80 (2)

A.P. Drake, M.F. Fuller, and A. Chesson

The digestibility of wheat(S) starch reached its *in vivo* level at around the 13.25 hours whereas at this time the wheat(L) and the maize were still 0.12-0.15 lower than the *in vivo* value. Both wheat(S) and wheat(L) *in vitro* had reached their respective crude protein digestibility values between 10 and 12 hours which matched the pattern of crude protein digestion for the protein meals shown inTable 12.1. In the case of maize, even after 18 hours' dialysis, the *in vitro* value was still 0.05 lower than the 24 h *in vivo* value.

It would appear from the literature that the simulation of maize protein digestion is a well recognized problem in conventional *in vitro* assays. Hung and Kermorgant (1982), measured the pepsin digestibility of crude protein in high-protein feedstuffs and found a close correlation with *in vivo* bioavailability only if they omitted corn gluten meal. Cave (1988), using a pepsin + pancreatin digestion to compare *in vitro* protein digestion of plant feedstuffs with *in vivo* values, found that the correlation coefficient was reduced when corn gluten was included because of its high true amino acid availability *in vivo* and its very low solubility *in vitro*.

Table 12.5. Time course of digestion of wheat and maize with Termamyl in a pre-digestion (0.125ml Termamyl/assay) and as a supplement to pancreatin (0.25ml Termamyl/assay). Values are means of two replicates.

	Starch digestibility						
Dialysis time (h)	2.5	4.25	7.0	10.75	13.25	22.75	*in vivo*
Wheat							
Freeze milled	0.24	0.54	0.64	0.80	0.97	0.97	
As fed (S)	0.33	0.53	0.68	0.77	0.92	0.94	0.95
As fed (L)	0.29	0.45	0.61	0.71	0.81	0.80	0.92
Maize							
Freeze milled	0.32	0.56	0.63	0.82	0.82	1.00	
As fed	0.27	0.44	0.58	0.75	0.78	0.93	0.90

	Crude protein digestibility					
Dialysis time (h)	8	10	12	14	18	*in vivo*
Wheat						
As fed (S)	0.59	0.64	0.71	0.68	0.75	0.69
As fed (L)	0.55	0.61	0.66	0.69	0.70	0.60
Maize						
As fed	0.36	0.39	0.44	0.44	0.54	0.59

In attempting to discover a way of increasing maize protein digestion *in vitro* various supplementary experiments were undertaken. We added an incubation with a range of polysaccharidase activites with the aim of disrupting intact cell walls to expose protein but this had no effect. A separate incubation step with deoxycholic acid (bile salt) was included, also with no effect. Walker and Hope (1963) had shown previously that the presence of sodium deoxycholate at 0.1% increased the rate of starch hydrolysis of maize by 30%.

There is a difference between maize and wheat in the gelatinization temperatures of their starches. In maize there are three stages (Jaska, 1971). The first stage corresponds to reversible hydration and swelling, the second, defined by loss of birefrigence or swelling measurements, occurs at 62-74°C at which some granule structure still remains; the final stage occurs when the last of the structure is broken down at 74-92°C.

Table 12.6. The effect of the time and temperature of preincubation on the digestibility of maize. Values are means of 2 replicates.

Treatment		Crude protein digestibility	Starch digestibility			
		Dialysis time (h)	Dialysis time (h)			
		11.5	4	6.5	9.25	11.5
2 h	80°C	0.55	0.50	0.59	0.75	0.87
	60°C	0.53	0.44	0.53	0.78	0.83
	40°C	0.45	0.38	0.50	0.75	0.77
1 h	80°C	0.49	0.64	0.72	0.80	0.87
	60°C	0.45	0.51	0.59	0.78	0.85
	40°C	0.43	0.29	0.59	0.64	0.78
15 min	80°C	0.51	0.46	0.73	0.87	-
	60°C	0.43	0.36	0.59	0.80	-
	40°C	0.42	0.37	0.50	0.76	-

- missing value

Table 12.6 shows the results of an experiment in which the preincubation (without Termamyl) was varied in time and temperature. Both time and temperature of preincubation clearly increased the crude protein digestibility after 11.5 hours of digestion. The effect was noticeable for the 15 minute treatment for which there was a 0.09 difference between 40°C and 80°C. Starch digestion was increased by raising the temperature but not by increasing the time of preincubations. It appeared that, with maize, a higher temperature improved both crude protein and starch digestion. Therefore, a high temperature preincubation was incorporated into the assay and tested for all the feedstuffs. The complete assay is set out in Table 12.7. The results of an experiment using this procedure for all the feedstuffs are shown in Table 12.8. In addition to the 14,000 molecular weight cut-off Visking tubing (size 5, as used previously, labelled 'High'), a second, labelled 'Low', Spectra/PorR6 with a molecular weight cut-off 1000, was used for comparison. This low molecular weight cut-off membrane was first introduced by Gauthier *et al.* (1982) for the purpose of limiting the number of molecules that could be dialysed to those of a size that can be absorbed by the intestinal mucosa.

Table 12.7. Complete assay procedure.

- Weigh sample containing 17.96 mg nitrogen into a boiling tube
- Add sodium acetate buffer 9 ml, pH 6.0 0.05M and 0.1 ml Termamyl - stopper, mix and incubate at 80°C for 1 hour with mixing 3 times during the hour
- Adjust pH to 1.9 with 1 M HCl and cool the tubes
- Add 2.5 ml of 0.05 M HCl containing 10 mg pepsin
- Incubate at 39°C for 30 minutes
- Add 1 M NaOH to neutralise and 4 ml pancreatin solution (containing 80 mg pancreatin) and 0.1 ml of Termamyl
- Transfer to 10 cm strips of dialysis tubing, seal and place in 1 litre of borate buffer 0.05 M at pH 7.5 with 190 μM Thimerosal (sodium ethylmer-curithiosalicylate, Sigma Chemical Company Ltd.) and calcium chloride 10 mM.
- Incubate at 39°C over a time span of 18 hours with samples of buffer being withdrawn for analysis throughout this time period

---

Parallel curve analysis using the Maximum Likelihood Program (Lawes Agricultural Trust, Rothamsted Experimental Station, 1987) showed there was no significant difference between the high and low molecular weight dialysis membranes except in the case of rapeseed meal ($P<0.05$).The digestibility of crude protein for both soyabean meal and rapeseed meal appears lower in the earlier stages when the low molecular weight membrane was used. By 16 hours there was no significant difference between the values. A time of 10-12 hours predicted the apparent crude protein digestibility for all the feedstuffs well except wheat(S) which required two extra hours. The time taken to reach the 'true' crude protein digestibility was a little longer and less consistent.

Table 12.8. Time course of digestion with an 80°C Termamyl preincubation. The effect of using either high or low molecular weight (MW) dialysis membrane was also investigated.

Crude protein digestibility

Feedstuff	MW	6	8	10	12	14	16	in vivo apparent
Soya	Low	0.55	0.65	0.72	0.78	0.82	0.85	0.74
	High	0.61	0.70	0.76	0.80	0.83	0.85	
Sunflower	Low	0.52	0.61	0.67	0.71	0.74	0.77	0.70
	High	0.49	0.59	0.66	0.72	0.77	0.80	
Rape	Low	0.38	0.47	0.55	0.61	0.67	0.72	0.59
	High	0.45	0.54	0.60	0.65	0.69	0.72	
Wheat (S)	Low	0.49	0.58	0.64	0.69	0.72	0.74	0.69
	High	0.49	0.57	0.63	0.67	0.70	0.72	
Wheat (L)	Low	0.46	0.54	0.59	0.63	0.66	0.68	0.60
	High	0.41	0.50	0.57	0.63	0.68	0.72	
Maize	Low	-	-	-	-	-	-	0.59
	High	0.44	0.53	0.60	0.65	0.69	0.72	-

Starch digestibility

Feedstuff	MW	6	8	10	12	14	16	in vivo
Maize	High	0.59	0.68	0.74	0.79	0.82	0.84	0.90
Wheat (S)	High	0.80	0.89	0.94	0.97	0.99	1.00	0.95
Wheat (L)	High	0.75	0.85	0.92	0.96	0.99	1.00	0.92

- missing values

The best correlations obtained between the *in vitro* crude protein digestibility and *in vivo* crude protein digestibility are shown below.

Ten hours *in vitro* dialysis (X) and apparent *in vivo* crude protein digestibility (Y)

$$Y = 0.104 + 0.8604X \qquad (12.1)$$
$$\text{SE of the Y estimate} = 0.035 \quad r = 0.88$$

A.P. Drake, M.F. Fuller, and A. Chesson

Twelve hours *in vitro* dialysis (X) and 'true' *in vivo* crude protein digestibility (Y)

$$Y = 0.230 + 0.702X \qquad (12.2)$$
$$\text{SE of the Y estimate} = 0.039 \quad r = 0.79$$

The starch curves show that 11 hours is adequate to achieve the starch digestibility *in vivo* of both wheat(S) and (L) but the maize starch digestibility remains 14 percentage points below the *in vivo* value.

Having achieved a reasonable correlation for crude protein, the assay was tested for its ability to predict the digestibility of individual amino acids.

From the same experiment samples of buffer were taken for amino acid analysis and the data were compared to *in vivo* apparent and true digestibility data as for the crude protein. Again there was no significant difference between low and high molecular weight cut-off membranes except in the case of lysine in rapeseed meal.

This suggests that the products of protein digestion of the test feedstuffs were predominantly amino acids or peptides with less than six residues, which, according to Gauthier *et al.* (1982), is the critical size in practice for this membrane. This also suggests that those mucosal enzymes of the small intestine that were not included in the *in vitro* digestion are indeed unnecessary in the simulation. If a lower molecular weight cut-off membrane such as a 500 membrane were to be used, the conclusion might have been different.

Predictions of *in vivo* ileal essential amino acid digestibility values were poor as shown by the low correlation coefficients.

The best linear regression equations obtained were as follows:

between apparent essential *in vivo* amino acid digestibility (Y) and essential amino acid digestibility after 13 hours *in vitro* dialysis (X)

$$Y = 0.565 + 0.116X \qquad (12.3)$$
$$\text{SE of the Y estimate} = 0.114 \quad r = 0.14$$

between true *in vivo* essential amino acid digestibility after 13 hours *in vitro* dialysis (X)

$$Y = 0.654 + 0.142X \qquad (12.4)$$
$$\text{SE of the Y estimate} = 0.087 \quad r = 0.23$$

The reasons why, despite the relatively good correlations for crude protein, those for amino acids should be poor are unclear.

The necessity for a high temperature pretreatment raises the question of what is happening *in vivo* to digest the maize to the extent that is achieved by heating to 80°C *in vitro*. It can be argued, from a pragmatic viewpoint, that it does not matter if a condition such as high temperature, obviously not a direct simulation of the

172

digestive system, is employed *in vitro* provided that it produces the appropriate end products of digestion. However, such arguments are dangerous, for if a wider range of feedstuffs were investigated the digestibility values achieved might not correlate with all the feedstuffs because some element of the *in vivo* system was not directly simulated.

Several workers have shown that diets containing cereals have extended *in vivo* incubation times in the stomach in comparison to diets without cereals (Braude *et al.*,1976; Clemens *et al.*,1974; Cunningham *et al.*,1963; Low *et al.*,1978). It may be that the high temperature treatment had the effect of simulating an extended *in vivo* incubation. The rapid disruption of the maize structure during starch gelatinization at 80°C may have had an effect in allowing protein accessibility to enzymes similar to a prolonged hydration period *in vivo*. How differences in transit times *in vivo* affect digestion is not well understood and could be a key question in modelling digestion *in vitro*.

Discussion

The experiments presented in this paper illustrate how, through manipulation of reaction conditions, the *in vitro* digestibility of feedstuffs can be altered so as to more closely predict values measured *in vivo*. However, a considerable amount of extra work is required if such an assay is to be developed to the point at which it could find wide application. The outstanding requirement is an improvement in the prediction of amino acid digestibility and investigation of a wider range of feedstuffs. Since *in vivo* procedures essentially do not simulate endogenous secretion, they are simulating true rather than apparent amino acid digestibility. It is possible that the poor correlation values obtained between *in vivo* and *in vitro* essential amino acid digestibility data reflect the problems of using protein-free diets to correct for endogenous amino acid flow at the terminal ileum (Sauer *et al.*, 1977b). The best method of accounting for endogenous flow at the terminal ileum is still debatable. The difficulties in handling maize in the assay underline the complexity of the *in vivo* system that is being simulated. It is equally likely that feedstuffs not tested in this study such as animal proteins and high fibre feedstuffs, will bring further problems of their own.

References

Akeson, W.R., and Stahmann, M.A. (1964) A pepsin pancreatin digestion of protein quality evaluation. *Journal of Nutrition* 83, 257-61.

American Society of Agricultural Engineers (1967) Methods of determining modulus of uniformity and modulus of fineness of ground feed. *Agricultural Engineering Yearbook*, ASAE; p. 301.

Barker, R. (1971) *Organic Chemistry of Biological Compounds*. Prentice-Hall, Inc., Englewood Cliffs. N.J., p. 96.

Braude, R., Fulford, R.J., and Low, A.G. (1976) Studies on digestion and absorption in the intestines of growing pigs. Measurements of the flow of digesta and pH. *British Journal of Nutrition* 36, 497-510.

Camus, M.C. and Laporte, J.C. (1980) Proteolyse *in vitro* de caseine et de gluten par les enzymes pancreatique. *Reproduction, Nutrition et Developpement* 20, 1025-39.

Cave, N.A.(1988) Bioavailability of amino acids in plant feedstuffs determined by *in vitro* digestion, chick growth assay, and true amino acid availability methods. *Poultry Science* 1, 78-87.

Clemens, E.T., Stevens, C.E. and Southwarth, M. (1974) Sites of organic acid production and pattern of digesta movement in the gastrointestinal tract of swine. *Journal of Nutrition* 105, 759-68.

Clunies, M. and Leeson, S. (1984) *In vitro* estimation of dry matter and crude protein digestibility. *Poultry Science* 63, 89-96.

Cunningham, H.M., Friend, D.W. and Nicholson, J.W.G. (1963) Observations on digestion in the pig using a re-entrant intestinal fistula. *Canadian Journal of Animal Science* 43, 215-25.

Ford, J.E. and Salter, D.N. (1966) Analysis of enzymatically digested food proteins by Sephadex-gel filtration. *British Journal of Nutrition* 20, 843-64.

Galibois, I., Savoie, L., Nunes, C.S. and Rerat, A. (1989) Relationships between *in vitro* and *in vivo* parameters of amino acid availability. In: Southgate, D., Johnson, I. and Fenwick, G.R. (eds), *Nutrient availability: Chemical and Biological Aspects.* pp. 340-42. Royal Society of Chemistry, Cambridge.

Gauther, S.F., Vachon, C., Jones, J.D. and Savoie, L. (1982) Assessment of protein digestibility by *in vitro* enzymatic hydrolysis with simultaneous dialysis. *Journal of Nutrition* 112, 1718-25.

Gauthier, S.F., Vachon, C. and Savoie, L. (1986) Enzymatic conditions of an *in vitro* method to study protein digestion. *Journal of Food Science* 51, 960-64.

Hahn, D.H., Faubion, J.M., Ring, S.H., Doherty, C.A. and Rooney, L.W. (1982) Semiautomated *in vitro* analysis of sorghum protein availability via pronase hydrolysis. *Cereal Chemistry* 59, 132-6.

Hinton, J.J.C. (1953) The distribution of protein in the maize kernel in comparison with that in wheat. *Cereal Chemistry* 30, 441-5.

Holm, J., Bjorck, I., Asp, N.G., Sjoberg, L.B. and Lundquist, I. (1985) Starch availability *in vitro* and *in vivo* after flaking, steam-cooking and popping of wheat. *Journal of Cereal Science* 3, 193-206.

Hsu, H.W., Vavak, D.L., Satterlee, L.D. and Miller, G.A. (1977) A multienzyme technique for estimating protein digestibility. *Journal of Food Science* 42, 1269-73.

Hung, N.T. and Kermorgant, J. (1982) Protein digestibility and "true availability" of plant and animal feedstuffs. *Proceedings of the Maryland Nutrition Conference for Feed Manufacturers,* 5-10.

Jaska, E. (1971) Starch gelatinization as detected by Proton magnetic resonance. *Cereal Chemistry* 48, 437-44.

Jenkins, D.J.A., Thorner, M.J., Wolever, T.M.S., Jenkins, A.L., Venketsghwer Rao, A. and Thompson, L.U. (1987) The effect of starch-protein interaction in wheat on the glycaemic reponse and the rate of *in vitro* digestion. *American Journal of Clinical Nutrition* 45, 946-51.

Kennedy, J.F., Noy, R.J., Stead, J.A. and White, C.A. (1989) A new rapid enzyme digestion method for predicting *in vitro* quality (PDD index). *Food Chemistry* 32, 277-95.

Low, A.G., Partridge, I.G. and Sambrook, I.E. (1978) Studies on digestion and absorption in the intestines of growing pigs. 2. Measurements of the flow of dry matter, ash and water. *British Journal of Nutrition* 39, 515-26.

Miflin, B.J., Burgess, S.R. and Shewry, P.R. (1981) The development of protein bodies in the storage of tissues of seeds: Subcellular separation of homogenates of barley, maize, and wheat endosperms and of pea cotyledons. *Journal of Experimental Botany* 32, 199-219.

O'Hare, W.T., Curry, M.C. and Allen, J.C. (1984) Effect of buffering capacity on a commonly used assay of protein digestibility. *Journal of Food Science* 49, 498-9.

Pedersen, B. and Eggum, B.O. (1981) Prediction of protein digestibility by *in vitro* procedures based on two multienzyme systems. *Zeitschrift für Tierphysiologie, Tierernährung und Futtermittelkunde* 45, 190-200.

Robbins, R.C. (1978) Effect of ratio of enzymes to substrates on amino acid patterns released from proteins *in vitro*. *International Journal of Vitamin Nutrition Research* 48, 44-53.

Satterlee, L.D., Kendrick, J.G., Marshall, H.F., Jewell, D.K., Ali, R.A., Heckman, M.M., Steinke, H.F., Larson, P. and Phillips, R.D. (1982) *In vitro* assay for predicting protein efficiency ratio as measured by rat bioassay: Collaborative study. *Journal of the Association of Official Analytical Chemists* 65, 798-809.

Sauer, W.C., Stothers, S.C. and Parker, R.J. (1977a) Apparent and true availabilities of amino acids in wheat and milling by-products for growing pigs. *Canadian Journal of Animal Science* 57, 775-84.

Sauer, W.C., Stothers, S.C. and Phillips, G.D. (1977b) Apparent availabilities of amino acids in corn, wheat and barley of growing pigs. *Canadian Journal of Animal Science* 57, 585-97.

Saunders, R.M., Connor, M.A., Booth, A.N., Bickoff, E.M. and Kohler, G.O. (1973) Measurements of the digestibility of alfalfa protein concentrates by *in vivo* and *in vitro* methods. *Journal of Nutrition* 103, 530-35.

Savoie, L., Parent, G., Charbonneau, R. and Galibois, I. (1989) *In vitro* technique to evaluate amino acid availability. In: Southgate, D., Johnson, I. and Fenwick, G.R. (eds), *Nutrient availability: Chemical and Biological Aspects.* pp. 343-45. Royal Society of Chemistry, Cambridge.

A.P. Drake, M.F. Fuller, and A. Chesson

Sheffner, A.L., Eckfeldt, G.A. and Spector, H. (1956) The pepsin-digest-residue (PDR) amino acid index of net protein utilization. *Journal of Nutrition* 60, 105-20

Walker, G.J. and Hope, P.M. (1963) The action of some amylases on starch granules. *Biochemical Journal* 86, 452-62.

Wedermeyer, K. (1899) Zur Methode der Kunstlichen Verdauung stickstoffhaltiger Futterbestandeile. *Landwirtschaftlichen Versuchsstationen* 51, 375-85.

Discussion - Part 2

In the multi-enzyme assay there is some interference from materials with a bone content such as meat meal or fish meal because of the possible acid binding affect of calcium. The group that originally worked with the method had examined some of these factors. Working with rats, a much better agreement was found using the pH stat method compared with the pH drop method, especially with animal proteins which give a rapid pH drop.

There was a good deal of discussion on sampling. With samples of 1.5g it is difficult to obtain a representative sample. Special sampling techniques are required for small samples. Part of the error of *in vitro* methods may be due to failure in sampling technique; perhaps larger samples should be used.

Tannin content of materials like beans affects digestibility. In the method for estimating water in soluble cell walls, samples containing tannin are associated with much more protein in the residue. A correction must be made for this. In relating water soluble cell walls to NDF cereals had exactly the same value but the protein sources were different. This relates to the solubilization of water in soluble pectic substances, not to protein itself.

Concern about *in vitro* methods overestimating AME may be overcome by regression analysis but this might require a separate calibration for each ingredient. It would be difficult to combine, for example, lupins and rapeseed because, although both are protein sources, their fibre is so different.

There was discussion about the use of the regression method to estimate true amino acid digestibility. This is based on the assumption that the endogenous secretion does not change with the level of protein intake. With some proteins this seems to be valid; for example, digestibilities of 100% have been recorded indicating that ileal amino acid flow was the same when the protein was fed as when a protein free diet was given. With other proteins of lower digestibility, this might not be true, especially if they affected transit rate. It was pointed out that the endogenous nitrogen which was not re-absorbed tended to have a distinctive composition, with high levels of a few amino acids and contributions also from amino sugars. The fact that regressions with different proteins show a common intercept suggests that a standard endogenous correction may be valid.

Endogenous losses might be reasonably consistent with normal ingredients but other materials, containing antinutritional factors, increase the secretion of endogenous materials or increase the rate of transit of the digesta thereby increasing the amino acid flow at the ileum. That is a handicap that would be reflected in the apparent digestibility value. If the actual endogenous loss was subtracted the handicap would be removed; it would be more appropriate for formulation purposes to estimate the real value of the food by subtracting a standard endogenous correction related to the way in which the material was fed.

There was also discussion on the relative merits of using sterilized intestinal juice compared with a mixture of enzymes. There was uncertainty about the value of unknown factors in intestinal juice but comparisons which had been made between intestinal juice and enzyme mixtures had not shown a difference. It might be difficult to guarantee the consistency of the composition of intestinal juice. It was suggested that *in vitro* systems based on unsterilized gut contents would, given sufficient time, degrade extensively materials which would be very little digested *in vivo*.

The question was raised as to the relevance of an *in vitro* assay taking 8 hours to digestion in the small intestine of a bird which took considerably less time. The *in vitro* systems were likened to a model in slow motion; the aim was to estimate the time required *in vitro* to give results equivalent to what was found *in vivo*. One could also examine the pattern of amino acid release after 10, 20 or 50% of the nitrogen had been released. In this respect, the *in vivo* measurement of amino acid uptake into the blood is appropriate in order to study the kinetics of the system *in vivo*. Obviously transit time varies greatly between species and, from that point of view, it would be unlikely that any one system would simulate digestion in all species.

It was suggested that in future systems of *in vitro* digestion might be based on the use of immobilized enzymes which would remove the problem of feedback control. Criticisms of the pH-stat method included its susceptibility to the buffering capacity of the food; it is also sensitive to the mineral content of the material. Furthermore, it could not yield estimates of, for example, amino acid release although it could rank samples in order of digestibility. The difficulty found in the degradation of maize starch *in vitro* is perhaps not surprising since maize starch is highly branched and if only α–amylase is used, small oligosaccarides, able to pass through the dialysis membrane, will not be produced. It would be useful to add other enzymes, able to break α-1,6 links and terminal glucose links in starch. It would be useful to add maltase in addition to pancreatin.

Concern was also expressed about the variability in amino acid analysis. Attempts to increase precision in digestibility assays would be futile if the actual amino acid content of the material could not be determined with equal accuracy. Variation between samples can be attributed to differences in variety, husbandry, processing and other factors. There was a good deal of discussion on how best to take account of the endogenous secretion which determines the difference between apparent and true digestibility values.

178

Part 3

The way forward

Chapter 13

The Future Requirements of the Feed Industry

B. Hardy

The Feed Industry

The primary function of the feed compounder is to provide the farmer with cost-effective diets and appropriate advisory services that should in a profit for both the feed compounder and the farmer customer. Practical application of feed products and feeding programmes should take account of the appropriate type of animal production, i.e. reproduction, meat, milk, eggs, wool and be geared to a predicted level of output. This whole approach should be flexible to take account of changes in the cost of the nutrient inputs and the financial return obtained for the output. To achieve this there is a need to have knowledge of the dose-response relationships for the major nutrients in relation to different types of animal output and also detailed information on the ability of each raw material to supply nutrients. This forms the technological base required to prepare diet specifications prior to use of computerized feed formulation systems to produce the least cost dietary solution.

Assessment of Nutrient Requirements

The farmer measures the nutritive and economic values of the diet and of the feeding programme through the physical and financial performance of his livestock. Measurements such as daily liveweight gain, feed conversion ratio or lean and fat content in the carcass are commonly used for meat-producing animals, e.g. pigs, broiler chickens, turkeys or ducks. In the case of laying poultry, feed intake, mortality, egg numbers and weight are more appropriate.

The level of animal performance has shown tremendous increases over the last 20 years. Much of this has been due to genetic improvement, but with associated developments in nutrition, health and management. Estimates of the nutritional requirements of farm livestock published in the literature often do not relate to genetically improved stock or to modern methods of animal production, hence commercial companies frequently conduct their own research to assess the nutrient responses of animals kept under modern farming practices. An alternative

B. Hardy

approach to establishing nutrient requirements is to have knowledge of the metabolic requirements for nutrients, which then allows factorial calculation of dietary requirements for maintenance and for production. Knowing the composition of the tissue and the efficiency with which nutrients are utilized, the dietary requirement can be calculated by the factorial approach for any level of production. It is obvious that there are many factors involved in the loss of nutrients within the animal system. An assessment of these by application of digestibility and availability coefficients for raw materials is needed to enable the nutritionist to specify diets in terms of digestible or available nutrients. This is particularly important for the key nutrients such as energy, amino acids, fatty acids and some minerals, e.g. phosphorus.

There have been a number of recent reassessments of digestible nutrient requirements for pigs (Agricultural and Food Research Council, 1990; Stranks *et al.*, 1988) and for pigs and poultry by commercial companies (Rhone Poulenc, 1987, 1989).

Energy

The actual energy content of a raw material will depend on its chemical composition since all organic components have an energy yielding value. The proximate chemical analysis of a raw material will, therefore, give a general indication of its energy potential, high oil being associated with high energy and high crude fibre with low energy.

Fig. 13.1. Relationship between TME and AME.

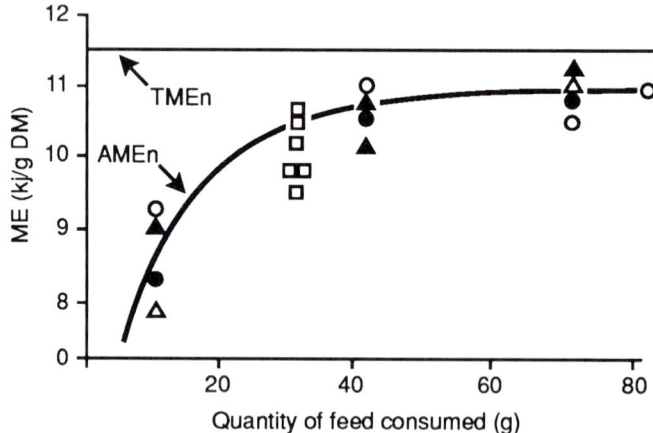

There is a need for an accurate assessment of the energy value of each raw material for each species. Whilst the same concepts of energy evaluation are applicable to all non-ruminant species, the physiology of poultry necessitates the

182

use of the metabolizable energy system, whereas dietary energy values for pigs can be assessed by either the digestible or metabolizable energy system.

Poultry

There are two ways of expressing metabolizable energy for poultry, apparent metabolizable energy (AME) or true metabolizable energy (TME). The TME system involving force-feeding of poultry (Sibbald, 1976) has three main advantages to the feed compounder. Only a small sample of the raw material is needed for the test which is rapid and repeatable. The AME system has the disadvantage that birds are fed *ad libitum*, which necessitates the use of larger feed samples and takes a longer time to complete. The relationships between TME, AME and feed intake is shown in Fig. 13.1 (Fisher, 1983). With normal practical feed intakes the difference between the two systems is very small. For the routine evaluation of raw materials, the feed compounder prefers to use the TME system.

Pigs

The digestible energy (DE) system is considered to be independent of genotype, sex and age of the animal (Henry and Perez, 1982, 1983). It can overestimate the values of raw materials with high protein or high fibre contents, as it does not take account of losses in urine or methane. It also underestimates the value of dietary fats when they are utilized for body fat deposition rather than used as an energy source for total metabolism. In general, DE values are determined by overall digestibility coefficients derived by means of pig metabolism studies. The values derived are apparent DE as there is no correction for endogenous losses.

The metabolizable energy system (ME) takes account of energy losses in urine and therefore makes adjustment for high protein levels in raw materials. Since practical feed formulation assumes additivity of individual raw material values, it is important that ME values of raw materials are determined by the technique of substitution in an appropriate basal diet to simulate a complete feed, otherwise the ME value of high protein raw materials can be understimated.

In the United Kingdom the DE system has been adopted for the formulation of pig diets. As a consequence any new raw material made available to the feed industry must either be evaluated in a pig metabolism study to determine its DE value or a calculation has to be made based on its chemical analysis and assumed digestibility coefficients to estimate the DE value.

Net Energy

The best energy system should be net energy (NE) as it evaluates the proportion of energy used for maintenance and production. The different efficiencies of utilization of ME for maintenance and production, e.g. for protein, fat and milk, are taken into account. The drawback is that NE cannot be determined directly and published prediction equations are frequently based on animals inappropriate for today's production systems.

Amino Acids

The main determinant of the protein quality of any raw material is its amino acid composition. The way in which amino acids are used by the animal will influence the biological value of the protein. In practical feed formulation only five of the ten essential amino acids are normally considered in setting the nutrient specification of the diet: these are lysine, methionine, total sulphur amino acids, threonine and tryptophan. More knowledge is available on the animals' requirements for these amino acids than for others and, therefore, the non-essential amino acids have to be supplied by the crude protein level set in the diet specification. The first limiting amino acid in pig diets is usually lysine and in poultry feeds methionine. The second limiting amino acids will vary according to the type of raw materials used. For instance, in the United Kingdom, threonine will usually be the second limiting amino acid in pig diets based on wheat, closely followed by methionine when peas are used as a replacement for soyabean. In the United States of America, where pig diets are based on maize and soyabean, tryptophan is likely to be the second limiting amino acid after lysine.

Table 13.1. Examples of digestibility coefficients of some common ingredients.

	Corn		Soyabean meal		Meat meal	
	Mean	Standard deviation	Mean	Standard deviation	Mean	Standard deviation
POULTRY						
Lysine	84.7	0.5	91.4	0.6	78.6	4.1
Methionine	93.9	1.9	89.3	0.6	85.3	2.4
Cystine	92.9	2.5	84.9	6.1	63.0	3.2
Threonine	93.1	0.2	89.4	1.0	76.8	3.9
PIGS						
Lysine	73.3	5.3	89.7	0.3	68.6	4.1
Methionine	86.3	3.4	91.2	1.2	84.0	1.8
Cystine	81.4	4.1	84.7	1.8	71.3	5.1
Threonine	80.1	8.0	85.1	0.8	64.2	3.9

Many feed compounders are still using total amino acids to specify animal diets. In future it will be necessary to use digestible amino acids to allow greater accuracy in the prediction of animal performance. There is a need to determine the animal's utilization of amino acids and this can be achieved by assessing digestibility or availability. The methods in current use normally measure digestibility of amino acids *in vivo* by the use of surgically modified pigs, e.g. with ileo-rectal anastomosis (Picard *et al.*, 1984), and by force-feeding techniques in poultry, first developed by Sibbald (1979). Although there is data to indicate species differences in amino acid digestibility (Table 13.1), for simplicity in practical feed formulation systems, pig and poultry amino acid digestibilities are assumed to be the same when setting raw material values.

To optimize amino acid utilization by the animal it is necessary to maintain the amino acids in a balance suitable for the particular type of animal production. For example, the amino acid balance deemed most suitable for the production of protein (lean meat) in the growing pig is shown in Table 13.2. This balance of amino acids is known as 'ideal protein' (Agricultural Research Council, 1981). Since the level of animal performance achieved is closely linked to the animal's daily energy intake it is important to maintain the correct balance between the amino acid and energy concentrations in the diet. The ratio of amino acid to energy will change in different stages of growth in meat-producing animals due to the rate of protein deposition changing with age or weight.

Table 13.2. Recommended balance of amino acids.

	ARC (1981) % of protein	ARC (1981) % of lysine	Wang & Fuller (1989) % of lysine	Proposed Balance % of lysine
Lysine	7.0	100	100	100
Methionine & Cystine	3.5	50	63	55
Threonine	4.2	60	72	65
Tryptophan	1.0	14	18	18
Isoleucine	3.8	54	60	60
Leucine	7.0	100	110	110
Histidine	2.3	33	-	33
Phenylalanine & Tyrosine	6.7	96	120	120
Valine	4.9	70	75	75
Essential Amino Acids	40.4	-	45	44.5
Non-essential Amino Acids	59.6	-	55	55.5

B. Hardy

Diet Specifications

Knowing the type and level of production expected, together with the anticipated daily feed consumption, the nutritionist can set an appropriate nutrient specification for each diet within the feed programme to supply the required daily amounts and balance of nutrients.

An outline of typical diet nutrient specifications is shown in Table 13.3.

Table 13.3. Nutrients specified in diets for pigs and poultry.

	Min	Max		Min	Max
Oil			Moisture		*
AOil	*	*	F.F.A.		*
Protein	*	*	C16.0	*	*
Fibre	*	*	C18.0	*	*
Ash	*	*	C18.2	*	*
Calcium	*	*	D.Lysine	*	
Phosphorus	*		D.Methionine	*	
D.Phosphorus	*		D.M+C	*	
Salt	*	*	D.Threonine	*	
Sodium	*	*	Tryptophan	*	
Potassium		*	NDF	*	*
Magnesium		*	Energy	*	
Copper	*	*	Starch	*	
Pigments	*		Sugar		
TIA		*	T.Amino Acids		
Declared Energy	*				

Raw Material Nutritive Values

The raw materials that are allowed in animal diets are controlled by legislation (Ministry of Agriculture, Fisheries and Food, 1988). The description of the raw material and compulsory declarations, as used between buyer and seller, are far too general to be of any assistance to the nutritionist trying to obtain information on the nutritive value to the animal. A wide range of chemical, physical and microbiological tests are used in the laboratory to produce a better nutritional description of the raw material but these analyses still do not take account of utilization by the animal during the digestive and absorptive processes.

It is particularly important to have knowledge on the content of key nutrients, such as energy and amino acids in raw materials. These should preferably be described in digestible terms, which normally necessitates animal metabolism studies. There are several factors that can affect digestion and absorption, including antinutritional factors, e.g. trypsin inhibitors, tannins, glucosinolates, lectins and Maillard products formed during raw material processing. These need to be evaluated and taken into account when deriving the digestible nutrient values for any given raw material.

Table 13.4. Common raw materials used in pig and poultry feeds.

Cereals	-	Wheat, Barley
Cereal by-products	-	Wheatfeed, Ricebran, Maize Gluten, Human food by-products
Vegetable proteins	-	Soyabean, Rapeseed, Sunflower, Peas, Beans
Animal proteins	-	Fish, Meat and Bone, Blood
Other	-	Molasses, Fats

Table 13.5. Typical chemical composition of some common raw material.

	Oil %	Protein %	Fibre %	Ash %	Starch %
Wheat	2.0	11.5	2.3	1.7	59.0
Wheatfeed	3.5	15.5	8.5	4.8	22.0
Soyabean 48	1.4	48.0	3.5	6.0	1.0
Rapeseed (Double Low)	2.7	35.5	11.0	6.5	0.5
Peas	1.0	21.5	5.8	3.0	31.0
Sunflower 30	1.4	28.5	25.5	6.5	-
Fish (Capelin)	9.5	65.0	0.5	16.0	-
Meat and Bone	12.5	47.0	3.0	29.7	-

The feed industry is primarily a user of by-products and as a result handles a wide range of raw materials, including cereal grains and by-products, whole leguminous seeds, extracted oilseed residues, animal by-products and human food by-products (Table 13.4). The typical chemical composition of some of these is shown in Table 13.5. However, even within a given raw material there is much variation (Table13.6).

Many feed compounders trace their raw materials back to a source, classifying them according to plant variety, manufacturing or processing plant, country of origin, etc. to reduce the variation and to treat each source as a separate raw material (Table 13.7).

Reducing the variability of any raw material allows for a more precise set of nutritive values to be used. Without this, wider safety margins need to be applied to diet specifications to reduce the effect of raw material variation on the performance potential of the diet. It is clearly essential to have a good description of the raw materials used in practical feed formulation, to take account of digestibility as far as possible, to reduce variation and to allow better prediction of animal performance from a better definition of the daily nutrient supply.

Table 13.6. Analytical variation in maize gluten feed from two UK sources.

Nutrient %	Source			
	A		B	
	Mean	Range	Mean	Range
Oil	5.90	4.40 - 7.30	2.20	1.60 - 3.00
Protein	21.50	19.40 -24.20	19.40	16.10 -21.20
Ash	6.60	5.70 - 7.90	7.90	6.80 - 9.00
Calcium	0.03	0.01 - 0.04	0.88	0.77 - 0.93
Sodium	0.21	-	0.69	0.60 - 0.80

(Dalgety)

Table 13.7. Variation in true amino acid digestibility from different sources.

Raw material	True digestibility (%)			
	Lysine	Methionine	Cystine	Threonine
Extracted Soya				
Source A	86.8	91.8	86.3	88.1
Source B	84.2	90.5	84.8	86.3
Full Fat Soya				
Temperature A	91.6	90.8	87.0	90.0
Temperature B	84.5	82.3	76.5	77.8
Meat and Bone				
Source A	81.7	84.6	70.4	79.2
Source B	90.9	95.6	71.6	88.7
Peas				
Variety A	87.7	94.3	78.4	82.5
Variety B	88.8	93.9	83.2	84.8
Variety C	93.1	96.1	82.4	90.7

(Dalgety)

Manufacturing Processes

Manufacturing processes have changed dramatically in recent years and continue to do so. This has been seen in those industries supplying by-products as raw materials to the feed industry as well as in the animal feed manufacturing plants themselves. These processes can have marked effects on the individual nutrients supplied by the raw material and also on the overall feeding value of the diet. An understanding of how these processes affect the physico-chemical properties of the substrates is vital in attributing appropriate nutritive values to the raw materials.

In the modern feed mill, post-grinding rather than pregrinding systems are now often used. This means that all raw materials are passed through the same grinding screen. A wide range of particle sizes results which can affect surface area and digestibility. Long-term conditioners may be used in which ground materials are kept at 80-85°C for 20 minutes prior to pelleting. Other processes include pelleting, double-pelleting and the use of extruders and expanders to enhance the digestibility of feedingstuffs. All exert different temperature and pressure effects on the raw materials. Temperature can range from 70-140°C which influences gelatinization of starches and hence the energy value of raw materials and complete feeds.

Legislation

Legislation continues to have a major effect on the feed industry, with controls on raw materials and feed additives used in animal feedstuffs (Ministry of Agriculture, Fisheries and Food, 1988) and increasing demands for more information to be declared on the feed label.

Table 13.8. Equations for calculation of energy value of feeding stuffs for declaration purposes.

POULTRY (compulsory)		
MEn (MJ/kg)	=	0.1551 x % Crude Protein
		+ 0.3431 x % Fat (acid hydrolysis)
		+ 0.1669 x % Starch (polarimetric method)
		+ 0.1301 x % Total Sugar (expressed as sucrose)
PIG (proposed)		
DE (MJ/kg)	=	17.49 + 0.157 x % Fat (ether extract)
		+ 0.078 x % Crude Protein
		- 0.325 x % Total Ash
		- 0.149 x % Neutral Detergent Fibre
RUMINANT (proposed)		
ME (MJ/kg DM)	=	0.14 x % Neutral Cellulase Digestibility
		+ 0.25 x % Fat (acid hydrolysis)

B. Hardy

Currently, oil (acid hydrolysis), crude protein, crude fibre and ash need to be declared. By January 1992, the declaration of energy will be compulsory for all ruminant, pig and poultry feeds as well as total lysine and total methionine for pigs and poultry respectively. The proposed equations to be used for the calculation of energy content for declaration purposes are shown in Table 13.8. These demand new analyses in the laboratory, some of which involve enzyme digestion stages.

It is therefore important to have a well-equipped laboratory that can evaluate incoming raw materials, check on the manufacturing process and ensure that the complete feed conforms to both the nutritive specification and the necessary legislation.

Analytical Techniques

The laboratory uses a wide range of methods to fulfil its function. Some methods are official to conform to legislative requirements (Ministry of Agriculture, Fisheries and Food, 1982); others are for routine assessment of raw materials, whilst new ones are continually being developed and tested to improve the assessment of the nutritive values of feed ingredients for use in animal diets. In general, as diet specifications become more comprehensive and precise, so laboratory methods need to become more sophisticated.

Many new analytical methods have been developed for complete feedingstuffs e.g. Neutral Cellulase Digestibility and Neutral Detergent Fibre. These are incorporated into the equations to calculate energy values of feedingstuffs for declaration purposes in ruminant and pig feeds respectively. Whenever new methods are developed they must be assessed for robustness. This normally requires a ring test between at least ten laboratories, including those of MAFF and of the EC. The coefficient of variation should ideally be less than 5%. When these methods involve an enzymatic step it is essential that the quality of enzyme is adequately controlled by the supplier or the assay method for the enzyme is made available. At least two companies must be able to supply the enzyme, to cover unforeseen circumstances. Any internal standards necessary must be readily available in the long term.

The feed compounder needs methods for the determination of the values of raw materials (rather than of complete feeds); these are assumed to be additive to predict the value of the complete diet. *In vitro* digestibility techniques have been used by the feed compounder to assess raw materials for ruminants, i.e. Rusitec or Tilley and Terry. The limitations and applications of these have been reviewed by Faithfull (1984). Appropriate techniques for non-ruminants are now required.

Future Requirements

The feed industry needs methods which can be used to establish the digestible nutritive values of a wide range of raw materials for different types of farm animals. The methods need to be robust, repeatable and preferably rapid.

190

It is anticipated that in future Near Infra Red techniques will be more widely used to replace wet chemistry in the determination of the basic chemical characteristics of raw materials. For diet formulation purposes these results must be converted to digestible nutritive values. This may be feasible through the use of regression equations derived from research data. There will, however, be new raw materials or blends of raw materials not included in the data set used to derive the regression equation. Appropriate methods of analysis or predictive relationships based on chemical analyses need to be established for assessment of these raw materials. To do this, the effect on nutritive value of each chemical component, of any antinutritional factor or of processing technique needs to be known.

The development of *in vitro* digestibility techniques could reduce the need for *in vivo* studies. This will become increasingly necessary due to concerns over animal welfare and ethics associated with experimentation, involving animals kept in metabolism crates and the use of surgically modified animals.

Due to problems of access, security, ethics and personnel, the feed compounder cannot easily use for routine assessment of raw materials methods that require animal fluids. *In vitro* enzymatic simulation of animal digestion is, therefore, of interest in the assessment of raw material nutritive values. The feed industry will need convincing that any values derived from such a system are reliable for use in practical feed formulation systems and will produce predictable animal responses such as could be measured *in vivo*. The major challenge would appear to be developing *in vitro* systems that could be considered typical of an animal population, bearing in mind all the factors that affect nutrient digestion and absorption.

References

Agricultural and Food Research Council (1990) Technical Committee on Response to Nutrients, Report No.4. Nutrient requirements of sows and boars. *Nutrition Abstracts & Reviews Series B. Livestock Feeds and Feeding* 60, 383-406.

Agricultural Research Council (1981) *The Nutrient Requirements of Pigs*. Commonwealth Agricultural Bureaux, Slough.

Faithfull, N.T. (1984) The *in vitro* digestibility of feedstuffs - A century of ferment. *Journal of the Science of Food and Agriculture* 35, 819-26.

Fisher, C. (1983) Report on a ring-test to evaluate the proposed EEC equation for declaration of ME values poultry. ARC Poultry Research Centre, Roslin, UK Occasional Publication No.3.

Henry, Y. and Perez, J.M. (1982) Les systemes d'evaluation de l'energie dans l'alimentaton du porc (1) *Les Dossiers de l'Elevage* 5 (1), 51-66.

Henry, Y. and Perez, J.M. (1983) Les systemes d'evaluation de l'energie dan l'alimentation du porc (1) *Les Dossiers de l'Elevage* 5 (2), 49-64

Ministry of Agriculture, Fisheries and Food (1982) Statutory Instrument 1982

B. Hardy

No. 1144 Agriculture The Feedingstuffs (Sampling and Analysis) Regulations 1982, HMSO, London.

Ministry of Agriculture, Fisheries and Food (1988) Statutory Instrument 1988 No.396 Agriculture The Feedingstuffs Regulations 1988. HMSO, London.

Mounsey, H.G. (ed) (1990) *Handbook of Medicinal Feed Additives 1990-91.* HGM Publications, Bakewell, Derbyshire, England.

Picard, M, Bertrand, S., Genin, F. and Maillard, R. (1984) Digestibilité des acides aminés : intérêt de la technique du shunt iléo-rectal chez le porc. *Journées de la Recherche Porcine en France* 16, 355-60.

Rhone Poulenc (1987) *Tables AEC - Recommendations for Animal Nutrition,* 5th edn AEC, Commentry, France.

Rhone Poulenc (1989) *Nutrition Guide - Feed Formulation with Digestible Amino Acids.* AEC, Commentry, France.

Sibbald, I.R. (1976) A bioassay for true metabolizable energy in feeding stuffs. *Poultry Science* 55, 303-8.

Sibbald, I.R. (1979) A bioassay for available amino acids and true metabolisable energy in feedingstuffs. *Poultry Science.* 58, 668-75.

Stranks, M.H., Cooke, B.C., Fairbairn, C.B., Fowler, N.G., Kirby, P. S., McCracken, K.J., Morgan, C.A., Palmer, F.G. and Peers, D.G. (1988) *Research and Development in Agriculture* 5, 71-88.

Wang, T.C. and Fuller, M.F. (1989) The optimum dietary amino acid pattern for growing pigs 1. Experiments by amino acid deletion. *British Journal of Nutrition* 62, 77-89.

Chapter 14
The Scientific Challenge

J.M. McNab

There is a continuing demand from the compound feed industry to have a rapid *in vitro* method capable of assessing the nutritional quality of both the raw materials which make up the diets fed to farm animals and the diets themselves. *In vivo* techniques are expensive to carry out, require personnel with special skills and frequently call for large amounts of raw materials. Furthermore, many are coming under increasing criticism on ethical grounds and it is felt that this pressure is likely to become more intense. The hope is that in the medium term - say, five to ten years - this meeting might help towards the establishment of a standard assay which predicts the nutritive value of feedingstuffs accurately without the need to carry out experiments with animals.

As has not been uncommon in the past, pigs and poultry have been grouped together, largely because the digestion and utilization of nutrients by both classes of livestock are perceived to be similar, if not the same. This reasoning may not be well founded and several speakers have drawn attention to differences which are claimed to exist between the species, particularly the much longer time that the digesta spend in the gastrointestinal tract of the pig and the more extensive fermentative activity within its hindgut. However, it does not yet seem to have been clearly established how important these two factors are and whether the consequences have any effect on the performance of the pig relative to that of the chicken. There is an obvious need to establish just how differently pigs and poultry digest the same food, not only to assist in the development of appropriate *in vitro* assays, but for economic reasons. It must be of considerable value for food compounders to know whether some feedingstuffs are digested more effectively by pigs than by poultry (or *vice versa*) and to direct a particular raw material into the diet of the species which is going to utilize it best. Boisen (Chapter 10) obviously considers that fermentation in the caecum of the pig is sufficiently important to include an enzyme, viscozyme, in his *in vitro* assay, in an attempt to mimic, and hence take into account, the activity of the hindgut microflora.

This workshop consisted of three clear parts. First, there was a session devoted to providing background information on *in vivo* digestion in which the digestive enzyme systems of the animals, the gastrointestinal microflora, the physical and chemical composition of the foodstuffs and the possible interactions among all three were discussed. Second, there was a substantial session, in which current *in vitro* methods and results from them were presented and in which the rationales for the procedures adopted were defended. Finally, there was a concluding session in which an attempt was made to predict what the compound feed industry of the next decade would require from an *in vitro* assay, and the challenge that this presents to those active in the field.

Digestion *In Vivo*

Longland (Chapter 1) described how the polymeric components of the foods - the proteins, the carbohydrates and the fats - are broken down by pigs, poultry and sometimes rats into the nutrients required for growth and production. The roles of the digestive enzymes of the different species were explained and it was shown that the efficiency of digestion depends on the substrates being exposed at the correct time to a series of enzymes the secretion of which is under hormonal and neural control. Attention was drawn to the importance of pH, the presence of the correct cofactor (such as calcium ions) and environmental factors such as temperature. It was suggested that it would be virtually impossible to mimic exactly all these conditions *in vitro*. Furthermore, there are the probable problems caused by end-product inhibition, which can affect not only the extent of enzymolysis, but the rate at which reactions occur. The importance attached to this barrier to digestion *in vitro* was illustrated by Savoie (Chapter 11) and Drake *et al.* (Chapter 12) who both carried out their reactions in dialysis bags.

Ratcliffe (Chapter 2) was even less optimistic about our ability to create a system capable of simulating the microbiological conditions in the gastrointestinal tract. It was shown how the microflora in the gut influence not only the extent to which the food is digested directly, but also the recycling of the endogenous components of the digesta. This was to become an important theme of the meeting, continually cropping up as a problem in the measurement of digestibility (of protein, particularly) *in vivo*, but a complication which was absent from *in vitro* systems. It seems important that the magnitude and significance of endogenous protein and the factors which affect its appearance and disappearance during digestion are given more attention in future research programmes. Endogenous loss from poultry and its measurement are of paramount importance in the derivation of true metabolizable energy (TME) values. Uncertainty over its size and constancy have prevented universal adoption of the TME system as a means of assessing the energy status of feedingstuffs for poultry.

At this point it seems relevant to raise the issue of what biological response

194

should be used to judge the quality of both feedingstuffs and diets. It seems unfair of those working with animals *in vivo* to be continually reminding those who are developing *in vitro* assays of the impossibility of their task, when there is as yet no consensus among nutritionists on the preferred method for assessing the nutritive value of a food *in vivo*. Throughout this meeting there have been frequent debates on the relative merits of apparent and true digestibility, of apparent and true metabolizable energy and of ileal and faecal digestibility. Net protein utilization, chemical score, protein efficiency ratio and blood amino acid concentrations have also been used as criteria of a diet's value. Even growth and food conversion efficiency, the ultimate tests of the quality of a diet, but more difficult to apply to dietary ingredients, have been used.

To provide those developing *in vitro* methods with a realistic goal, it is arguably important to establish what *in vivo* procedure is most appropriate to assess the nutritional quality of a feedingstuff. However laudable this objective is, it seems as remote as ever. In my own field of study some believe that apparent metabolizable energy (AME) is the most meaningful measure of dietary energy status, whereas others argue cogently that TME should be the system of choice; and that is before it is even debated whether either should be adjusted to zero, or some other level of nitrogen balance. There does not even appear to be agreement as to which method is the more precise, Carré (Chapter 5) arguing that AME_N is superior to TME_N, whereas I believe Parsons (Chapter 7) and I would argue exactly the opposite. The same lack of general agreement exists in the assessment of protein quality *in vivo*: true or apparent, ileal or faecal, digestible or available. For example, Ratcliffe (Chapter 2) considers that the role of the microflora in the digestion of food is so important that it casts severe doubts on the validity of techniques based on the analyses of ileal contents.

Although these are issues of considerable importance and currently of fairly vigorous research activity, they should not prevent the quest for an appropriate *in vitro* test being pursued simultaneously. Most, if not all, of those working with *in vivo* assays are aware of their limitations. It should, therefore, be kept in mind that if a less than satisfactory relationship is derived between an *in vivo* and *in vitro* method, both assays should be scrutinized for their suitability and not, as is often the case, only the *in vitro* technique.

There are many other challenging aspects to setting up a single successful *in vitro* assay and these have been highlighted in several of the papers. Longland (Chapter 1) drew attention to the observation that not only the species of animal but also its age and physiological state (e.g. whether it is gestating or lactating) may affect its digestive enzyme activity. While it is implied that differences such as these affect the extent to which a food is digested it is unclear exactly what effects they exert on nutritive value. Both Ratcliffe (Chapter 2) and Graham (Chapter 3) drew attention to the wide variation with which components of foods falling within the same chemical classification could be digested by monogastric animals. For example, 8 to 50% of the acid detergent-insoluble fibre fraction could be digested before the terminal ileum by pigs and 0 to 60% of the non-starch polysaccharide fraction. If this is the case then the present classification of non-starch polysaccharides is patently unsatisfactory. Graham also illustrated in Chapter 3 how small variations in carbohydrate structure, which did not affect the category into which the polysaccharide was classified, could markedly alter the extent to which it was digested. Whether interactions between the fibre fraction and the microflora are the cause of these apparent discrepancies is speculative but warrants investigation. In this context it may be significant that microflora are present and active throughout the entire gastrointestinal tract and not restricted to the hindgut.

Pusztai *et al.* (Chapter 4) delivered the final blow to those trying to devise *in vitro* assays based on known *in vivo* activities when they argued that it would simply not be possible to take into account in an *in vitro* system many of the digestive constraints imposed by the presence of certain antinutritional factors present in quite a large number of animal foodstuffs. Illustrating this point with some elegant experiments using lectins extracted from legumes, it was demonstrated how their properties were influenced by both the receptor sites on the intestine of the animal (which were highly species dependent) and the nature of the resident microflora. It is difficult, if not impossible, to envisage how such interactive effects could ever be incorporated into an *in vitro* assay and it would therefore appear to be essential that components such as these should be detected in potential feedingstuffs and eliminated before using an *in vitro* assay to predict biological performance. We were also reminded how the development and practice of gene transfer in plants could result in the increasing likelihood of the presence of previously unknown antinutritional factors. These could easily be introduced into potential foods by plant geneticists on the basis of protective properties which they confer on the plant against possible predators. Nutritionists must keep themselves aware of developments in this rapidly advancing area of research.

Digestion *In Vitro*

Despite the gloomy forecasts made by the animal nutritionists, that *in vitro* techniques were never likely to simulate realistically conditions *in vivo*, it is a measure of the resilience of the remaining speakers that they tackled the predicted problems with enthusiasm, innovative skill and, as judged by correlation coefficients and residual standard deviations, some considerable success. Although I believe it is correct to point out that no single *in vitro* assay is ever going to reflect rapidly and precisely each nutritional nuance of every potential animal feedingstuff, some of the fire directed at *in vitro* technology was perhaps a little unfair. While it is possibly reasonable to expect a system to be capable of predicting what is the value of fructans to pigs and poultry, it seems unnecessary to challenge it (as Graham described in Chapter 9) with onions and Jerusalem artichokes, two unlikely animal feedingstuffs.

The value of simple methods which would allow feed compounders to reject very quickly poor batches of feedingstuffs was shown by Parsons (Chapter 7). Although these methods were much less powerful at detecting small changes in quality within a particular raw material, there seems to be scope for improving their applicability and precision. If the chemical bases of the differences and the influence of particle size were better understood there would be clear pointers as to how these methods could most effectively be developed. It is simply not helpful to say that it has probably got something to do with the tertiary structure of protein or its cross-linking with carbohydrate. The correct application of modern physico-chemical techniques could unravel exactly what has happened in structural terms and allow the assays to provide information on the changes that have occurred and whether these are likely to have been beneficial or detrimental. Greater collaboration between food technologists and physical and organic chemists is essential to allow progress to be made in this potentially exciting area.

Carré showed in Chapter 5 how, by careful preparation of water-insoluble cell walls, he was able to develop an assay capable of predicting the ME values of poultry diets and feedingstuffs of plant origin with considerable precision and efficiency. The fact that equations based on this component of the feed are not empirical and have reasonable coefficients is important and lends credibility to the technique. It was comforting to hear that a prediction equation, despite having a high correlation coefficient, was rejected because the coefficient of the non-starch polysaccharide component did not reflect the likely extent of its digestion (Graham, Chapter 9). The extension of Carré's equation to a wider range of feedingstuffs is encouraging and progress will be monitored with great interest and anticipation. The innovative approach being pursued by Assoumani (Chapter 6) will also be followed with considerable interest. Lysine availability in foods is still a crucial issue in animal nutrition, particularly in heat-treated proteins. The problems of food contamination in the UK are leading to the increasing use of sterilization and the sensitivity of lysine to heat is sure to sustain interest in the assessment of its availability.

Furuya showed (Chapter 8) a good correlation between true ileal digestibility *in vivo* and an *in vitro* technique using intestinal fluid taken from pigs. The significance of applying the term 'true digestibility' as the criterion of quality was stressed and the importance of using the same intestinal fluid for all comparisons was also underlined. A standard feed (as a control) is now included in all assays, to enable feedingstuffs assayed at different times to be related to each other. This feature of the assay is likely to prove very important as concern was frequently expressed that the composition and, hence, the enzyme activity of the isolated fluid may vary from pig to pig, from day to day and throughout the day. It would seem fruitful to evaluate this technique in an interlaboratory experiment where the same feedstuffs are tested by different people using different samples of fluid at different places and times. It would be interesting to discover whether the 'enzyme cocktail' isolated from sweepings from the laboratory floor (Graham and Löwgren, Chapter 9) was as effective a source of enzyme activity as the intestinal contents of the pig.

Furuya also emphasized that values generated *in vitro* could only be related to true and not to apparent digestibility coefficients. Regression lines for raw materials tested by substitution experiments all had a common intercept and, although this appeared to persuade some that the endogenous nitrogenous component had not been influenced by either the nature of the diet or its protein concentration, this may not necessarily be the case. Any linear increase in endogenous nitrogen loss with increasing dietary protein (say) would result in the same intercept. Boisen (Chapter 10) rather neatly sidestepped the issue of endogenous nitrogen loss by including it in the undigested component of the assay.

As predicted, most *in vitro* assays have difficulty in coping uniformly with the wide range of raw materials that are included in diets for pigs and poultry. Particle size appears to affect values obtained from *in vitro* assays and is obviously an issue that has to be addressed. The fact that two different feeds both pass through a 5 mm screen does not necessarily mean that they have identical distributions of particle sizes. The importance of this factor in *in vitro* assays needs to be more clearly understood.

Finally, different people have different expectations of an *in vitro* assay. If the object is to predict the response of an animal, then the painstaking approach described by Savoie (Chapter 11) would be the method of choice, but would only give information on the quality of the protein. For that reason the approach described by Drake *et al.* (Chapter 12) will perhaps be preferred, insofar as it tried to take into account the contribution made by both carbohydrate and protein to the nutrition of the animal. Curiously, as Hardy pointed out in Chapter 13, none of the *in vitro* assays described made any attempt to simulate the digestion of fat, an important component of animal diets.

However, if the preference is for a rapid assay capable of ranking feedingstuffs then the methods described by Parsons (Chapter 7) will probably be preferred. The application of modern physico-chemical techniques, such as near infra red reflectance and nuclear magnetic resonance spectroscopy, to describing foods will undoubtedly increase the amount of information available on the chemical structure of the nutrients in these foods. The scientific challenge is to translate this information into the prediction of nutrient availability to animals.

Discussion - Part 3

In the final discussion five major areas were considered. These were:

1. the aim of the assay;
2. the *in vivo* measurement to which it should be related;
3. the need for a single test for all raw materials as against individual assays for particular feedstuffs or classes of feedstuff;
4. the choice of appropriate grinding or other preparation for an *in vitro* assay;
5. the relative requirement for precision in discrimination between samples as against obtaining absolute estimates of digestible nutrients that could be used in formulation.

It was pointed out that a number of different aims had been identified. Some assays had been developed in order to maximize the discrimination between samples of one material varying widely in quality. Others had the aim of developing an accurate simulation of the digestive processes so as to estimate the net yield of the nutrients released by the enzymatic activities of the animal. There were also suggestions that the eventual aim might be not simply to predict digestibility but the utilization of nutrients for growth, etc.

There was lengthy discussion of the appropriateness of ileal digestibility as a standard against which to evaluate *in vivo* assays. Since there have been various reports of substantial disappearance of non-starch polysaccharides before the terminal ileum the question arose as to the involvement of the microflora and the extent to which that involvement might differ between animals and in different test conditions. There was evidence that cannulation *per se* did not alter digestibility values compared with those derived by slaughter methods. It was pointed out that although there was considerable discussion about the standardization of *in vitro* methodology there had been little discussion about the standardization of *in vivo* measurements. Any collaborative effect towards standardization of *in vitro* methods needed to be accompanied by a comparable effort to standardize *in vivo* estimates. This would need to include standardization of feeding level, protein content and particle size distribution. In the case of ME values for poultry this had been undertaken by the World Poultry Science Association. Such activities require a great deal of effort in developing and maintaining a system for collating information.

It was pointed out that *in vitro* assays are unlikely to be able to take account of many anti-nutritive factors, especially those which act by altering the response of the digestive system to the food. There was considerable discussion on the endogenous losses in digestion. Such factors as feeding level and protein concentration in the diet alter the relative endogenous contribution to digesta. The general aim of an endogenous correction was to remove the effects of differences between measurements in such factors as feed intake or protein level; differences in digestibility that could not be accounted for by these factors would be attributed to the feedstuff whether or not they involved the alteration of the endogenous component. This involved an assumption of additivity which would be especially important in the case of those feeds which, by their content of particular anti-nutritive substances, altered the contribution of endogenous sources to the digesta. There was discussion about the appropriateness of the standard technique of protein-free feeding to estimate endogenous losses. However, the observation that ileal amino acid flow was no higher in pigs given a diet with 10% casein than with a protein-free diet suggested that protein feeding *per se* does not necessarily influence ileal losses. However, the practice of expressing endogenous losses per kg of dry matter intake was obviously absurd when related to the starved bird with no intake at all.

Concerning the need for a single assay for all materials, it was felt that the convenience of a single assay should be set against the undesirability of introducing bias in the prediction for one material by specific problems of another material. However, it might be possible to have one assay incorporating different prediction equations for different raw materials. The answer to this question related to the aims of the assay. There was on the one hand the scientific need for the simulation of the digestive processes and on the other a need for a pragmatic system of discriminating between samples. The first would require close and absolute representation of the *in vivo* processes; the second could rely on empirical relationships, perhaps including a combination of a simple *in vitro* test with near infra-red reflectance or other routine assays.

It was felt important that any *in vitro* assay could predict the digestibility of a material as it was fed. In many assays the material was ground very much more finely than it would be in practice. Is it necessary to anticipate the effective particle size of materials during their passage through the digestive tract? What is the importance of mechanical breakdown of food materials? Clearly, since digestibility does vary with particle size both *in vivo* and *in vitro* any evaluation system must take this factor into account.

The relative need for precision and accuracy in an *in vitro* test was seen to be related to the aims of the assay. Precision would also be needed, but where the aim was primarily to discriminate between samples accuracy was of less importance. If the aim was to develop predictive relationships bias might be removed by developing different prediction equations for different raw materials or by including terms which describe other easily measured characteristics of the material.

The value of *in vitro* simulations in stimulating further research was emphasized. Simulation allowed one to propose a hypothesis or model: by examining ways in which the model did not conform to reality, new lines of investigation might be developed.

The final discussion addressed the question of future directions for work in this area and the possible avenues for collaboration. The sharing of samples of raw materials was seen as an important way in which the development of methodologies might be accelerated. If those laboratories making measurements *in vivo* would be prepared to provide those working *in vitro* with samples and with their *in vivo* data this would allow a much larger data base to be built up for validation studies. Practical users would be looking for alternative methodologies to avoid the use of animals and the ethical implications of that. There is a wide range of materials available to the feed formulator and these materials must be characterized in terms of their net nutrient contents, bearing in mind all the changes that might be introduced by particular methods of processing. This means that methods which merely rank materials are not adequate; absolute values are required which can be used in a formulation matrix. There is a need to continue both with the approaches based on analysis, such as that of Carré, and with the *in vitro* simulations such as those of Savoie and of Drake *et al.* Some doubts were expressed about the validity of the *in vivo* data against which *in vitro* methods were compared. In the literature there is considerable variation in assays of the same feedstuff made by different laboratories. It must be recognized that *in vivo* estimates also have an error and it would not be right to assume, if an *in vitro* method did not agree with the *in vivo* measurement, that it was the *in vitro* measurement that was in error. Comparisons based on slaughter methods, with measurements of fat or protein gain might be needed to provide absolute answers but there would have to be careful control because of variations in the efficiency of utilization arising from factors other than digestibility. It was emphasized that the methodologies we develop need to be based much more on an understanding of what really happens in physiological and biochemical terms in the animal; this would confer much greater credibility on any new methodology. It was recognized that the task of developing appropriate assays to cover all the needs of the feed industry was probably greater than any single company would be prepared to undertake. It was agreed that some basic information was still needed to underpin the development of *in vitro* assays and these scientific investigations would probably require considerable effort from a number of laboratories. One such area was to understand the factors affecting endogenous amino acid losses. Another was to understand the importance of time in enzyme action, both *in vivo* and *in vitro*. Several participants offered to provide samples of materials at their disposal for others to evaluate using their own methods. Although it was recognized that the eventual beneficiaries of the development of *in vitro* systems were the feed industry and its customers the greatest common interest amongst these would be in developing the basic understanding of the physiological realities of digestion which could then be applied in

a range of *in vitro* systems. The components on which we need to focus include the enzymatic and microbiological processes and the contribution of non-protein nitrogen to endogenous secretions. We also need to understand how each of these components contributes to the overall measurement of digestibility. Putting this information together would also allow one to understand, in the whole animal, the consequences of using apparent rather than true digestibility values. It was also pointed out that better definition of the source of ingredient, the raw material and the processing method and the preservation of the identity of individual samples would all be valuable in reducing the variation in raw material evaluation.

Participants

Dr Ir. H. Boer
Head of Laboratory
Department of Animal Nutrition
Wageningen Agricultural University
Haagsteeg 4
6708 PM Wageningen
The Netherlands

Dr David G. Cieslak
Cargill inc
P.O. Box 301
Elk River
MN 55330 USA

Mme Marcelle Eudaimon
Eurolysine
16 Rue Ballu
75009 Paris
France

Dr B. van Gils
Hendrix' Voeders b.v.
Postbus 1
5831 JN Boxmeer
The Netherlands

Dr G. Gordon
Dalgety PLC
Group Research Laboratory
Station Road
Cambridge CB1 2JN

Dr D.D. Hall
Purina Mills Inc
PO Box 66812
St. Louis
MO 63166 USA

Dr G. Perrott
British Sugar plc
PO Box 26
Oundle Road
Peterborough PE2 9QU

Mr Johan Inborr
Development Manager
Finnfeeds International Limited
Forum House
41-51 Brighton Road
Redhill
Surrey RH1 6YS

Dr Oscar A. Isquierdo
Duquesne-Purina
1, Place Charles de Gaulle
78180 Montigny-le-Brettonneux
France

Mrs Helen M. Lee
J. Bibby Agriculture Limited
Head Office
Adderbury
Banbury,
Oxon OX17 3HL

Ms C.A. Makkink
Department of Animal Nutrition
Wageningen Agricultural University
Haagsteeg 4
6708 PM, Wageningen
The Netherlands

Ing. A. Mul
Hendrix Nutrition Nederland BV
Business Group Feed and Animal
Products Benelux
PO Box 220
5830 AE Boxmeer
The Netherlands

Mr S. McDonald
Colborn Dawes Nutrition Ltd
Heanorgate
Heanor
Derbyshire DE7 7SG

Dr Matti Näsi
University of Helsinki
Department of Animal Husbandry
SF-00710 Helsinki
Finland

Dr Martin Owers
Pauls Agriculture Ltd
PO Box 39
47, Key Street, Ipswich
Suffolk IP14 1BX

Mr F. G. Perry
BP Nutrition (UK) Limited
Wincham
Northwich
Cheshire CW9 6DF

Dr Sue Perry
Unilever Research
Agribusiness Research Group
Colworth Laboratory
Colworth House
Sharnbrook
Bedford MK44 1LQ

Ms Carol Pletcher
Cargill inc
P.O. Box 301
Elk River
MN 55330 USA

Dr. J. Radisson
Purina Europe
Excelsiorlaan 13,
1930 Zaventem
Belgium

Dr A. Veldman
CLO Institute for Animal Nutrition
de Schothorst
PO Box 533
8200 AM Lelystad
The Netherlands

Dr R. Washam
Ralston Purina International
Checkerboard Square
St Louis,
Missouri 63164 USA

Index